The MADNESS of Modern Parenting

The MADNESS of Modern Parenting

Annie Ashworth and Meg Sanders

HODDER

First published in Great Britain in 2006 by Hodder & Stoughton
A division of Hodder Headline
An Hachette Livre UK company

First published in paperback in 2007

Illustrations by Claire Clements/Miekeljohn

The names and identities of the people
quoted in this book have been changed.

A CIP catalogue record for this title is available from the British Library

ISBN 978 0 340 92342 9

Typeset in Sabon by Hewer Text UK Ltd, Edinburgh
Printed and bound by Mackays of Chatham plc, Chatham, Kent

Hodder & Stoughton policy is to use papers that are natural, renewable and
recyclable products and made from wood grown in sustainable forests. The
logging and manufacturing processes are expected to conform to the
environmental regulations of the country of origin.

Hodder & Stoughton Ltd
A division of Hodder Headline
338 Euston Road
London NW1 3BH

www.hodder.co.uk

To our wonderful children,
who have proved that madness is inherited.
We got it from you.

Contents

Introduction: Once Upon a Time   1

1. Welcome to Planet Parenting   8

2. Babies: Let's Start at the Very Beginning   29

3. Trial by Party Bag   60

4. School Entry: Admission Impossible   82

5. School Life: Forgery and Fraud   101

6. Food: A War of Nutrition   130

7. Family Holidays: Travelling Hopefully   152

8. Slaves to the Schedule   174

9. Consumerism:
   Can I have one too, pleeeease? Can I?   188

10. Teenagers: The Hormone Himalayas   207

11. And Then I Woke Up . . .   230

Once Upon a Time . . .

The sun is setting at the end of another lovely day. The children are singing together in the back of the car and giggling, planning the make-believe game they are going to play when they get home. You all unload the shopping they helped you choose at the village shop – Oh, how Lizzie loves those little organic yoghurts and of course Jamie wants broccoli with his steamed fish tonight – and your teenage son helps you put it all away in the cupboard before making you a cup of tea and going off to do his homework. You put on your pinnie, ready to make a crumble for pudding from the apples from the orchard, and smile to yourself, secure in the knowledge that your husband will pull up on the drive any minute and you can share the happy stories of your day.

Yeah. As if . . . In reality, you have just schlepped round the chaotic out-of-town supermarket and frantically crammed in over-priced organic vegetables and the pizza you know you shouldn't have bought but did anyway because it's quicker, and thrown them in the back of the car along with the child who has whinged the whole way round the supermarket pestering you for a packet of bubble gum, which of course you gave in to. Then you screeched out of the car park in your 4 x 4 which you bought because you read it was the safest means of transport for children and pulled up outside school for the third time that day to collect a stroppy thirteen-year-old who is covered in mud and hungry and spurns the apple crisps you offer shouting that he wants a Mars Bar, then goes on the computer instead of getting washed and on with his homework while you try to find room in the fridge for the food and find your daughter's ballet shoes because in ten minutes you have to leave for a class which you have read is good for her balance and posture, while chivvying up your ten-year-old who doesn't want to go to karate even though he nagged you about getting him in and sat on the waiting list for three months before a place came up and you bought the uniform. Your husband calls to say he's going to be late after all and the dog is sick on the carpet and your mother is coming over for lunch tomorrow, then the office email to say that report you aim to deliver on Monday has to be done for tomorrow or they'll lose the client.

That, dear reader, is modern family life. A catastrophe of optimism over the grim reality of 'parenting'.

The word 'parenting'. Now what exactly is that all about? I parent, you parent, he parents . . . (well, usually she, actually). Since when did 'parenting' become a verb? It is no coincidence that it appeared in the lexicon about the same time as networking, down-shifting, interfacing and other management-ese 'ings' because it has suddenly become a profession. A career. Something on the CV to be taken ever so seriously.

Ask your parents if they ever used the word 'parenting' and they will probably snort with laughter (they laugh at everything else we do). They were our mums and dads, they didn't do *parenting*. Any more than they *incentivised*, or had *interpersonal solutions*. No, parenting is a late twentieth-century phenomenon like yuppiedom and upward mobility. They may have invented sex in the sixties, but we invented parenting. It's not even a skill any more – it's a science. We know that because someone called Dr Margot Sunderland has written a book with that very title.

Why has this happened? The problem is there isn't any one single answer. Just look at the world we are living in, for heaven's sake. It's about as straightforward as trying to put a nappy on an octopus. Look at us: you can send an email to Costa Rica in seconds, but you can't drive more than 10 mph round the Hanger Lane gyratory on a Monday morning. People are on waiting lists for hip replacements and handbags. Footballers are paid the equivalent GDP of a small African country to wear a certain brand of hat. We have machines that cook pizza in seconds and yet we get stressed about leisure. We even use words like 'leisure'. On TV we watch total strangers locked in a house or stranded on an island together and call it entertainment.

The paradoxes are enough to scramble your brain. It's a mad world; no wonder we are all mixed up. No wonder what was once the most natural thing in the world – raising a family – sends us into a frenzy of self-doubt. We are surrounded by an information superhighway, but it seems to contradict itself all the time. And everywhere is spin, spin, spin that creates a tyranny of fear.

You want to raise a family that is happy and thriving, but have to do this in a world where it has become harder and harder. So we invented the concept of 'parenting' because we had to give it a name. It couldn't be something that just happens. If we name it, we can control it and have theories about it, and talk about it. Is it a result of our own upbringing? Doubt it – it all seemed a heck of a lot easier when you got two shillings pocket money and were in bed by eight thirty. We didn't get sent to podiatrists, homeopaths and cranial osteopaths because we weren't picked for the netball team. Nor did our mums and dads track us with GPS systems like criminals.

The only mistake they made was to launch us into a world where we expect to be happy and perfect, because we have been told we could be.

Even though our rational heads know it is nonsense and all we need to be is *good enough*, we still find ourselves buying into this ideal. We are held to ransom by the headline writers and cover line writers of magazines. Take titles like *Green Parents* which had a letter from the editor, pictured sitting with her two rosy-cheeked children on a hay bale, that goes on about how she chose the 'natural birth and gentle mothering approach for her daughters'. We read about contributors whose favourite place in the world is their kitchen because 'each time I put the kettle on I'm standing in the spot where I gave birth'. And we ask ourselves:

why am I reading this smug pap, but know it's because we picked up the magazine like a brainwashed automaton lured by the cover line: 'Ethical Chocolate – Would You Let Your Children Eat Anything Else?'

Unable to break away, our eyes wander back to the news-stand and any one of the squillion parenting magazines there to torment us. 'How to be happy', says one. 'Your toddler – how to make the most of quality time', crows another. 'Is your baby too fat/too thin/too tall/too stupid?' 'How hopeless are you? Try our quiz and find out!' 'Working? You terrible mother, how could you?' 'Be a more successful parent'. Okay, we made some up, but bet you can't work out which we didn't.

There's the pressure: I must succeed. I must make them happy. They must be perfect. And I must make it look as easy as a walk in the park, the swings and slides of which have been passed by Health and Safety.

We realised, when we were writing our novels, *Goodbye, Jimmy Choo, Warnings of Gales,* and *The Xmas Factor,* that we were starting to explore the craziness of these new modern families – creating characters who were trying desperately to juggle everything and be brilliant at all of it. But it was only when we started this book that we realised how all-pervasively mad the modern family has become. In fact, the weirdest part was getting people to own up to their vulnerability and, on occasion, lunacy. They knew exactly what we were getting at – and always knew someone else who'd done something really barking – but were still reluctant to admit they were struggling to get it right themselves. 'Don't quote me!' squealed a lot of people, as if they were owning up to something illegal or perverted.

Penny Wilson was the co-founder of a regrettably short-lived magazine called *Wipe*, intended to be the antidote to self-congratulatory, patronising parenting magazines, with frank articles with headlines like 'Sex? I remember that'. Tell it like it is, was the motto. The response to its launch was massive. 'We were inundated with letters from people,' says Penny, 'all saying, "Thank God! Thank you for being honest."'

How odd is that? The biggest requirement of being a parent these days seems to be the ability to be a masterful liar. We have to pretend that we are fulfilled, that we aren't tired, that the baby is sleeping, and we manage seven orgasms a week. Life has become like some gingham-pinnied Doris Day fantasy – oh, and in your spare time you are chief executive of a multinational corporation. Or if you aren't, you probably have an MBA in stay-at-home motherhood.

Remember the heroine of Allison Pearson's novel *I Don't Know How She Does It* who systematically distresses mince pies so people will think she has made them? It wasn't enough to say, 'I have a high-powered, full-time job – sorry, no time for baking.' She *had* to fake it.

The question is always in our heads. Am I failing? Am I doing it right? Small wonder when our role model is the Tom Cruise School of Parenting where celebs buy their own ultrasound machines. And this is held up as a good thing?

We have all been sucked into this charade – even people we once thought sane. But hey, sisters and brothers! It's time to stand up and say, 'We are Mad Modern Parents, with Mad Modern Families, and now we'd like to go and have a little nap please. Wake us when it's all over.'

I

Welcome to Planet Parenting . . .

. . . A world you never even thought about until you crash-landed here. Beware, the air is thin and the day much longer than you are used to. As in all worlds there are tribes here, some friendlier than others, but as sure as ovaries is ovaries, you will be sucked in to one of them. Or worse, you might take on the characteristics of several.

Craft Mummy

Her house is a chaotic mess of creativity where good taste and wedding present Bridgewater china on the kitchen dresser have been buried beneath works of art fashioned from fusilli pasta and Mexican dough. A moth-eared Father's Day card from a couple of years back, the 'I Love You' formed from screwed-up bits of yellow tissue paper and glued, takes pride of place. It's the family's year catalogued in craft.

Pinned to the fridge by a cheeky magnet will be a tatty piece of paper on which is scribbled the recipe for home-made playdough, gleaned from a friend at nursery, and in a big plastic box from B&Q will be crammed every last bit of string, old Christmas cards or interesting piece of fluffy fabric that has been squirrelled away until friends of her daughter's come over to tea. Then they will be offered home-made biscuits, misshapen but charming, the packet of Haribo your child arrived with secreted away in the top of a cupboard, and the art fest will begin.

Craft Mum runs herself ragged mopping up spilt PVA, because the warm conviction she has deep inside that creative time is wholly good does not completely quash her terror of red and blue finger marks all over the Farrow & Balled walls. Her real intention is to make you feel woefully inadequate because all you will have time for, on a return fixture, will be a trip to the park and a Mr Whippy. Enough to make you feel like sniffing Pritt stick. As you leave with your paint-covered child, Craft Mummy will carefully hand you a collage of leaves and grasses that is 'not quite dry'.

It will be immediately sat on by the dog in the back of the car.

Too Posh to Push Parents

For Sarah, pregnancy is a wonderful excuse to go shopping. Since the moment she squealed the exciting news to all her girlfriends – not forgetting to drop in that it had been conceived in the Maldives – she has been in a credit card-flashing frenzy, securing a stash of Elle McPherson maternity underwear and plundering the rails in Bumpsville and Blossom. The only fly in Sarah's ointment is that Prada don't do a range. Determined that, not for one second, will she look frumpy pre or post partum – did you *see* those pictures of Britney in *Hello!*? – she wears her bump as if it were a designer accessory, dreamily rubbing in Japanese Camellia Oil to keep those pesky stretch marks at bay, and has acquired an air whereby she appears to float in an aura of fragile femininity; if Gwyneth can do it, so can she. She takes life gently, does a bit more shopping and meets the girls in Beauchamp Place for something light for lunch (though she could murder a bag of chips).

Truth be known though, Sarah has been flicking quickly past the bits in the baby book about the actual *birth* – it can't really be that gross can it? – which is why, as they are just out of the catchment area for the Chelsea & Westminster, she has persuaded husband Nick to stump up for a private delivery. The hospital literature makes it sound more like a hotel (she likes the words 'ensuite' and 'deluxe') and it even does à la carte. Of course it will all be lovingly recorded on camcorder and announced in *The Times*, though friends will be able to see a picture of the baby via the web thanks to the hospital's picture posting system. Her mother, who drops by occasionally to visit her expanding daughter, wafting Dior as she goes, will approve, though of course in her day they 'lay in'.

Sarah also finds the consultant's soothing words about 'a section if we feel it is necessary' very reassuring. It will fit in nicely around Nick's work schedule and what does it matter if she takes a bit longer to recover? She'd rather that than an episiotomy – yeuch! – and the maternity nurse starts the moment they get home, so why worry?

Everyone agrees that it's sensible to give the baby the best possible start in life, and, anyway, it's already down for the best schools, so that's the whole thing sorted.

For Sarah, motherhood was a wonderful
excuse to go shopping.

The Sensitive Man

Chris has been sick with nerves since the moment, twelve months ago, Abby told him the pregnancy test was positive. Obviously he was proud as hell, relieved that he wasn't firing blanks because he couldn't have borne being told to 'provide a sample' at a clinic, but a lifetime of responsibility, school fees and insurance policies looms ahead. During the pregnancy he was in awe and admiration of Abby as she blossomed and swelled, and he remembered to listen attentively to all the details of her antenatal visits. He even sat through NCT classes while the instructor stuffed a purple-haired troll enthusiastically through a plastic pelvis in the absence of a doll to demonstrate the 'birth journey'. Now that Freddie has come into the world, Chris's life has changed for ever and having the little mite around has helped him forget the twenty hours of labour torture. He'd been told rubbing Abby's back was a good idea, so why did she tell him to bugger off? Somewhere a voice tells him that pacing the corridors with a cigar would have been preferable but he would rather have eaten the placenta than admit it.

He took his allocated paternity leave, is rather proud of the fact that he's an expert on the contents of each nappy (and he changes as many as he can), and nods sympathetically when regaled about the trials of lactation. More supportive than a nursing bra, he can bore for Europe at kitchen supper parties with other new parents, as the wives breastfeed shamelessly at the table, and finds common ground with the other men about the pros and cons of different buggies, knowing exactly which one fits best into an Audi.

But deep down he's panic-stricken that he's lost his wife for good and is desperate for a Saturday morning shag like the good old days. Meanwhile, he's wanking for Britain.

Eco Mummy

There's a bit of a funny smell in Belinda's house, but you don't really want to ask. Is it the ever-present bucket of nappies soaking in the corner or the jam jar of alfalfa sprouts, left a bit too long on the windowsill? Take care not to accept a drink. She'll pass you a mug of Barleycup with several rings still in evidence – she'd never dream of having a dishwasher cos of the impact on the environment – but if you are quick you can tip it into the weeping fig. Little Jerome, gurgling happily in his sustainable wood highchair, doesn't care that all his unbleached cotton romper suits are now a lighter shade of grey – no optical whiteners in this house, thank you very much.

But his older sisters have realised something's up. Desperate for invitations to houses where they get Jaffa Cakes and can watch TV, they try to make new friends by offering the wholemeal contents of their lunchbox, but to no avail. Their classmates turn up their noses at bio-dynamic felafel and organic mushroom pâté. Belinda's offspring – home deliveries every one (it's a wonder they didn't name the youngest Ocado) – live in constant hope of an invitation to a McDonald's party, but know that if one came their way they wouldn't be allowed to go.

Obsessive to the point of mania, Belinda is determined that she will single-handedly make the world a better place for her children by driving a thirty-mile round trip to the only recycling plant that takes Tetrapaks.

As you leave, picking your way out through the hallway cluttered with bikes, overflowing bags on their way to the charity shop and the box of organic veg delivered weekly, you feel completely traumatised at the thought of your carbon footprint and the terrible harm you've done your children by allowing them to have drinks from plastic bottles. And who could have imagined there were so many pesticides in a carton of apple juice? Belinda's clear-eyed zeal and fresh-faced evangelism has you in a frenzy of self-doubt. You go home and empty your cupboards of all the cleaning products that actually work – then have to buy in a new stock when that odd smell you detected round her house starts to pervade the atmosphere of your kitchen too.

The Foodie Parent

Richard and Sophie's kitchen is a shrine to the senses and a temple to the finest food the world can provide. Their children know it, your children know it. In fact, everyone knows it, because the Foodies keep telling them so.

No ingredient is too recherché for the family. Sophie consumes cookbooks like most people do novels and is on the phone to Valvona & Crolla weekly. Each meal is a 'menu gastronomique' with a perfect balance of little courses, each seasoned to perfection. On the table at mealtimes are Halen Môn salt crystals, wasabi (which your child thought was snot), and vinaigrette (made with their home-brewed vinegar, using a matrix they picked up in northern Italy, donchaknow).

Their children's gourmet palates have been developed since before they entered Little Sod's Nursery. No fish fingers in this establishment! Sophie's idea of fast food is seared scallops. Thanks to intensive highchair training in 'super little places' on foodie pilgrimages through Europe, Foodie kids can identify a Maris Piper from a Pink Fir Apple at a single bite – although they've never been near a chip. Their lunchboxes would have Michel Roux in tears of envy. The only chocolate they've ever tasted is Valrhona. Is there any other kind?

When you tremulously offer the Foodie kids pasta on a play date, they ask you to be more specific: linguine? Eliche? Penne rigate? They'll reject the shop-bought pesto, cos it's not made with extra virgin olive oil, but they wouldn't mind tapenade. You're frantically searching the larder, wondering if Marmite would do, when salvation comes in the unexpected form of a bag of Cheesy Wotsits. You tell them they're Japanese rice crackers and they munch away contentedly.

Quality Time Mum

Probably working in some high-powered job she refuses to give up (it took her so long to get there), Rebecca is racked with guilt. About everything – all the time. At work for not being at home, at home for not being at work. She virtually gave birth in her lunch hour, having finished off a presentation in the early stages of labour before taking a taxi to the hospital. She chose a place that provided a fax machine and broadband in every room. With an epidural, she could carry on with phone calls to Frankfurt until the midwife forcibly removed the handset from her grip.

She was back at work within a week, half the time spent crying out the hormones in the lavs and the other half trying to staunch the flow of breast milk on her Ungaro silk shirt. She made Nicola Horlick look like a slacker. Her permanently knackered three-year-old, who's kept awake by the nanny until 'Mummy gets home' has come to dread these twenty-minute intensive fairy cake-baking sessions with her mother, a virtual stranger who has a phone glued to her ear talking to the office. Rebecca knows she is gushing every time she comes home (late) to make up for lost time, yet screeches in on sports day at the last minute and pretends she saw her daughter come fifth in the egg and spoon. Half her salary goes on the nanny but they both know the family couldn't survive without her.

She has to keep everyone happy, so Saturday mornings are 'Daddy and Mummy time' – while CBBC babysits – then she makes herself feel better by meeting colleagues with children for a power Sunday brunch on Upper Street; but 'it's a treat for the kids, isn't it?' She collapses into bed at the end of each day, thanking her lucky stars for the fact that she has so many choices available in her life. I am woman – hear me snore!

Helicopter Mum

What's that strange whirring noise that accompanies little Hector wherever he goes? Why, it's Tamsin, his mummy, hovering at a safe distance, far enough away to allow him to interact, at least a little, with other people, yet close enough to swoop should she judge it necessary. Always ready with an opinion, an answer, a wet-wipe or a snack, she's as connected to him now as she was by the umbilicus, and as crucial to his wellbeing, or so she would have you (and him) think.

He's never quite on his own, Hector, although Tamsin did once leave him with the trusted Mrs Arkle who cleans - while she went upstairs to change. At five he has yet to speak because Tamsin does it for him. She refers to him as 'We', as in, 'Oh, no, we never have butter on our bread,' or, 'We had a bit of a late night, I'm afraid, so we might be a wee bit grumpy today.'

Tamsin is particularly noticeable at parties, where she enters like an avenging Health and Safety Officer to scan the room for potential hazards. Of course she always stays, offering to help. How kind, how thoughtful, you think, until you notice that the only thing she's interested in helping with is Hector. She ignores any other child's request for juice, takes over refereeing Musical Statues to make sure he wins and refuses to help with the washing up, because she can't actually see him from the kitchen.

At school, she resorts to helping in class so she can keep an eye. At the playground on Saturdays she shadows his progress on the equipment, her car keys clenched in her hand, her knuckles white, just in case they have to dash to A&E. Don't bother trying to engage her in conversation. She's constantly looking over your shoulder to check on his status and won't hear a word you say. If you'd really like to speak to her, go and chat to Hector. She'll be there like a shot, ready and eager to respond.

Taxi Driver

The world looks a better place from an SUV. And with everything she needs stashed away in that copious glove box, Anne secretly relishes her driving hours although, with all the eye-rolling and tutting she does, you'd never guess. Between 8.07 and 8.52 precisely she braves the morning traffic, her route honed to perfection, as she transports William and Catriona, plus all their paraphernalia, to their respective schools, chanting tables, conjugating French verbs and handing out wet wipes to remove all traces of breakfast on the move, all at breakneck speed.

The rest of the day feels oddly flat, although, of course, she has to shop to restock the glove box/larder (the menu limited to foodstuffs you can hoover up with a Dustbuster), and tries to meet up with friends to compare their packed schedules in case they can lift-share. (The hidden agenda is finding out if anyone has discovered a new and more interesting activity she should be plugging into.) Then from 3.17 until whenever, she swerves the kids from one improving activity to the next, getting home just in time for a quick bath before bed.

Anne has, so far, resisted in-car DVDs but at least the

kids would be able to watch *Muzzy*, still in its wrapping and gathering dust at home, and it would be a good use of driving time. Shame she has to pick them up early from pottery so as to make sure they only miss the first five minutes of tai kwando, but there's no other way. Thank heavens she did that chart on the computer so she can work out which of the many sports bags she has to stow on which day.

The children, exhausted but resigned, change their clothes as required in the back. All they really want is to cuddle up in the sitting room and watch *Blue Peter* once in a while so they can join in the conversation at school, and eat shepherd's pie at the kitchen table with a real knife and fork.

Double-parked outside the leisure centre, Anne is free, for twenty-five minutes at least, to flick through *Vogue*. It's a punishing schedule for her. Still – when you have such gifted children – there really is no choice . . .

The 'Been There Done That'

Jenny has climbed the foothills of babies and toddlers, negotiated the glaciers of the tween years, cramponed and ice-picked her way up the north face of teenagers and has reached the summit. From the privileged position of one who has children for whom A levels are a distant memory, she looks down on you as you battle the challenges below. A bit like an older sister, she listens with a slight smile as you rant and rail about recalcitrant behaviour, common entrance or incompetent teachers, and you take her smile for support and sympathy. In reality it is wry and knowing, even a tad patronising. She nods reassuringly, 'it's only a phase', which is as helpful as telling someone in the middle of root canal work 'it'll soon be over', then utters those magnificent words that fill your heart with dread: 'This is nothing. Just you wait.'

Thousands of miles ahead of you on the parenting trail, Jenny can discuss GCSE options and theory driving tests, knowing you will have no comprehension of what she is talking about. She's an expert on gap years and UCAS forms – it's all so different now, you know – can tell you why geography is better at Loughborough than Newcastle and refers to them all as 'uni'. When you visit for coffee she struggles to find a biscuit suitable for your toddler, and leaps up with, 'Don't touch that, sweetheart,' as he lunges for her son's mobile phone. Said son then strolls in and picks up the keys to the Mini Cooper from the table. Do children really get that big?

Jenny, who dresses a bit like your mother, smiles indulgently but don't be fooled. All that nonchalance hides a ball of anxiety, but she'll never admit how easy early parenting is compared to the horrors of having children who are no longer an 'een' and who are about to flee the nest and, ergo, her clutches.

Designer Parents

Function follows form for Giles and Daisy. Every purchase, every item in the house is an *homage* to their highly developed aesthetic taste – and that goes for the baby stuff too. It was a bit of a shock, that first trip round Mothercare. All that plastic! All that colour! It seemed there was just no way you could make a baby minimalist!

Things have moved on a bit now, thank goodness. Now that babies are a recognised fashion accessory, DPs are far better catered for. From the Bill Amberg papoose to the huge Bugaboo, there's plenty to satisfy their retail longings. Gracious, Armani even do a baby range. With cashmere bootees from Brora and Alice Temperley rompers, they'll match Mummy's cardi and frock beautifully. Daisy can use the kids as an excuse to visit all her fave shops and there's always a chance you'll bump into little Apple, or Lila with nanny in tow, or even (oh, joy) their mummies, while you're browsing the racks.

The problems may arise when the kids start to assert their own taste – sadly, their choice of telly programmes doesn't bode well. There's no way you could ever call a Boobah chic, even in an ironic way, and as for *Balamory* . . . Overalls? I don't think so!

The PTA Parent

Ever since she was chair of the Junior Common Room at UEA, Mandy has been able to smell a committee at five hundred yards and she can't resist being *involved*. Her motivation this time, though, is that she is in awe of Ben's teachers – the closed staffroom door making it no more accessible now than when she was at school – and she feels it's so important to be a key player in school life.

She has made certain inroads by always making herself

available to accompany school trips and positioning herself next to the form teacher on the coach, but the woman remained irritatingly unresponsive to leading questions about Ben's progress, even though Mandy bought her coffee in the science museum café!

She's pretty pleased that the head now calls her by her first name, achieved thanks to her persistence in signing herself that way on emails to him, but she can't help thinking that, by joining in the fund-raising for new computers, she'll cement the relationship even further. The fact that she's single-handedly organising the Auction of Promises supper might be valuable when Mr Cafferty marks Ben's Victorians project. He's bound to be wowed by the postcards they've stuck in which shows they did the museums and didn't just Google it.

Mandy is always there early for collection at 3.15 so she can collar people and ask them to help with raffle tickets, but they all seem to be deep in conversations or have to rush away. Well, she complains to the mother of Ben's best friend as they wrap gel pens for the tombola, they'll never raise the necessary funds flogging a couple of fairy cakes at the school fête. Someone has to be committed. They'll have her to thank, though, when there're two lovely new computers in the library.

Touchline Dad

Greg looks forward to Sunday morning mini rugby with mixed emotions. William takes a bit of persuading, especially when it's zero degrees outside, but Greg's enormous investment in 'battle gear' shoulder pads and a fluorescent green gum shield was a worthwhile bribe just to see the lad jog out on to the pitch in his strip.

Greg's enthusiasm is greater than the quality of his own schoolboy rugby, as he barely scraped the thirds – though, as he recalls, it was a particularly good year group for second row players – but time has healed the wound and now he invests all his boyhood ambitions in young William. Sport at St Lawrence School is derisory, and the only option anyway is football which everyone knows is for wusses, so minis on the Sabbath it is.

The volume at which he bellows 'Get stuck in, son!' makes one wonder just what decibels he could reach during a nail-biting Calcutta Cup clash at Twickenham, but Greg keeps up the verbal pressure. You just never know: a county talent-scout may be lurking by the corner flag. William, at once both confused and embarrassed, looks across at his Barbour-wrapped father on the touchline, because he is nowhere near the ball anyway. Nor does he intend to be, because it hurts, his legs have turned blue and he can't feel the ends of his fingers.

His father's verve is equalled if not surpassed by his mother's, who sits at the end of the pool at swimming galas and times his backstroke on the stopwatch facility on her mobile, explaining away his poor performance to others with excuses about late nights and being 'under the weather'. Why can't she see he's never going to be quicker than Henry, who must have webbed feet, and who cares anyway? William just wants to go home and play with his Lego.

William is six.

'Come on son, you'll never get to Twickenham that way!'

Crop Top Mum

Lou got her figure back really fast after pregnancy – well, never lost it, actually – and, boy, does she let everyone else know! It's hard work staying so hot, but worth it because it means she and her daughter are more like sisters – bezzie m8s. And that's got to be good – right? Her signature crop top, worn whatever the weather, also reveals her belly button piercing, much to her eleven-year-old, Laura's, embarrassment, but it was the price that had to be paid for being allowed to get her ears pierced. Now Laura just has to convince her mum that low-slung trousers are so *yesterday*, and that long sweaters are in.

Lou and Laura have always been on first-name terms – because they really respect each other as individuals. That doesn't stop Lou from appropriating all her daughter's slang, textese, dance moves and tastes in music. She also insists on chatting to her friends and wants them all to feel really at home in her house, all the better to spy on what they're wearing and copy it. Her role model is Peaches Geldof.

When Lou offered to take Laura and all her mates to see Robbie as a birthday treat, who was up at the front, arms in the air, singing while Laura cringed, scarlet with humiliation, in the loos? Your daughter, by contrast, thinks Lou's really cool and demands to know why you don't take more care of yourself.

You always feel about a hundred when you go to Lou's house to pick up your daughter. It seems like a permanent sleepover party there, with Lou serving up bowl after bowl of popcorn, watching DVDs with the girls. Still, at least your daughter doesn't keep you waiting. In fact, she's desperate to leave once you appear because you're so drab, and she doesn't want Lou to spot your awful old M&S Footglove shoes and haggard, make-up-free face.

The Tate Parent

India was a late and unexpected blessing in Jane and Harry's marriage. She is the most perfect creature they could imagine and she never tries their infinite patience. Granted, the adjustment has been, well, frankly immense and Harry has had to put a lock on his study door since the day she crawled in there and shredded his notes for Monday's lecture on Eastern European economics. But she coped very well with last year's trip to Peru and looked like a native in her little papoose on Jane's back.

Jane is frankly terrified of her daughter, especially when Harry goes off to work in the college department that also used to be the centre of her world until she had to give it all up – a nanny? Unthinkable! – and she is faced with the long day ahead. She looks at her daughter's faintly menacing expression as she chews on a wholemeal crust in her highchair. Getting her down will be not unlike unleashing the dogs of war, and Jane has spent hours of reasoned bargaining with promises of extra *Tickabilla* if she will only stop terrorising the cat.

India will almost inevitably be artistic given the family genes on both sides, and no doubt she will absorb culture by osmosis, but there's no harm in helping nature along.

Hence the family days out to significant art galleries and museums. Harry, in a voice loud enough to benefit anyone else standing close by, crouches down beside India in her buggy and explains, in the simplest terms he can, the influences behind Vorticism. At twenty-four months, India is mad as hell at being strapped in so whines and twists her body in protest. Her parents, keen that she should be able to express herself, release her and watch with glee as she waddles towards the Rachel Whiteread installation. What a glorious sight to see their precious daughter captivated by such a profound artistic statement! They retire shortly afterwards for refreshment in the café, exhausted by attempts to stop her clambering all over it.

Perhaps, Jane wonders as she sips her green tea, the Eden Project might engage her more.

The Mother of All Teenagers

Lucy has dealt with more confrontation and negotiation in the last twenty-four hours than Kofi Annan has ever had to contend with. She has tried the softly, softly approach and has now got as far as 'because I say so', but has fallen short of raising her voice even further because if that doesn't work, she'll have exhausted her arsenal.

Tash remains resolute. Natasha seemed such a pretty name to choose for their daughter, and seemed to suit so well the biddable little thing who used to put her arms around her mother's neck and tell her she loved her to the moon and back. It doesn't seem to suit this . . . this alien standing here in the kitchen, her jeans hugging bony hips,

27

her arms folded, her face as hard as nails, informing her mother that it is totally unreasonable not to let her stay over at the house of a friend of a friend of her mate Georgie's, the address of which is uncertain. Lucy would love Alan to be here to help, but her husband is totally at a loss to understand this oestrogen-driven fifteen-year-old who occupies their house like a malign wraith, and he finds sales meetings at the office a blessed relief.

Unsure whether she should be suggesting the Pill, but worried it might be planting the wrong message in Tash's head, Lucy tries very hard not to nag with questions, knowing it's the quickest way to alienate her daughter. During the day, however, she can't resist going through her room, on the pretext of tidying it, and picks up the scantiest of knickers from the floor, discarded with her FCUK T-shirts, and wonders, with a large dose of panic, just who they are intended to attract. This all seems light years away from the Laura Ashley dresses and innocent kisses of *her* far-off teenage years.

The only thing Lucy and her daughter have in common is that they both think the mobile phone is the greatest invention since penicillin. For Tash it's a means of directing her social life and confirming to her friends that her mother too is totally 'sad'. For Lucy it's a substitute umbilical cord – Tash can't ignore a 'where ru?' text message, can she? – but it's a mixed blessing at 3 a.m.: Oh, God, why hasn't she replied?

2

Babies: Let's Start at the Very Beginning

Obviously a child is the basic accessory we need to qualify as a parent. That's nothing new; parents have been having children for years. But these days becoming a parent suddenly needs to fit in to some *grand scheme*. A life plan. It's all very thought through and deliberate. It's one of the many things we hope to achieve before we turn forty. Like doing a parachute jump, or buying a BMW.

The trouble is, for women at least, the scheduling starts just about the time we choose our A levels.

Preconceptions

Here's how it seems to go: we choose a career path and hurtle along it, then, once we've established ourselves and got the company pension, we form a partnership with someone who shares our vision and set up a base that reflects our corporate beliefs. After that expansion seems the logical thing to do. Yes, it's a serious project, doing the baby thing, but with the right research and plenty of investment, eminently doable.

At this early stage, though, the only contact most of us have had with the end product is through books, magazines and ads on TV, and the occasional specimen you see out and about at weekends. Yes, it's odd. Before we get interested in babies, we never notice them. Even when we start looking, they're a bit thin on the ground. So where are they all?

But it doesn't matter. We think we know all the important stuff already. We know where the best people go to give birth; that we can get our figure back within days; that we can get a designer baby carrier; that we can buy it cashmere mittens; that playing Mozart will guarantee a genius. We know because we've done the research. We know we'll be the best parents ever. And the baby will be the best baby the world has ever seen. So let's get stuck in. After all, it's not fair to make the world wait any longer.

What we didn't factor in was the immensity of this particular project, and that those who had already beaten us in the egg and sperm race would be longing to tell us all about it.

'We'd decided to try for a baby and I was at the health food shop,' Lydia remembers. 'I'd just bought some pre-conceptual vitamins that looked pretty good, and I felt very pleased with myself, when this woman with a baby in one of those enormous three-wheeler buggies came in. I said hello to the baby and the woman seemed friendly. She looked at my vitamins and laughed knowingly. "I did a complete detox before I even started trying to get pregnant, and there are far better supplements than those – organic ones." I felt crushed but at the same time, I just wanted to get all the same stuff she'd got. So I wrote it all down feverishly. That was just the start of it.'

Suddenly it dawns on us just how high the bar has been set. If we're not right up there with an MA in Pregnancy, we've failed and failure is simply not an option. If we're not chanting pre-conceptual mantras, guzzling zinc (or whatever) and making our partners wear big baggy boxers for months before we even jettison the condoms, it's virtually child neglect. We get a nasty feeling in our stomachs – and it's not morning sickness – that we are being sucked into something. A bit like suspecting the person being so nice at the airport is a Scientologist. Our rational brain says, 'Hold it right there! I'm not falling for this.'

But we *do*.

Welcome to the madness of modern parenting.

The Thin Blue Line

Wham! Whether we managed to get pregnant straight away, or had to endure the living hell that is fertility treatment (ever been judged on the quality of your eggs before?), the realisation that we've created a new life brings a mixture of elation tinged with downright panic! Suddenly it feels as though the carpet has been pulled from under our feet. It's a new life all right – ours – and suddenly the old, predictable, under-control one starts to slip away.

If you're a bloke, there comes the validation that not only are you virile, you've joined the ranks of the grown-ups. And that makes you partnership material – the big swinging dick. But deep down, you're thinking, Help! Do I have to look as if I want to take six months' unpaid paternity leave? Or will that be as good as waving good-bye to promotion? How does the New Man get perceived at work – *truthfully now*? Damned if you do, damned if you don't.

If you're a woman, there comes the validation that you're fertile (phew!), but what the hell happens to *your* brilliant career now? The happy news can elicit the strangest response from those around you, especially at the office.

'When Dave announced at work that I was pregnant, everyone slapped him on the back,' says Carrie. 'When I announced it, people were nice but it was treated more like a problem. Was I going to be coming back straight after? What was I going to do about childcare? Would I go part-time? I could almost see the gleam in my colleagues' eyes as they thought about sharing out my clients between them.'

And to cap it all, your body no longer even feels like your own.

There you are – boobs like Dolly Parton's (but so sore, you can't bear your partner to touch them), constant puking, knackered all the time. And when you go to the antenatal clinic for the first time, you are sharing a waiting room with a load of tattooed teenagers. They must be in here for another reason surely. Then the midwife writes down on your notes that you're an 'elderly primagravida'! This was not what you signed up for!

Pregnancy is a great leveller all right.

Your New Club

At this stage parenting is terra nova, and we don't have a map, but there are compensations. We've become members of a new club without even having to apply, and our belly is our membership card. Our stamping ground becomes the previously unexplored maternity clothes and baby equipment shops. We had no idea there were so many retail opportunities, did we? Pregnancy, as a shopping experience, is hard to better, and spending shed loads of money is an excellent preparation for parenthood.

At last we've found the other parents, in the few shops they can get their enormous buggies into, and now we can set about observing them close up, and deciding what kind of parents *we're* going to be – in terms of style statement, that is.

For men, there's not too much choice in terms of role model. Obviously you're not going to go the Steve Bing/ Dwight Yorke route – cads that they are – but are you prepared to be as soppy as David Beckham or Jamie Oliver? You're dead proud too, of course, although not in a nasty macho way. But is it compulsory to have a tattoo? You're also completely terrified that you've lost your partner as you once knew her for ever, because she's acting so weird and moody, and the idea of natural birth scares you rigid, yet everyone's expecting you to be the strong one. How are you going to cope with all that? The same way other blokes do. By buying a huge great state-of-the-art buggy, of course. Suddenly Maclaren is the new McLaren.

Charles felt his Bugaboo definitely gave him
an edge, even with no baby inside.

'I've become obsessed with all the gear,' says James. 'I go up to couples in the street and ask them about their buggies. And the amazing thing is they all want to tell you about it, especially the blokes. Where once you'd be talking about the performance of your car, now all you can talk about is which buggy has the best handling. It's amazing how competitive it is to get the best.'

For pregnant women, there are all too many role models out there; trouble is, they're all uniformly gorgeous. Why, there's even a book called *The Yummy Mummy Handbook*. How nauseating is that? The reality for most of us, once our pregnancy starts to advance beyond the puking stage, is that we look and converse like a Teletubby, and that's on a good day. But we drag our knackered and ever increasing behinds to all those aqua natal classes, and slap on make-up to contrive that 'natural glow' we read about, but are still hoping for – because we're damned if anyone else is going to know how bloody hard we're finding it all. No point complaining about the competition any more – we're the competitors.

Buy the book

It's all so confusing, isn't it? Thank goodness for all the advice out there. Alarmingly, much of it is written by people who have only had one child and it's all so contradictory. But they're celebrities, so they must know what they're talking about.

Now every woman who has ever given birth could bore

for Britain about the details of her pregnancy and delivery. It's a brief spell when we're the centre of attention before being shunted aside by people wanting to gawp at the baby. You'll know, if you've been on the receiving end, just how dull it is, but if you let other couples bore you there's a chance they'll let you bore them in return.

If you're a celebrity, however, the normal rules don't apply. Everything they do is interesting – even when it's boring. This is why the list of celebrity pregnancy and parenting guides keeps getting longer and longer. They only have to have a bit part in *Holby City* and get up the duff. Suddenly they have a book deal, and now we can pay to be bored rigid by someone we've never even met. And, yes, they'll even tell us that pregnancy was a life-changing experience – like we didn't know that.

Cindy Crawford did it, Mel Giedroyc did it, Melanie Sykes, Libby Purves and Jools Oliver have all written books about motherhood. So, you may be asking yourself, what do they know? But if it's a choice between them and Gina Ford, you can begin to see the attraction.

Raising the perfect child

Have you noticed that, just when one theory of baby care becomes established, another one, saying completely the opposite, comes along? Perhaps all those experts get together and plan it that way, just to make sure they go on selling books? And why do we need to be told what to do by experts anyway? The very titles of their books are designed to make us anxious, so we need to buy the book to allay the fears they create. How about *Potty Training in One Week*? No pressure there.

'I can't prevent myself from buying these stupid books,' rants Louise. 'It's the titles. *The Contented Little Baby Book*, for goodness sake. Well, how can you say no to that? And *The Complete Secrets of Happy Children*. Not buying it seems irresponsible. And some of them even sound like management books, like *Seven Secrets of Successful Parents*. Or pet care manuals, like *The Baby Whisperer*. Bookshops are more of a threat to my health than unpasteurised Brie.'

Very public pregnancy

Pregnancy has never been so out there! Remember the Diana days when pregnant ladies disguised their condition behind tent-like dresses and coy euphemisms, and would disappear for a while, reappearing only when the yucky stuff was over, holding a swaddled and indistinct pudding. It was career death, of course, for working women and a woman never quite regained her pre-pregnancy glamour and sex appeal, moving immediately to the next generation up.

But that all changed in 1991, when famed celebrity photographer Annie Leibovitz photographed actress Demi Moore, naked and pregnant, for the cover of *Vanity Fair* magazine. This became one of the hottest selling issues in *Vanity Fair* history and a landmark of liberation for pregnant women everywhere. Liberation? Yeah, right. Only if you look like Demi. Semi Demi was no good at all.

Now it's open season for pregnant celebs. In terms of magazine circulation, the two very best sellers are celebrity pregnancy and celebrity drug rehab. And pregnancy has better photo opportunities. You can't open a glossy without coming nose to navel with the latest pregnosaur, from A-list downwards through the alphabet. They all seem to be at it and they're huge – at least in circulation terms – although rather less so in sheer physical terms. But more of that later.

In fact, pregnancy can be the making of a celebrity. And although it would be horribly cynical to imagine that parenting is part of a greater PR plan, there are plenty who owe their new-found high profile to the bun in the oven. Star mummies sell, both themselves and an idealised image of pregnancy and parenting. They look fantastic, they say they feel fantastic, they say they feel more fulfilled than ever before in their starry little lives. We flick the pages avidly, asking ourselves, does anyone actually believe this crap? Then find ourselves comparing our bovine form to Mrs Famous Bump's neat little silhouette. We know it's all hype, but doesn't it just get under your rapidly expanding skin?

Yummy pregnancy

In the late fifties, even Sylvia Plath, not known for her sunny outlook, wrote contentedly about being 'cow-heavy and floral' when she was pregnant. Today, the prevailing attitude towards the heavily pregnant body verges on disgust. So now we have to look sexy, gorgeous and available as well. It's enough to make your morning sickness last all day.

'It was the first time in years that I just ate what I felt like eating,' says Kate. 'It was incredibly liberating. But then I met this woman with a little neat bump, and lots of black Lycra (registered trade mark), and she kept going on about how she hadn't had to buy any maternity clothes. She was a whole month further on than me too. So, do you know what? I lied and said my baby was due before hers.'

Some of us react by taking weight control too far. A midwife says, 'I've known women go on diets *before* getting pregnant so they won't get too heavy by the end. The pregnancy and the delivery are all about them; it's almost like they've forgotten there's a baby involved. And I've seen them struggle to get into their pre-pregnancy jeans before they leave the hospital. The scariest thing is that some of them manage to!'

There is even a rumour that women have been asking for Caesarean sections to be scheduled as much as four weeks early, to avoid putting on that extra dollop of fat at the end of their pregnancy. Good to know they have their priorities straight. Which brings us on to . . .

Birth pangs

A survey carried out by *Mother & Baby* magazine found that three-quarters of new mothers they asked found childbirth 'more painful than they'd ever imagined'. Well, doh! Trying to expel a watermelon through your nose would probably be less daunting. And it's not as though we don't have time to think it over. Almost forty weeks, generally. And what goes up, must come down – usually the same route!

Once there was no option. You had your legs shoved into stirrups and pushed against gravity and the surgeon only went in if things got tricky. The problem for us now is the appearance of too much choice. What's on the menu? We can plump for scented candles, whale music and dimmed lights, or opt for three thirty on Tuesday afternoon in the operating theatre at a private hospital. Elective Caesareans are on the up and up – very much the celebrity choice – and the big advantage is that this high-tech route fits into the busy schedule and no loss of dignity. It's hard to see why anyone could imagine that recovering from major abdominal surgery and six weeks without being able to drive is somehow less inconvenient than the scenic route. Or maybe they're hoping to maintain their 'honeymoon freshness' – a repulsive expression that would make the most hardened want to gag.

Like all things these days the answer seems to be to throw money at it. We're so used to consumer choice these days that we apply it to the most unconsumer thing in the world. Most of us have Hobson's choice: NHS or NHS and though the whole creaking system tries to provide an amazing service, despite the best efforts of government, you've got to admit it's a time when a bit of luxury wouldn't go amiss. Actually, a clean loo with a door that locks would be a start.

Lucky for the Haves, these days, the only limit to their comfort at this trying time is the size of their bank balance. In London, the main private choices are the Portland Hospital, the Lindo Wing at St Mary's Hospital, the Hospital of St John and St Elizabeth (John and Lizzie's), and the Birth Centre. Each has its own philosophy and adherents.

'Posh labour has become like a holiday choice – you have the brochures,' says Sarah cynically. 'Will you go five star or barefoot luxury? You book yourself in at a time that suits you and pack your Louis Vuitton and away you go. Then you come back, fresh and relaxed, with your snaps and your little souvenir.'

The Portland attracts the likes of Liz Hurley, Posh and Zoë Ball, and is renowned for its luxury and excellent food – at a price. The Lindo hosted the royal deliveries of the Princess of Wales and Princess Michael of Kent. For the groovier boho set, anxious to start on earth-motherhood as they mean to go on , the Hospital of St John and St Elizabeth in north London, with its charismatic founder, Yehudi Gordon, emphasises über-natural childbirth: Jerry Hall, Heather Mills, Cate Blanchett, Elle McPherson and Kate Winslet, Sadie Frost and Emma Thompson pushed and grunted there. Birthing pools are standard and the luxury is of the laid-back variety. More democratic and distinctly low-tech, the Birth Centre in Tooting has tended to the needs of Davina McCall, Jane Horrocks, the late Paula Yates, Thandie Newton, Stella Tennant and Doon Mackichan. Hilariously, the Birth Centre justifies its fees by comparison with other purchases, including school fees, sofas, mortgage payments, two weeks in Barbados and weddings.

'I have two friends who gave birth in completely different ways,' Sarah continues. 'One high-tech and the other natural, and each is convinced her way is the *only* way to go. They corner me on their own and bang on about the pros and cons, trying to recruit me to their gang! It's a bit like being back in the playground. And their babies both look and smell the same to me.'

Still not sure what you want? You could always follow Madonna's example and flee the country altogether. What about France, you hear yourself thinking, because you read somewhere they give you a glass of wine after the birth. Beats NHS tea any day.

Sadly, there is no definitive research about the effect different birthing methods have on the children the babies become. Are Zen-born ones really calmer than those ripped untimely? When he's screaming blue murder in the supermarket queue, it all seems wonderfully irrelevant.

Telling tales

Whatever happens during the delivery, we have to commit it all to memory, because we will dine out on it for the next few years and, like the Ancient Mariner, we find ourselves stopping people and relating our gory tale whether they want to hear it or not. What! Only one in three? The other two got off lightly.

This cringe-making frankness astonishes our mothers who were so coy about their own experiences they failed entirely to mention that they had you in under two hours.

Now you know why you had Millie in the hospital car park. Or that they laboured for thirty-six hours. You'd have gone for a section straight away if you'd known.

If you've already started swapping stories on the circuit, you'll already know that the best-in-show rosette will always be reserved for the women who struggled through hours of agonising labour, fully conscious and unaided, bravely turning away pethidine and sticking remorselessly to their birth plan. If you had an elective section, you might as well give up and go home. No one wants to hear about it. You loser.

Delivery Dads

Only a generation ago, the only active role a man had in the birth of his child was to pace up and down and hand out the cigars once everything was done and dusted. Now 90 per cent of dads are present – and there's a lot of pressure for them to be there. How on earth did that happen? And did anyone think to ask if that's what anyone wanted?

In the 1960s, one father-to-be in Chicago had to hand-cuff himself to his partner's trolley so he could not be removed from the delivery suite! One similarly eager dad, more recently, had been to all the classes and read all the books, but it didn't prepare him for what happened. 'I was all ready,' he whines, 'with ice chips in a flask and tennis balls in a sock to massage Lydia's back. She turned into a complete harpy, and screamed at me to "**** off" with my ice chips. And she squeezed my hand so hard, it took weeks for the sensation to come back properly.'

Nowadays, fathers are more likely to have to chain themselves to the vending machine if they don't want to be part of the birth. It takes a brave man to come right out and say he doesn't want to be there. One of the few who've done so is the chef Gordon Ramsay, no stranger to stressful situations, who admitted that he did not attend any of his four children's births. Funny. They're all so keen to be there for conception.

Nick, a father of four, says: 'I managed to avoid being at the birth with the first three. The first time I was at work. With the next two, being quite close together, I had to look after the older ones. With the last one, though, I'd run out of excuses. I tried everything. Going out to make phone calls, offering to go home and check on things, going to the loo. I really thought I was going to faint. I stayed well away from the business end, I can tell you.'

But nowadays daddy is expected to be in the delivery room witnessing every stage of baby's arrival – even if it is a Caesarean. 'An operating theatre, seeing his wife having major abdominal surgery, is not the right place for a man to be,' says a seasoned obstetrician. 'It's hard for medical students first time and they're not even emotionally involved. The best place for a man to be during a Caesarean is somewhere else.'

Instead there they are with the camcorder, getting in everyone's way, recording every pant and grunt. The end result you subject your friends to is somewhere between *Alien* and a soft porn flick. *Emmanuelle Bears Down*?

Get Real

Thirty years ago, no one expected very much of women when they had delivered. They could spend three weeks in their dressing gown and learn the scary lessons of new motherhood in the privacy of their own home, with the help of their mum or a starched maternity nurse.

Now you are expected to have pinged back into shape just like Liz Hurley, and to be a dab hand at changing nappies straight away. It's like suddenly being asked to fly a jumbo jet without the training. And it's a conspiracy of silence! Why won't somebody break rank and just say how bloody hard it is? Let's face it, most of us have still not regained our shape twenty-two months after giving birth and some of us will still be waiting for it to happen after twenty-two years. Yet apparently 97 per cent of us feel 'unhappy about our bodies after having a baby'.

So if everyone else is as fat and blobby as we are, why are we so bothered about it? It's the elastic celebs that are the freaks, not us.

And then there's the baby to contend with. 'Motherhood hit me like an oncoming train,' admits Polly. 'I had absolutely no idea what was coming. Nothing in my education has prepared me for it. Why couldn't I get him to sleep? How hard could it be? I've got an MBA, for God's sake.'

Bloody hard – that's how hard – and it's no easier for the over-educated. This is when the panic sets in. Everyone else seems to be finding it so easy, don't they? The happy truth is they're not, actually. Everyone's finding it as tough as you are but, like admitting to being hopeless in bed, it's the hardest thing to confess to.

You have this sneaky feeling that because you brought it on yourself, you have to grin and bear it, and it's ten times worse if you struggled to get there in the first place.

'We did IVF eight times,' says Gail. 'How could I admit to being less than ecstatic 24/7 when the whole process had taken years and cost us about as much as a family car!'

It's like your mother used to say when the stilettos you'd insisted on started to pinch: you've only yourself to blame. You're damned if you'll admit it, and if everyone else seems to find it easy you'd better pretend you do too. It's no wonder we flounder.

Tizzie Hall, an Australian sleep guru, says we are the most inexperienced mothers in history. 'We don't grow up with small siblings to practise on, we don't see babies around us. Often the first baby we ever hold is our own. And we live far from our families so have little support or advice.' She may be talking about the thousands of miles between Sydney and Perth, but when you have a colicky newborn, Sydenham to your mother in Purley can seem light years away.

Jenny remembers, 'Everyone said, "Follow your instincts, follow your instincts, your instincts will take over." And it just didn't make any sense to me. The only instinct I had was to run away.'

Fran winces at the memory: 'Oh! Those early days of motherhood; being left with a tiny baby and wanting to yell to my husband's departing back, as he headed off to work and the sanity of the adult world, "Please don't leave me, what am I supposed to do?" So I tried to build structure in the day. I would go to various drop-ins and spent a great deal of my time at the clinic having Harvey weighed. It became a pretty full-time occupation.'

Most of us cope, just, but, out of our skulls on hormones and fatigue, it's usually all we can do to find ourselves a clean pair of knickers. Where did the chick in the snappy suit and the briefcase go?

She's out there all right. She's that Super-Mum. The one who's chairing a meeting forty-eight hours after delivery. The one who's in full slap when you haven't had time to wash your hair for three weeks. The one who's making you feel totally inadequate as you lumber with your pram. Rest assured it's nothing compared to the pressure she's putting on herself.

'When I see women for their six-week check,' says a GP, 'the ones I don't worry about are the ones with their sweatshirts on inside out, who tell me they haven't slept since the birth and they feel like a blob. That's perfectly normal. It's the ones who've put on make-up and have ironed their co-ordinated outfits and say everything is fantastic that worry me. They're the ones trying to live up to unrealistic standards.'

Post-natal depression? Moi?

Tits Up

Breast is best! Breast is best! (So anything else is complete pants.) That may not be exactly what they say, but we all know that's what they mean. Okay, it may be natural, but

47

it's far from simple. Breastfeeding has gone on for as long as women have had boobs, but we make it horribly tricky for ourselves these days, trying to fit it in with our busy, busy lives.

'There was this really thick girl in hospital, right across from me,' says Amanda, a merchant banker. 'A real pramface. And she was managing it no bother – baby latching on, good supply, the lot. And the way she looked over at me, so smug. Well, to be quite honest, it was probably the way I'd have looked at her in any other context in the world. I was really floundering and I bet the midwives were thinking, Bloody career women. And, just for the record, let me say there's nothing more stressful than being told to relax all the bloody time.'

And even if you do manage to get feeding going, the advice is still completely contradictory. But what's a girl to do? You've got Gina Ford telling you to feed to a schedule, you've got another batch of experts telling you to feed on demand. If you feed to schedule, there's a good chance your supply of milk will decrease. If you feed on demand, you'll never get a routine established. So which is it?

'I can't believe what's happened to me. I used to be able to do things,' says Jane. 'And I'm sitting here, advice book in hand, on the phone to my breastfeeding counsellor, with cabbage leaves down my bra, tits like boulders and a screaming baby.'

Lucy gave up trying, but still felt the pressure. 'I did go to my after-birth yoga class with the baby and lied about it and said I was breastfeeding. And the baby's not even a week old!'

These days breastfeeding is the Battle of the Boobs. 'I became obsessed with other women's tits,' says Helen. 'If I saw a woman with a baby and enormous knockers I'd want to stab her!' And the self-satisfaction of those who can!

'I was sitting at a post-natal get-together of my NCT group – I still think of them as ordeal by home-made flapjack – and Tom was fractious,' says Verity. 'He just wouldn't feed and I knew it was because I was tired and production was low. One of the other mothers looked over at me sympathetically, baby to her breast, and asked, sweetly, if I'd like to use some milk from the fridge she'd expressed earlier! I never went back.'

Of course all good cows are judged by their milk production quotas, but what is it that makes people who were once our friends – intelligent, sensitive women – suddenly lose all modesty and brag about their skills at lactation?

Dawn is amazed by it all: 'I was sitting recently with a group of woman having coffee,' she says. 'One admitted she was struggling with breastfeeding and worrying about having enough milk, then this insensitive cow – careful choice of word there – pipes up with, "Oh, God, when I was breastfeeding I just had SO much of it, I couldn't get it to stop. I'd lie in the bath and there'd be, you know, a layer of cream forming around me. It was amazing!" Horrified silence all round . . .'

If you did manage it and it's all systems go, then good on ya, Daisy. The World Health Organisation loves you. The NCT loves you. Every childbirth and parenting pundit loves you. But enough of this love fest. If breast-feeding is good, why are we still finding ourselves squatting in bathrooms trying to nurse, fumbling with shawls, apologising all the time, being asked to leave restaurants and coffee houses, and treated like social pariahs? You'd think, wouldn't you, that in these liberated times you could get your boobs out without being vilified for it?

At least if our mothers did it (which few of them did – it interrupted cocktail parties) they did it in the privacy of their own home, with a fag and a G&T to while away the boredom. Our problem, silly us, is that we still want to make like single girls and meet girlfriends for coffee. Tits and caramel macchiato don't mix.

Naming or shaming?

Choosing a name for the baby ought to be the fun bit – especially when we, as a generation, have such boring names. We were all called Katherine or James. A bit of creativity in the naming department is the reward for necking all those vitamins, going to all those NCT classes and hospital appointments. It's the only thing in the uncertain world of birth and labour that you really do have control over, so there's all the more pressure to get it right. Is a single word capable of telling the world just how utterly perfect your child is going to be?

Naturally the celebs take the Oscars for absurdity here. Gwyneth's Apple and Moses, Helen Hunt's MaKena Lei, Cate Blanchett's Roman, Heidi Klum's Leni, Courteney Cox Arquette's Coco: they sound like Chihuahuas, poor little sods. But they are not the only ones who completely lose the plot when they name their babies. Quite a lot of parents seem to have this shameless urge to be original and unique. To make their babies into a limited edition. Exclusive.

But with all the weird and wacky names around, why is it getting harder and harder to choose something? It is a sign of the times that a new book, *Cool Names for Babies*, by Pamela Redmond Satran and Linda Rosenkrantz, has recently been published. All this competition has given rise to a terrifying new trend, 'Name Rage'.

'We spent ages coming up with the name for our baby,' says Mary. 'And my stupid husband went and confided in a friend. Soon after that a friend of the friend got in first and used *our* name for *their* baby. I was livid. We never speak to them now.'

'I called my daughter Nutmeg,' opined one old hippy, 'because I felt it would help her to build her character.' Well, let's hope she builds enough to turn round and give her parents a sharp slap when she is tall enough.

Why, oh why don't they save up the wacky ideas for middle names? Or, better still, get themselves a cat.

However, the ramifications of getting the name wrong are terrifying if recent research is to be believed. Psychiatrists have found that men named Wayne were more likely to be considered malingering, feigning and personality-disordered in diagnosis than those called Matthew. So that cuts down the choices a bit. The study concluded that doctors may stereotype patients on the basis of their names. What would they make of Tiger Lily and Dweezil?

Sleep – please?

It is a universal truth that a baby is a nocturnal creature, sleeping adorably during the day and yelling blue murder from 9 p.m. onwards, making any attempt at civilised meals or conversation between parents utterly impossible. After being passed from parent to exhausted parent for a few hours, the baby will sleep intermittently from about 11 p.m. until 2 a.m., when it will wake again and require constant feeding to nourish it for a hard day of sleeping from about 9 a.m.

Terrible sleepers are probably nothing new. Mothers thoughout history have paced the nursery floor singing lullabies, but that was all very well in the days when they had all day to sleep with them. Or nannies to do the pacing. But when you have just got home from a sales conference, or have two other children to consider, it's living torture.

Our mistake is that we are guilty of *trying to get back to normal as soon as possible*, of kidding ourselves it won't be like that for us, so we ignore the voices of warning.

Instead we run around like headless chickens at 3 a.m. trying to find solutions. John admits, 'We tried everything: swaddling, black-out curtains, white noise, formula top-ups. Most of the things we tried did work – once – and we'd think we were on to something. But the next night, we'd be back to square one. One night, at about 3 a.m., we even moved the cot so it was lying north–south rather than east–west. Then it was magnetic mattresses. Anything!'

The next mistake we make is to believe that other people's babies are always sleeping more than our own – it's a ripe area for one-upmanship and since you're not there at midnight to check, the big fat liars can get away with it. At least some of them 'fessed up in another survey by *Mother & Baby* magazine, which found that during the first four months, mothers average fewer than four hours' sleep a night. Sometimes the media can be our friend!

And, naturally, where there is a problem, there'll be someone out there prepared to tell you you're doing it all wrong. Thanks again, Gina! But wouldn't you pay anything to make the baby sleep through? Now you can hire a night-time nanny to solve the problem for you. In just two nights, they claim to be able to get your baby into good sleep habits. Basically, you pay them to leave your baby to cry. How crazy is that?

'My partner actually had to restrain me to stop me going to Tim when we decided to try controlled crying,' says a quivering Tracey. 'I think I was crying more than the baby by the end of it, and even though in my heart I knew I didn't agree with the advice in the baby manual, I went along with it like a lemming.'

But fear not, Tracey. A scientist has come to your rescue. A study has shown that the best way to ensure your child grows up as a 'calm, healthy adult' is to let him sleep in your bed *until he is five*. Never mind that you will get no sleep from his wriggling, you'll have offspring with good chi and there'll always be plenty of room in the bed because your partner will have buggered off in despair ages ago.

53

'We've got to get to lunch on time. I don't
want them to twig she isn't sleeping through.'

Mama wars

With all the world today in strife, you might think we would cut each other some slack. That motherhood, the great leveller, would serve as a safe house where civility and mutual respect prevail. If only. Working mothers and stay-at-home mothers have been staging a vicious, guer-rilla war against each other since the Equal Opportunities Commission first opened its doors.

Jackie says, 'There's nothing yummy about being a stay-at-home mummy. I love Ella to pieces, but it's the hardest work I've ever done and it's more than full-time. I get so pissed off with people asking what I do and then looking over my shoulder to see if there's someone more interesting when I say I'm a full-time mother. They make me feel as though I've taken the cop-out route.'

Celine sees it from the other side: 'My partner is a composer and he works from home. I'm a teacher and I can't work from home. What could be more logical than for me to go out and him to stay with Charlotte. But you'd think I was Cruella DeVil the way some of the stay-at-home mums treat me. And when he takes Charlotte out shopping, just because he's a bloke, he gets all these women helping him! Meanwhile I'm racked with guilt.'

Alex is more direct: 'I'm doing the job I spent years training for. Why should I feel guilty about that?'

Then there's Rachel: 'I'm fed up of being the only mother at mother and baby groups. Most of the other women there are nannies and they won't talk to me.'

It seems we can't do right for doing wrong! So much

expected, so little help and society so ready to blame. We decide to climb off the career ladder and we are a parasite. We decide to stay on it, and we are a bad, bad woman. The legislation is pretty much in place to allow parents to return to work, if we want or need to, yet we still feel like second-class citizens.

Men can't win either. One (male) business director admits: 'I wouldn't let on to doing the school run or wanting to be at one of my kids' events because it might affect how my peer group perceives me. I opened my briefcase in a meeting the other day and there was a copy of *Little Red Train* in there. I slammed it shut quickly before anyone noticed as if it was a dirty magazine!'

'If I was in a pinch, I'd only turn to another working mother,' confides Sally, an estate agent and the mother of two young boys. 'Even my closest friends lord it over me. One really close girlfriend sighed deeply when I asked her to collect Dan from swimming for me because I'd been held up with a viewing. "Oh, you career girls," she said. "Always putting work first!" I could have slapped her!'

Of course the working mum will get her own back when the children have flown the nest and the stay-at-homer decides to embark on the tricky route of career rebirth. But then she did give her children the best years.

Life after birth: it's a social life, Jim, but not as we know it

Remember that moment in *Sex and the City* when Miranda, new mother in denial, tries to rejoin the normal world and takes her baby out to a restaurant with her mates. 'Nothing has to change. Just think of this as a big purse.' The big purse promptly vomits.

So is it possible to combine a baby with a social life these days? Well, no. Not really. Child-free friends quickly come to the conclusion that we're part of an evangelical cult, trying to recruit new members to parenthood. We, meanwhile, have to construct a new life for ourselves among the Parent People, who know Milton isn't necessarily a poet and where we can talk about our piles and stitches with complete strangers, and nobody looks at us funny.

Outside that safe and lovely place, there's the awful realisation that we have become social pariahs.

'I have to confess that these days I try and avoid my friends with babies,' says Caroline, unreassuringly. 'They are so boring, with their endless chat about nappies and their contents. They can never come out and when they do they keep yawning, spend the whole time looking at their watches then worry about their boobs leaking.'

Then that huge car we bought is too big to park. We can't take that lovely big buggy into any of the shops we want to go to because it won't fit through the doors. We can't live the life we did before because no restaurant really wants us there. There's nowhere to change the baby that's quite clean enough and nowhere we feel comfortable breastfeeding. Parks are full of huge menacing two-year-olds and, frankly, with all the clobber we were talked into, by the time we're ready to leave the house, it's time to come home again.

Now we know why we never really saw anyone with a baby out and about, in those far-off days of our pregnancy. They were all at home fretting, just like we are now, or at each other's houses, pretending to each other that their baby sleeps through.

The Top Ten Most Oppressive Book Titles Ever

The Seven Sins of Parenting an Only Child

The Baby Whisperer Solves All Your Problems

Brain Child: How Smart Parents Make Smart Kids

The Yummy Mummy's Survival Guide

Potty Training in Less Than a Day

Creating Kids Who Can Concentrate

Body After Baby: The Simple 30 Day Plan to Lose Your Baby
    Weight

Optimum Nutrition for Your Child's Mind

The Science of Parenting: Practical Guidance on Sleep,
    Crying, Play and Building Emotional Wellbeing for Life

365 Creative Days of Play

From Kid to Superkid

The Top Ten Silliest Childcare Book Titles Ever

125 Brain Games for Babies

Sippy Cups are Not for Chardonnay

101 Educational Conversations with Your Kindergartner-1st
    Grader

Fresh Milk: The Secret Life of Breasts

The Three Martini Playdate

Baby Signing (Publisher? Amazing Baby)

O'Baby: The Irish Baby Name Book

Laughin'fertility: A Bundle of Observations for the Baby-
  Making Challenged (Wince-making awful!)
Baby-gami: Baby Wrapping for Beginners
Fathers' Liberation Ethics: Holistic Ethical Advocacy for Active
  Nurturant Fathering (Zzzzz . . .)

Wisdom before the Event
(or things you wish you'd never said)
I'm going to give birth without pain relief
I won't talk about the baby all the time
I won't be one of those women/men who bore other people
  senseless
I'll breastfeed of course
I'd never use a dummy
Our baby will never sleep in our bed
I'd never smack my children!
I'll never bribe them with sweets
Having a baby will not change my life

3
Trial By Party Bag

Jelly and ice cream, jelly and ice cream. Oh, it used to be so simple then. Uncle George with his ukulele, a couple of rounds of Pass the Parcel and Pin the Tail on the Donkey, then settle down for a tea of bread and butter (which you had to eat first before you were allowed the party ring biscuits). The iced gems were always left on the plate because they were and still are disgusting. Then you'd run around the garden in your short white socks, knowing your mother would tear you off a strip for getting them covered in grass stains, until home time at half past five when you'd be handed a slice of the *home-made* cake wrapped in a paper napkin and, if you were lucky, a balloon, which would burst in the back of the car – though that was a good thing because it was obscuring your mother's view out of the back window anyway.

Your feet would hurt from the elastic on your blue patent party shoes, and your dress would have ripped when someone had stood on the sash when you were on the space hopper, but Uncle George had been funny – even though you'd seen the rabbit-out-of-the-hat gag six times before – and you had a trip to see *Bedknobs and Broom-sticks* with Gillian from 3B after half-term to look forward to, because her mum had booked it at the Odeon as her special birthday treat.

We didn't seem to have parties every year then, except for my friend Tracy who was quite rich and spoilt and a select group of us used to go to the leisure centre with her to swim. Our brothers had football parties, refereed by unfit fathers who would give away penalties unfairly and precipitate tears and time out in your bedroom 'until you have calmed down'. There might have been war games which involved hiding with water pistols behind trees or Kick the Can, which was scary if you were 'it', and the boys would go to any lengths, even resorting to violence, to get to the can before you.

So we progressed through the party years. Games got more and more daring – Blockey 1-2-3 in the dark with torches? – until we hit our teens and exploded in a burst of hormones. Instead of flicking ice cream at smelly George Dickson and playing Blind Man's Buff with him, you'd be pinned against the wall of the village hall trying to flick flirtatious looks at a now much taller (and strangely attractive) George Dickson and thinking about doing other things in the buff with him. We'd have hot dogs and fruit punch and shuffle to 10CC *I'm Not In Love*, while being held in the sweaty grip of a boy who wasn't George Dickson, until someone put the lights back on because it was eleven thirty and Dad had arrived to collect you in the Ford Sierra.

Your own party would have passed in a haze of excitement and a vague feeling of nausea brought on by too much dandelion and burdock, and the hope that everyone would leave very soon so you could open that tantalising pile of presents, which would include a 6-inch single of 'Crazy Horses' by the Osmonds, a pink troll and a furry orange pencil case.

That was then . . .

Of course our birthdays used to come around slower when we were younger, but have you noticed how our own children's birthdays seem to arrive about a month after last year's? Or at least that's when you start planning the next one.

'What happened to the big celebration?' asks Gemma. 'When once only Big Birthdays, like the eighteenth and twenty-first, warranted Big Plans, now all birthdays seem to involve advance planning on the scale of a task force. We know people who I can't help thinking have peaked a bit soon with a tenth birthday bash. What will they do for an encore?'

Frankly, a party for a hundred adults is preferable to a shindig for twenty or thirty (or actually any number of) children. Children are now so unstinting in their judgements, with absolutely no grasp of the social graces whereby you pretend you are having a good time even if it's dire and you'd rather be anywhere else on earth. But don't you sense that this feeling of being judged is now heightened to such intense levels thanks to the weight of expectation?

And that is the crux of the Birthday Party Angst that has us all in its grip: *expectation*. No longer will simple, brief and easy suffice. In fact their first birthday, when they are more interested in the paper and the cardboard box, is the one and only time when we seem to be able to get away with anything. Trouble is no one told us at the time!

But added to expectation – and we have to be big and brave to admit this – isn't it just possible that a birthday party is our once-a-year chance (and more if you have several kids) to invite all our friends and other parents in, and show them just what marvellous parents we are?

'Yup, that's me!' says Freya sheepishly. 'I hold my hands up and admit that I get a bit of a kick when other parents say, "Wow!" I mean, you've got to make sure they know how much effort you've put in, don't you? How else would they know?'

The Honeymoon Period: Ages 1–3

To be really prepared these days, you have to start thinking about birthday parties at about the point at which the child is to be conceived. Saddle yourself with a January baby and the options for parties are severely restricted as it gets older. 'Weather permitting' are words that strike fear into any party organiser's soul. Don't know about you, but not many people would dare risk a slaved-over Pirates Extravaganza being rained off and then be lumbered with thirty expectant faces turned to you for entertainment. No, really the only time we should be thinking about risking pregnancy is between August and December (though even that might be leaving it a bit late).

At least these early years are the simple ones when birthday parties are a genuine celebration of the miracle of our children. Most one-year-olds are pretty clueless about the birthday concept anyway, but know to smile benignly when a helium balloon is waved at them because it means lots of lovely attention. One friend does admit to staying up late the night before to ice out Happy 1st Birthday on the top of a chocolate cake, vaguely aware of the absurdity of what she was doing. Could the fact that her mother-in-law was coming over for tea the next day have had anything to do with it?

At least at this early stage you don't have to contend with the 'invite the whole class' dilemma and can only hope that the other mothers there will be as obsessed as you are with potty training so will fail to notice any shortcomings on your part – though, as with any gathering of other parents, that in itself brings on its own stresses! The Helicopter Mother will be around the table like a persistent bluebottle of course.

'It's feeble I know but I found myself apologising all the time!' Alison rants. 'I found myself justifying everything and saying weakly, "Oh, do you think so," when one Heli mum pointed out earnestly how bread sticks can be awfully sharp on their little mouths.'

The trouble is that, with a fairly poor level of conversational subject matter among the partygoers, you are left to converse with the other parents, who you hardly know but met at toddler group. They can't leave their offspring with you (thank God!), but the only thing you have in common with them is that you have children the same age, which makes you cling together like survivors in a shipwreck. No one will admit they are knackered but will tell you how many teeth their darling has and laugh, saying, 'Never mind, you don't see many adults with only four,' when you admit that your child has only popped the top and bottom two.

This is the only time in their lives that children seem to be unaffected by peer or commercial pressure. They think the adverts on ITV are part of the programme so won't be too judgemental about the level of the bash or the quality of the present. But it's not really about them, is it? It takes courage to buck the trend and get away with 'Come round for tea and a bit of cake'. But this party business is uncharted territory, isn't it? We can have friends round for dinner, and probably arranged our own weddings, but a Children's Party? Now that's a whole new challenge.

'I didn't sleep for two nights.' Beth laughs. 'And when the first child arrived, I broke into a muck sweat. I opened a bottle of wine and by the time the parents came to collect them, I was half cut!'

'Oh, God! I was so terrified that I ended up being horrible to my son – and it was his party!' wails Harriet. 'He ended up in tears and so did I!'

But we needn't worry if we are nervous about how we should handle the stress – there's plenty of advice out there in books and websites. Don't have the party at nap time; don't have balloons that may burst and startle children; offer carrot sticks and hummus or guacamole, for goodness sake; sweeten your cake with apple juice not sugar; don't offer chocolate . . .

'Talk to your toddler about what they would like for their party a few weeks before the event,' suggests one child guru. Come on! There are times when you can take inclusion too far. Don't they know toddlers have absolutely no idea of timescales and will think you mean tomorrow? Though of course you find yourself asking the little chap anyway because you don't want him to feel excluded. You are even given – and probably heed – advice on how to word the actual invitation. One supplier advertises ready done invitations with the words 'first impressions count'. What is this – a party invite or a job application?

The Tween Years: piling on the pressure

From four onwards, though, it's party-time *extraordinaire* when there is about one party a week at least and the pressure is more full-on than an A-list celeb's diary. School has started and with it a whole new seam of children and their parties and the ensuing party neurosis. You come home from collecting your child from a class-mate's Karate Party and think, How the hell will I top that? And implicit in the rave reviews your child gives of it is, How the hell will you top that? Or at least you read it that way.

A recent report by Virgin Credit Card reveals that over half of UK parents are suffering from 'Posh Party Syndrome', and we fork out over £1.25 billion a year on our kids' birthday parties. Not each one of us of course, though it may feel like it. That's an average of £181.50

per party – and if that's the average a scary number of us must be spending a lot more. In London it's about £221 per party, which means if you invited fifteen children that would be nearly £15 a head – probably more than the value of the gift they bring with them – and that's before you've bought a present for *your* child. According to another report, it's the fifth birthday that is the biggy with over half of 3,500 parents polled saying they'd spend over £500 on it. Based on population numbers, that's about £128 million being spent on children turning five this year alone!

These reports are done by banks and credit card companies – as well they might be as you'll have to remortgage to afford it – but the most alarming finding is this: over half of UK parents admit that they feel under pressure to compete with other parents. Oh, crikey, so that's it: we've been rumbled. It's not about giving our children the very best. It's not about imitating celebrity parties because your child is every bit as special as Brooklyn or Romeo Beckham. It's about what the *other parents think*. Another report – if you can believe companies carry out these things – states eight out of ten parents said that other parents are always trying to show off by throwing the biggest and best birthday bash. That's either sociological observation on the part of the respondents, or paranoia.

One party organiser we spoke to confirms it all. 'Parents get very nervous about parties,' she said. 'They want their children to look good in front of their friends and they want to look good in front of their friends. We always prepare tea and coffee for the parents who are staying at our parties and, at one party as people arrived, the hostess, ignoring the children, was running over to ask them what they wanted to drink. It was as if they might think she had failed in some way if she didn't ensure they had what they wanted.'

Another party organiser is more blunt: 'It is all about impressing other people.'

The bar is set pretty high, so what do we find ourselves doing? Like getting an interior decorator in to choose our curtains, we get in a professional to do our kids' parties, and what they offer now is a million miles from pinning the tail on the donkey. Perhaps in our agonisingly self-conscious desire to avoid anyone losing – how would they cope with the failure? – we studiously avoid competitive games and plump for pamper or makeover parties (from age six) where, in some sort of paedophiliac fantasy, little girls can all look beautiful as they have their nails painted and their hair done in any from a 'range of 14 styles' while they sip little cocktails and look like something from the Elizabeth Arden salon in the 1950s. Yippee! They can round it all off with 'some body art tattoos applied to finish your transformation to Pamper Princess, Disco Diva, or Teenage Belle' before – and here's the critical bit – 'being collected by shocked and *impressed* parents' as it says on one piece of sales literature. (Apoplectic more like.) Another one sounds so insincere we're not even sure they aren't being sarcastic: 'From 5 to 9 years – give your little darling's [sic] a birthday to remember'.

On the assumption that not many twelve-year-old boys

would go for beauty parties, we call in the SAS of party planners to exploit the testosterone rush with quad bike parties and paint balling at upwards of £200. But we fall for the set price, little realising that an impassioned adolescent can discharge 200 paint balls in no time and then come begging for seven quid to get a few more. Two hours later and we are writing a cheque to the organisers for £350. Yes, dear reader, that sucker was me.

'We did go karting,' whispers Penny (surname withheld), 'and I paid for half with a cheque and the rest with cash so my husband wouldn't know how much it had cost.' Marital deception? Things are getting out of hand.

Parties have taken on the same dimensions as corporate events. You find yourself going the whole hog. He wants action? You find yourself hiring a tank and Parachute Regiment lookalikes in combats. She wants a bouncy castle? Why stop there? Hire a fairground to come to your house. Yes, really, it's been done.

Party goods and party planning is a massive industry, though Peter Robertson of Twizzle, the society party planners with whom some parents spend over £10,000 a party, reckons it's not in response to parents wanting to get one up on the Joneses. It's hard not to think he's being a bit too charitable or concerned his customers might be listening. 'We do parties for busy working mums, often successful business women,' he says, 'who simply don't have the time. It's more than just trying to impress.' Though he did admit a look of satisfaction on the faces of the hosts as they smiled modestly at the gasps of admiration from collecting parents.

As if to compound the pressure, at the end of the credit card birthday spending report, published on the web, were links to websites with suggestions for themes and party games. Even as you look at them you can feel the pressure building. It isn't: 'Gosh that's a good idea. I'll keep that in mind.' It's: 'Hell, I've never done that. Should I have had a Piñata? And what is one anyway? Yoga parties – what?'

The wealth of information, advice, ideas, goodies to buy for this age group is frankly overwhelming, but it's the wording that is most alarming: 'We recognise the importance of a fantastic going home present . . .' or 'this theme is always a success'. It's meant to help, but all it does is heap on the pressure. If you don't heed the advice, is the underlying message, you might *fail*.

You may not approve but you daren't break ranks. So it is a certain madness descends: what happened to your sense of proportion? There you are at midnight, propped up by a glass of Glenmorangie, wrapping up a *Now That's What I Call Music* CD (you can please all of the people all of the time) inside layer upon layer of paper for Pass the Parcel, remembering of course to insert a little something between each layer so *no one loses out*. This is what writer Lesley Thomas calls: 'part of a new and rather cowardly style of parenting in which Mummy and Daddy never want to be the bad guy'. She goes on: 'I don't think it's kind to shield children from the lesson that "you win some, you lose some".'

Then there's the party bag. The thing that says as much about us as the car we drive. The yardstick of the success of our party, and therefore us as parents, is the contents of the party bag. So you find yourself stuffing water pistols and Top Trumps into a cheap but jolly plastic bag, racked with uncertainty: too much? too little? If it's not up to standard, will your child be invited to the next party? Yet you know deep down (and resentfully) that it will all be discarded and put in the bin anyway when they get home.

And then what you thought was okay seems so mean and tacky when you hear that at Georgie's party they got a little book as a going-home present, with a mini Mars Bar attached as a special treat. Okay, so Georgie's mum is in publishing and she is a good friend of yours, but somehow you feel a bit let down. She's played dirty and used her position to get one over on everyone. In the words of Dolly Parton: please don't do it just because you can.

You snarl for a bit and feel stupid until you and Georgie's mum can both laugh together when you hear about the total absurdity of the dinner dance, with linen tablecloths, black tie and 'champagne' reception with sparkling apple juice, for a five-year-old. Really.

Going solo

Of course party success (and, ergo, parent success) is measured in quite the opposite way too: by being the parent who *did it all herself* . . . We do this one of two ways: we hire not one, not two but five bouncy castles of different shapes and have an activity party, or we get all creative and have princes and princesses parties. 'I spent hours trawling places like Currys and stuffing giant-sized old washing machine boxes into the back of my car,' says

Jennifer. 'Then it took ages to make castles out of them. The children made their own crowns out of crafty bits I'd laid out on a table and they proceeded to wreck the boxes.' And how did she feel for her efforts? Just a teensy bit pleased with herself? 'Well, yes, I suppose I did feel a certain amount of satisfaction when the leisure-centre-party mothers came to collect their offspring and oohed and aahed in admiration.'

Of course the trickiest issue is The Cake. Naturally we all know that it will be cut, wrapped in a napkin, popped in the party bag and binned. So what do you do? Slave over it for hours, creating something that looks a bit like Hogwarts out of Royal icing, or do you nip into the supermarket for a ready made, iced, utterly disgusting version based around some TV theme? It's a tough call.

'I can do the hired-in entertainer,' says Helen, 'but I just can't bring myself to buy a birthday cake. I have to make it – it's a matter of principle – and the one and only time I did cave in and buy one the entertainer asked my daughter if Mummy had made it.'

Marie takes the whole cake-making issue so seriously she makes one for the candle-blowing-out ceremony, but it's such a work of art she won't actually let the children eat it. In fact no one eats it. It is simply photographed for the album and is left out to be admired until too stale to eat. Nope, she buys one in to cut up for the party bag.

Take that route though and there is always the danger a guest's mother will eat it from the napkin in the party bag; then what might she think?!

Upping the ante

Phew, as they get a bit older you heave a sigh of relief because you no longer have to fret about trial by Victoria sponge, nor do you have to invite the whole class. At last we can slough off that irritating whingey little child whose mother always hung around in case he proved to be allergic to the type of bread we were using for the sandwiches. She needn't have worried, they went untouched anyway, along with the hummus, but we had to provide them, didn't we? What we do have to do now, though, is seriously *impress*. Parties for anything over the age of eleven have to be very cool indeed and we end up feeling even more image-conscious than our coy, excruciatingly embarrassed pre-pubescent child.

A trip to the skating rink or the leisure centre just won't wash. Bowling? Too quick, too noisy – and the shoe-sharing? Yeuch. Laser Quest? Too last year. So you end up booking one of those wind-tunnel sky-diving flights which take an hour to get to, last ten seconds yet somehow make a serious dent in your credit card, and that's before we've bought the digital pics, the DVD, the T-shirt, and the pizza afterwards. 'I just wanted him to be cool among his friends,' winces Linda, mother of Rory, fourteen, 'and somehow the pain of the bill was dulled by the look of awe on the faces of the other kids. What will their parents top that with, I thought!'

Perhaps they'll do it with a limo. Of course, *you* know they are insufferably naff, but children never did have much taste, did they? And won't it look great when it turns up to take them all out? Beth wasn't impressed. 'My eight-year-old was invited to a private members' club in the middle of South Kensington and the mother was curiously insistent that we got there at 2.45. I thought there might be a time limit, but it turned out that there had been two classes of party invitations and there had already been a party in the morning. The second wave had to be there on time to be the welcoming party on the pavement as the limo pulled up with the more favoured friends on their way back from the morning jamboree.'

'They make more sense,' justifies a London limo company. 'If you are taking lots of kids to ice skating or bowling then one big car means you don't have to have lots of mothers delivering children.' But, it admits, people book cars in their fleet for a three-hour drive around to look at the sights (you could get halfway to Scotland in that time) and drink pop and eat in the back. You can pack in twenty-six little friends in a Hummer (four flat-screen TVs and a mirrored ceiling if the view gets boring) and it would be a snip at £685.

Wow! Any more? 'Well, we took fifteen fourteen- and fifteen-year-olds to paint balling the other day and their dad wanted the limo to stick around.' So while they splattered paint at each other the car sat there then brought them back again at a cool £1,285 for a six-hour hire. If that wasn't enough, it delivered them to a restaurant (fifteen kids remember), then presumably there were taxis home. You do the maths.

Well, at least there wouldn't have been any booze, them being under age and all. Forget it. While it's illegal for these companies to allow kids to drink while they are unaccompanied, put a parent there and a crate of alcopops and that's okay.

As boundaries have slackened so the teenage party becomes more an exercise in crowd control and the vice squad. We seem to have completely forgotten the boundaries our parents set for our parties – were we that hard done by? – and have a very tenuous hold indeed on the whole event.

'I can't believe myself,' says Sarah, whose daughter Anna is fifteen. 'I was brought up in a house where we weren't allowed to have friends around on a Sunday because it was quiet family time and here I am creeping downstairs to the sitting room at 3 a.m. when my daughter has friends over and bleating, "Soo sorry to interrupt but would you mind quietening down a teensy bit cos I'm trying to sleep."'

The sleepover party (or the no-sleepover) is one of the more irritating bloody things we have inherited from the States, along with baby showers and Mary Kate and Ashley. Didn't we used to just 'stay the night at someone's house'? So why this silly cute word? And sleep has nothing to do with it. When you finally get the horde into some sort of order, after they have trashed your sitting room watching *Legally Blonde* and getting high on Skittles and Pringles (then demanding toast) you then spend the next three hours trying to get a bit of quiet, aware that it will embarrass everyone if you lose your temper and get firm – they might dislike you, heaven forbid!

'We were woken at 2 a.m.,' remembers Ally, 'when a

girl burst into our room asking if I had any eye make-up remover!' And she probably found herself sheepishly getting some for her. Then it gets to 3 a.m. and you have a total sense of humour failure and let rip at 50 decibels, shocking the little sods into silence. As you drag yourself from your bed next morning, feeling as if you have been hit by a train, you vow that never ever again will you have anyone to stay over.

But, like childbirth, somehow you forget the pain and find yourself planning another one . . .

Even the sleepover is just about bearable if the only drink involved is Diet Coke. Alcohol is a whole new ball game. 'We were so naïve,' admits Lyn. 'When our daughter had her fifteenth birthday we said we weren't providing drink but they could bring some if they wanted to, and we imagined it would be wine and a bit of beer. Oh yeah? There was champagne, whisky, brandy, vodka. At about 1 a.m. a boy passed out and I called his mother. "Oh, he's allergic to alcohol," she told me. "If I'd known there was going to be drink I wouldn't have let him come!" At my younger daughter, Joey's, party I was wiser and frisked everyone when they arrived! I am amazed by how little other parents ask details about parties. It's either ignorance or laziness. When she was fourteen, Joey was invited to a sleepover party at a hotel in Eastbourne owned by the hostess's grandmother. Will you be there? I asked her mother. "Oh, I hadn't thought about that," she replied, and when I asked her how she was going to stop them all sleeping together, she said, "Well, you have to trust them some time." I didn't let her go.'

Ali thought her son Jake, fourteen, was at a New Year's Eve party in Brighton with the parents there until she got a call from outside a nightclub at 2 a.m. where he was throwing up his guts. Where was the host's mother? Goodness knows, but, says Ali, I had to believe her when she said she'd stay there with them. What else could I do?'

We aren't the first generation to fret about teenage parties – though I think when we were younger it was cider not Bacardi Breezers and spliffs – but where we differ from our parents is that we are so self-conscious or keen to be seen as chilled and uninterfering that we don't even bother to check what the children are going to be up to. 'I think we want to be considered cool,' says Jane, mother of Angus and Tom, sixteen and fourteen, 'which is odd when we spend so much time when they are little fretting about how safe they are. One minute we're not letting them play in the woods in case they hurt themselves or are abducted by some deranged murderer, and the next, as they become teenagers, we do the reverse and let them go out until all hours when the dangers are much more real. It's nuts!'

Ben, dad of Ed and Chloe, finds it hard. 'To maintain control is hard work. I can see why my dad insisted we were home by midnight – he wanted to go to bed. Now you have to be up till 3 a.m. when they get back and I can't be bothered. I have to admit I just close my eyes and hope to God they are being sensible.'

Mummy says I had a lovely time

And does any of this party angst get rewarded? Not likely. Have you noticed the way the thank you letter, like butter puff biscuits and Parma violets, has almost completely disappeared? While Boxing Day was once the worst day of the year as you were made to sit down and write to Aunty Mary to thank her for the Kerplunk game, you now find yourself looking back on it fondly. At least then we knew how to be grateful and now, on the rare occasions a thank you letter does arrive, it's like winning the Premium Bonds. So why aren't we making our children write them? 'Ah, no one does that any more,' says some achingly self-conscious thirteen-year-old, so you don't push the point because the last thing you want is for him to arrive at school with a pile of letters in neatly addressed envelopes and look geeky.

So, phew, at least that's it until next year. Just one thing: you have booked the venue, haven't you?

Many happy returns.

New types of party parties

Proms: that other irritating import from the US, and they don't just happen at the end of school life: there are proms at the end of the school year, the end of term, even at half-term probably. You trawl Topshop with your daughter holding up possible outfits for her sneering opinion, and she shakes her head in disbelief and continues to go through the T-shirt rail. But it doesn't just stop at the outfit. 'When your teenager gets invited to the school prom,' urges the dedicated party planning company, 'the last thing you want is for her to walk down the stairs in the expensive outfit you bought for her, looking like Magenta from the *Rocky Horror Show*!!! – Why not invite her friends around for the afternoon and have their make-up applied professionally and their hair styled – they will feel like the belle of the ball.' Well, that's something else to organise. And then there's the After Prom party. Time to hit Topshop again.

Halloween: what used to be the biggest non-event of the year now involves buying an outfit in Tesco with a range of plastic teeth and face paints that has been on display since the Easter egg range came down. Then there is the trick or treating, which anyone over the age of twenty thinks is nonsense, but we still find ourselves forking out four quid for a pumpkin and handing out Haribo to grasping little children who are clueless about what it's all about and actually think it's called 'trickle treat'.

Baby Showers: oh, come on. It's just an excuse for more presents.

Sixteenth Birthday Parties: these are on a par with the eighteenth and twenty-first in case they can't wait that long. Be careful you don't peak too early because where can you go from here?

Extreme Parties

'We once did a bar mitzvah for a hundred and twenty guests, twenty-five of whom were children. We did an upmarket music theme all in black and white. We made every table look like a grand piano. By the time we had installed the set, the forty-piece orchestra had flown in specially from Israel, the kids' table was already an afterthought and the budget – probably in excess of £100,000. Then we did a christening party for a one-year-old which was a Wild West Town complete with rodeo!'

Gary, party planner

4
School Entry: Admission Impossible

So we've got our prototype, and it's looking pretty fantastic. All that careful planning has paid off. And now it's time for the product launch. And on which lucky educators will we bestow the honour of nurturing our perfect and utterly gifted child? It's only a matter of time, surely, before they will be forming an orderly queue outside our house.

Hey, babe, wake up and smell the espresso. Getting our children into the *right* school these days is about as traumatic and complicated as swimming the Channel with your arms tied. In fact, in the face of huge demand for places and catchment area border disputes that make the Gaza Strip question look simple, there's not even any guarantee we will be able to get them into the *wrong* school.

Be under no illusion: when it comes to school entry, this is war. 'You're in it for the long haul,' says one battle-scarred veteran. There are no tactics, no dirty tricks to which we will not descend and the most alarming part of all is that casualties are usually the result of friendly fire and wholesale treachery. We think our friends are allies because they are on the same side, all united against the enemy – the massed opposition that is the admissions appeal committee. Don't you believe it.

And all this warmongering seems to bring out traits in our personalities that we never imagined were there. 'You say you won't be like that, but you are,' says another casualty. 'Something takes over. A certain madness will descend, and every principle that you have ever held dear will be abandoned.' It reveals levels of dishonesty that we won't contemplate employing anywhere else in our lives: we lie, cheat, play the wild card to get our offspring into the right seat of education, using espionage and subterfuge that would have made the KGB blush. The loss of perspective is terminal.

But can't they see how special we are?

Oh, the shamelessness of it all, because this ugly dogfight is not just to secure that last desk in the superest-dooperest school in the county so our children get the very best. It's about naked competition. It's about pimping ourselves and our families, because we're worth it (and therefore worth more than everybody else).

Naturally, whoever teaches our child will rapidly realise they're dealing with someone very special indeed. They'll never have seen such aptitude before – or such steely determination. And that's only us, the parents, we're talking about. Our main role as a parent right from the word go is as a facilitator and opportunity-provider in an ever more competitive world. We all know that if we play our cards right and choose the right pre-school, our children will be set fair for the best primary school, the finest secondary education, a first-class degree at a venerable university and a high-rolling job in the City.

But if we get it wrong . . . Well, the best our children can ever hope for is a fistful of ASBOs and a job flipping burgers while waiting for a lucky break working as a drug dealer. They will have miserable lives, and *we* will be to blame. We realize they can't all be winners. Some will lose. But it won't be ours.

So hurry up, there's no time to waste. The world is full of dangers and nasty rough people, so the sooner we can put some distance between our cosy little nuclear family and the great unwashed the better. Six-year-olds can take GCSEs now, A levels at eleven, then off to university at twelve, and then . . . Well, we'll have to think about that when the time comes, cos right now we're far too busy stimulating that beautiful little mind. Before long, our children will earn enough to look after us in our penniless dotage, once we've squandered every penny on their education.

Milestones or Millstones?

This pursuit of perfection starts early with the purchase of those educational mobiles, rattles and brightly coloured plastic structures that will dominate our home for the first few years.

It's not until we come out into baby society, like a blushing debutante at her first ball, with our brand-new change bag and pristine car seat, that we really become aware that we have been slow out of the stalls. We may have suspected, of course, because those blasted baby books had planted the seed of self-doubt, but now we know for sure. Because there are lots of people out there to tell us how they are already around the first bend.

'I went to an NCT member's house for a coffee morning,' remembers Rachel, 'and, taped all over the house, were these handwritten cards – door, chair, window. Our babies were four months old. But I was so freaked out, I went home and did the same myself. When my husband got back from work, he laughed himself silly.'

The pressure's on, isn't it? Despite our better judgement and despite all the things we may have said while we were pregnant, we find ourselves comparing our baby with every other baby we see. And suddenly, things like being able to roll over or playing with toes become pivotal to our very existence. And when it comes to walking and talking! Show me a baby that can walk at ten months at toddler group and I'll show you a dozen women who go home and spend the rest of the day urging their bendy-legged bundle to stand up and go it alone, without recourse to furniture. By the time they go to school, most children are walking and talking – aren't they? – so what's with the panic? Why do we lose our perspective? When did the developmental milestones become millstones?

Implicit in the achievements of other babies is some sort of reproach to your ability as a parent. What? You mean you haven't been stimulating your baby with vivid mono-chrome mobiles? You haven't been playing classical music to increase his IQ? You haven't been chugging fish oil capsules to enhance your breast milk? Of course, that

'I know, darling, it is tricky, but you do need
a second language for St Margaret's'

explains why he's a week behind the charts in being able to sit up. What have you been doing with your time for goodness sake? Wasting it away on cuddles and 'This little piggy'? Didn't you know a baby's brain doubles in size in the first year? Well, you might as well forget Oxbridge, then, because it's probably already too late.

'I thought Debbie was my best mate,' says Sam, 'and then we had children. Her daughter was always way ahead of my son and I'd be eaten up with jealousy and practise propping him up with cushions to make it look like he could sit up. Then, ha! He said "Mama" before she did. Eat my dust, sucker!'

Forget, for a moment, the fact that Einstein was a late developer; we must leave no stone unturned in our quest to enhance baby's mind at this crucial time. Fortunately, there are plenty of products to feed into our paranoia. And all created by experts. Now we can plonk our baby in front of the telly with a clear conscience, with DVDs like *Baby Einstein*, *Baby Genius*, *Baby Shakespeare*, *Baby Van Gogh*. They're never too young to learn. And we're never too old to be taken in by a new marketing ploy!

Nursery Crimes

Always assuming that we haven't been bludgeoned into submission by Steve Biddulph's propaganda, and are actually contemplating sending our child to nursery, we now have to choose the right place.

'I looked for a nursery when I went back to work,' explains Debbie, 'for my two-year-old and found what I thought was a really lovely place. Homely, welcoming, good Ofsted report, all that sort of thing. And then another mum said, "What second language do they teach?" And I couldn't believe she was serious. The child could barely speak English!'

Just like in Lake Woebegone, every child must now be above average. So instead of being allowed to play and actually have some fun, they are assessed for pencil grip, knowing their colours, ability to sit nicely at circle time – and so much more. It's like a production line, isn't it? Well, we'd better get used to it, because that's what education has become, with our child as guinea pig, being tested, assessed and judged from now on.

'I wanted my daughter to get into a very popular private school and the competition was fierce,' says Melanie. 'So I had to send her, at the ripe old age of three and a quarter, to be assessed there, and all I was thinking was, How can I get the highest mark out of her? We were not allowed in to witness the test, but obviously they're not doing algebra, so how are they judging these little toddlers?' You wouldn't credit it – one nervous child, when asked what blue and yellow makes, blurted, 'Blellow!'

Melanie continues: 'We tried not to worry our daughter, but the night before she had a huge tanty about what she was going to wear. So I put her in the car seat and drove her round for a couple of hours, just so she would go to sleep. I felt I couldn't leave it to chance because this is how the rest of her life, her future, is basically decided.'

The teachers are in the perfect position to witness the

lunacy of potential parents from close quarters. One teacher at a minor prep school remembers showing a father around. 'He was very insistent that his son should be fast-tracked. He kept stressing how bright he was and, basically, trying to get me to agree that we would move him through the school at an accelerated pace. I asked a bit more, and eventually it came down to when he might want to start in the school. That was when he told me his son was only six months old!'

This is just the start of a long campaign to get it right, but everybody else we know is at it too. Previously amicable dinner parties suddenly become a minefield of taboo subjects. You find yourself keeping your cards close to your chest. Or, worse, intentionally feeding false information to the enemy – I mean the other guests. Don't let on that little Flossie's Japanese tuition has paid off handsomely – the head was soooo impressed at interview – or that you've just exchanged contracts on a house three inches inside the catchment for Sunnydale Junior. Everything on a need-to-know basis only.

Primary school

Back in the good old days, before league tables, our main concern about primary school would probably have been how convenient it was to get to. But now there are some schools that are so desirable, some parents will stop at nothing to try to get their precious darlings in. It's like everyone in the neighbourhood trying to squeeze into the same hypertrendy restaurant on a Saturday night. But if we go somewhere else, are we really going to end up getting a bad meal?

'When my son was eight months old,' says Amelia, mother to Harry and foetus Piers, 'we thought we'd be efficient and sign him up for a school around the corner – a very exclusive school. And they virtually laughed in our faces and said we were far too late, and the waiting list was already closed. And they suggested – quite straight-faced – that what some parents do is to get pregnant, register the unborn baby, and then our son could come in as a sibling.'

So just how low would we now sink to get our child into the primary school of our choice? According to the BBC almost a third of head teachers in the highest-ranking state primary schools have been offered bribes or threatened by parents desperate for a place for their child. Of course, we could always move house – if we can afford to. The effect of a good school on house prices within the catchment area is staggering. It is featured prominently on house sale details even outside London. Sod the ensuite, what makes a res des these days is how close it is to the school gates. Trouble is, the catchment area keeps getting smaller and smaller – down to less than half a mile in some places *as the crow flies* – as all the local properties are snapped up by hopeful parents.

'My children went to a nursery based at the local state primary school,' says John, a desperate parent. 'The problem was that the nursery had twice as many places as the reception class, so basically half the children at the nursery wouldn't get a place. We used to scour the streets for removal vans, wondering if someone was going to move in with twins, closer to the school than we were, and rob my kids of their place in the school. It was a traumatic two years. The children are supposed to be enjoying playing with sand and splashing around with water while all the parents going home are weeping because their children aren't going to get into this school.'

The alternative is basically to lie about where we live. And plenty of people try it, giving a false address, or renting a tiny flat next to the school while keeping a nice big house elsewhere. Schools and education authorities are on to them, though, running checks through the electoral register.

'Two children had to leave the school because their parents had given a false address,' says Gerard, father of two. 'It was awful. The parents were called in and confronted with the evidence. They just disappeared. No one saw them again. Maybe they were sent to the salt mines. But nobody cared because it meant that two more places were available.'

A head teacher of a very popular state school says, 'All the effort these parents go to! If they sent their children to schools that still have places, and used even a fraction of the energy and determination they show trying to get into a school that's full, they could support the head and teachers, and the school would improve. Of course it would.'

Pray or pay?

But if we're not in the catchment area, and we're not ready to hand out bribes or invent a bogus address just yet, what's left? There are two strategic options. We either sell everything we own and go private, or we get religion, and fast. But not just a little religion, as Lucy saw at first hand.

'Just going to church at Christmas and Easter isn't good enough any more and wearing a little cross round your neck won't convince anyone. So my sister did the full going to Sunday school, going to church, being terribly helpful with the flower-arranging and all that kind of thing. She roped us all in, the entire family running stalls at the church fête to get the child into school. And it worked.'

And if you are a bogus born-again, be sure your sin will find thee out. In one popular Catholic school, baptismal certificates had to be called in to check that children had in fact been baptised before they had applied to the school. Several places became available after that. Rumbled!

So if we can't square a sudden conversion with our conscience, and no other school will do or have you, all that's left is to pay and just tough it out. And once we leave the state system, it can be hard to get back in until senior school entry comes along.

'I've had to do the lottery, stay up late doing Internet poker games, go to car boot sales and become familiar with eBay,' says a poor private parent. 'We live from term to term, not really knowing if they'll be able to go back. I do realise that this is true madness. But there doesn't seem to be an alternative round here.'

And this is all before the poor little thing has even turned five. 'There's the moment when we get our child into the nursery school or primary school of our choice,' says John. 'There's a sort of brief moment of elation – five minutes, tops – followed by a growing anxiety as the years rush past and we start to worry more and more about the next big hurdle: getting into secondary school.'

This is when we need to radio in for back-up.

Coaching for the slowcoach

At one time, having extra tutoring was regarded as a shameful secret – a bit like having webbed feet. But now at least one in four families in the UK gets coaching for their children in something or another. To pile on the pressure, there are always stories in the newspapers about freaky six-year-olds passing their GCSEs. There are even crammers that specialise in this kind of mental torture. And although we can see it's weird and wrong, a part of us has the uncomfortable feeling that maybe we should be doing the same for our child. Anything if it will help secure a place at the right school.

And as our kids get older, the pressure builds up these days. While selective state schools continue to exist, the iniquity of coaching for secondary school entry will continue and parents feel under huge pressure to coach because everybody else does. Some fee-paying primary schools seem to function as eleven-plus factories for grammar schools, charging a fortune to shove children through the entrance exams just to save the parents the money they would have spent on school fees for the senior years. Hmm – makes you think. Because state primary schools don't have the time to cram their pupils in this way, private tutors can clean up. One tutor notes, 'Generally a child needs at least two years' preparation for the exam. At £10 per hour, twice a week, that can cost over £2,000. But it's a lot less than paying for private school.'

Some parents will consider going even further with this madness. One father advertised recently on the Internet offering to pay for a copy of the entrance paper his daughter was due to take. The school found out and were not at all impressed. But what's the point? Many teachers are of the opinion that coaching distorts the whole system.

'If a child can't pass the exam without a lot of help, then they would be better suited to an education elsewhere. It wouldn't be fair on them to put them in an environment where they're struggling to keep up with their peers,' says one head teacher.

But parents are unrepentant. 'It's all a game, isn't it? But it's not a game – it's the World Cup!' says Darren shamelessly.

'Secondary school, we'll do anything basically. We'll do anything, whatever it takes,' Trevor says. 'It's not a level playing field any more. All these schools have got their good points and bad points. I'll do anything to get them in. It's a very, very, very good school. Too good for our kids to go to actually but I don't care, I'll do anything.'

Gerard knew that an early start was essential.

Bribery and extortion

It's not just the heads who are worth corrupting, of course. Bribery can work with children too and, when the stakes are so high, a decent bribe for passing the entrance exam is well worth offering. Trouble is there are no rules for where to pitch it.

'When I found out my son had passed his eleven-plus, I got him a great big ice cream. Then we met a girl who'd been promised that she could have her belly button pierced if she passed, and another kid who was bought a pony!' Jacqui laughs.

Schools are very well aware of the panic we succumb to. And if we hedge our bets and apply to private schools as well as state, there's a price to pay.

'For each private school we apply to, there's a fee to take the entrance exam and a non-returnable deposit. And we have to hand this over, of course, before we hear which state school our child has been accepted into,' laments Justine. 'It cost me hundreds, literally hundreds of pounds, just to keep our options open.'

There's a strange sort of tension that arises between state and private parents and those who go the grammar school route. There are undercurrents that can test the most established friendships. Our choice of school says so much about our worldview and it polarises people in the last couple of years at primary school. Suddenly you find yourself cosying up with the parents of kids who are applying to the same schools as you are – because someone you once liked has taken the traitor route and gone private. Adversity makes strange bedfellows.

Unappealing Parents

Despite government claims about now giving parents more choice, tens of thousands of children do not get places at the school their parents want for them. So what happens next? Don't take it lying down, brave warrior.

Some parents are paying hundreds of pounds to consultants because they are desperate to win their school appeals. Rather than taking no for an answer, and accepting that the school is full, they will challenge the decision and try to force their way in. Consultants offer their services, at a price, and claim they can increase the success rate of appeals from about 15 per cent unassisted to as much as 70 per cent. For an extra consideration, they will even appear at the appeals alongside the parents.

But would you want to be the parent who pushes the class size over the critical number? The crazy part is in state primary schools in particular, where class numbers for the early years are dictated by the government, just having one extra child can force the school to split the class and employ another teacher.

Susie remembers feeling resentful. 'We had these parents who pushed and pushed, and their appeals were granted. The class size was just too big. It meant the classroom was overcrowded and all our kids, who'd been there since the start, got less attention. It just seemed really selfish. We all used to glare at the parents in the playground. I don't think they noticed. They were so chuffed to have beaten the system.'

Best days of our life?

After living and breathing school entry for what feels like years and years, we finally get our child in somewhere or other. And if we end up just accepting the place we're allocated, it might turn out to be better than we feared.

'We gave up eventually and I remember thinking, Oh, well, I think this school will suit them perfectly after all, and everyone can relax and feel a bit happier,' says a resigned mother. 'We stopped hating our child, finally, after this long campaign, our child who was never good enough for a scholarship somewhere or a special place somewhere else. And then it begins again for another set of parents; the following year we're at the school gates with our younger kids and we hear them talking, and we know the hell they're going through. They're going to suffer exactly the same way that we did. They look for advice – we're reluctant to give it. Even after we got that place we don't want to share our information.'

The gamesmanship doesn't let up as the years go by. Another wave of lunacy takes over between GCSEs and A levels, when those of us who've slogged to get our children into lovely, privileged private schools suddenly get a wake-up call. Because of recent positive discrimination for the scallys from state schools, our cossetted darlings may not be able to swan into the uni of their choice. The solution? We hoick our kids out of private school at sixteen, then send them to state school to sit A levels. The children will already have benefitted from an elite education for most of their schooldays, and can probably withstand having to study with the common people for a couple of years. The university admissions officers, however, will assume they have spent all their academic life in a 'bog-standard comp' and will allocate their places accordingly. We just have to hope their cut-glass accents won't give the game away at interview. Estuary elocution lessons, anyone? The rine in Spine . . .

University challenged

So we've barged our kids through the education system as fast as we can. University awaits our under-aged boff and, with it, the reflected glory that the parents of a freakishly brilliant child can bask in. All those sacrifices we've had to make for our moment in the sun. But brace yourself: Oxford is considering a minimum age limit of seventeen as a response to child protection laws. So while we're waiting, our tiny genius will have to cool their heels and take another batch of A levels while learning to play the cor anglais, just to while away the years.

All that effort for nothing. And was it worth it? Will they thank us in the end? Alex doesn't think so. 'Sometimes, in a rare moment of sanity, I compare Jack's life to mine when I was a child. I wouldn't like to have his life. I'm always on his case about working harder. But I'm like that because everyone else is too. It's no wonder that children love books with heroes like Pippi Longstocking,

Harry Potter and Alex Rider. They're all orphans who can do what they like without parents bossing them around.'

A Dozen Daft Names

The following have appeared at least once among the 600,000 births registered in Britain over the past twelve months.

For her . . .
Ikea
Paprica
Caramel
Bambi
Fire-Lily
Skylark

For him . . .
Moet
Finchley
Ely
Rocky
Rivers
Red

5
School Life: Forgery and Fraud

Of course getting our children into the chosen school is just the start of fourteen years of obsession. And obsession it is. School talk dominates dinner parties, benches at the park, chats over a latte in Starbucks. There are forums on the Internet about it. It makes you wonder what we all talked about before. Babies probably.

Having children in school is a funny old feeling, isn't it? You probably haven't been near a school gate for fifteen years or so and suddenly, instead of being there as a pupil, you are delivering your offspring. The odd part is you have a mixture of emotions: the teachers still manage to make you feel as though, if you misbehave, you will be sent to see the head. The smell of a pencil case, the beautifully written labels next to the pegs, the cabbagey waft of school dinners. It all takes you back to those days of short trousers or long white socks, and you feel cowed and small again.

Then you remind yourself that the teachers are probably younger than you are.

Sending our children off to school brings out a whole new side to our personalities, and we become people we don't recognise. Granted we have moved house, lied, scraped or re-mortgaged even to get him into the place

anyway and we are, after all, handing over our pride and joy to someone else for about thirty-nine weeks of the year, so a little concern and involvement is natural. But instead of giving up our children to education on trust, it is here that modern parenting shows new heights of insanity.

'Teaching is the only profession where other people think they know best,' sighs Margaret, a pre-prep head with years of teaching experience at a private school. 'I mean, you don't appoint an accountant and then tell him how to do his job, or tell the dentist how to do an extraction. Parents these days are not in the real world. In the last ten years there's been a sea change in the way parents behave and it's warping the children's minds.'

'Government Guff', as she calls it, is partly to blame, and who can resist being alarmed by a feature on low-performing schools and the threat that your child is being sold short? There's a bit of jealousy there too: galling, isn't it, that your son's teacher might just know a side of him you don't? Suddenly he's learning things not from us but from someone else. But the real problem is that schools have become a service industry and we treat them like car dealerships.

State versus private

Which ones of us are the worst then? Those of us who pay or those of us who move heaven and earth to be in the right catchment area for St Top-of-the-League-Tables?

Private school parents, in response to the pain that results from paying through the nose, very definitely expect a return for their investment these days. And why shouldn't we? At the current rate – not allowing for inflation – we're forking out enough during their school careers to buy a small three-bedroom house. You can double that and a bit more if you take the boarding school route. Not surprising then that you want to make darned sure Jimmy is going to 'realise his potential'. And, while you're at it, the certainty of a lucrative job in the City or a partnership in the top law firm would be very nice too. So, just to make quite sure that's the way things are heading, we behave as if our children were comestibles.

'I was taking register one morning,' continues Margaret, 'and the door was thrown open by a mother, her face purple with anger. "Are you teaching my child nothing?" she shrieked. "Am I wasting my money here!"' It transpired it was all about a piece of extra homework she had demanded her child be given, which he had then refused to do. 'It's all about value for money.'

'One mother,' relates another long-experienced teacher, 'asked if she could have a video camera in the classroom so she could watch her child in school. Strangely enough we said no!'

But unlike a BMW, whereby the more you spend the higher the spec, it doesn't quite work that way with children. A few grand and your daughter's exceptional ability at drawing may not be enough to ensure she turns out a genius.

Margaret sees this pattern of expectation all the time: 'I had to tell one father that his son was not doing very well. "I'm amazed you are telling me the truth," he said. "I thought if I was paying for his schooling you would put a gloss on it"'!'

What we don't seem to want to accept is that we can throw all the money we like at school and education, but it won't make our children any more intelligent.

In state schools, we are just as pushy but in a subtly different way. It's the 'it's my right' mentality. We know that Barny might just develop later and we should leave him to find his way, but we can't resist, can we? We have to know where he is *now* in relation to other children. 'He's doing okay,' simply isn't a good enough answer, is it? We need to know success is happening already.

But what both payers and non-payers have in common is this growing 'parents versus the school' attitude. 'Letters from solicitors,' groans the head of the comprehensive in the north-east. 'I never used to get them before. Now I receive about two a week.'

They are usually growling threats of litigation, another influence from America no doubt, but the demands we place on schools seem to have got more absurd by the minute. At the lowest level we want them to potty-train our children and teach them how to hold a knife and fork. 'They've been so coached to perform at home before they start nursery that some can write their own names when they come in,' says one teacher, 'but they can't eat lunch. What on earth are the parents doing?'

At best we want results; at worst we want teachers to do our job for us. But it all gets a bit more sinister when it comes to playtime.

Where there's blame, there's a claim

Blame it on the Yanks, but we seem to have become obsessed with wrapping our children in cotton wool to the point that has made litigants of us all. Nothing new here of course – we've been an increasingly blame and compensation culture for a while now. Trip over a paving stone in the street and you can be sure your case will be taken on by a firm of lawyers advertising on daytime TV, who'll take the local council to the cleaners.

Trouble is the councils and, ergo, schools are now so terrified of legal action from us parents that they are banning anything that could be faintly contentious. Take playground games. There we are on one hand saying, 'Oh, it isn't like the old days, is it, when we used to string rubber bands together and play skipping games, or British Bulldog – remember that? Kids these days – no idea how to entertain themselves and have fun.' And then what do we do? Issue proceedings against the school because Annabel slipped and grazed her knee.

Unfortunately we can't go blaming other parents here. A Mori poll suggests that if their child suffered personal injury at school that they felt to be the fault of the school or school staff, then the majority of parents would seek compensation from the school. In fact only 15 per cent said they would never consider doing this.

Dr Sarah Thomson from the Education Department of Keele University published a report recently after studying three primary schools across three counties. She found that British Bulldog was banned in all schools; and conkers were viewed as offensive weapons. 'I even heard one member of staff talk about banning conkers because she linked conkers with nuts, which might expose children to nut allergies.'

Instead of sticking on a plaster, teachers now have to tell a child to dab a cut with a wet paper towel; well, imagine the consequences if the child proved to be allergic to Elastoplast. (Wouldn't you let the school know if your child was?) One school in Thomson's study had even banned skipping after some girls had tied their legs together with ropes for a three-legged race, and subsequently fallen over.

Suddenly, says Thomson, 'the children's choice of pastime and amusement must be regulated for both the teachers' and the children's protection.'

'We could not do otherwise,' says one head, 'or you are leaving yourself open. You say you are *in loco parentis* but really you are not. You have to ask permission to do anything, everything.'

Another head teacher admitted that he would like to 'ban all playtimes, as they are a nightmare'.

Is there something wrong with children these days? Do they have thinner skin or brittler bones? The crazy part is that Thomson observed 'many of the children's attempts to play were extinguished by the same supervising adults who complained that children "did not play".'

'We played British Bulldogs and we nearly killed each other,' one says, 'but that was the object! Children get hurt. We used to get hurt when we were playing it. People used not to bother in those days. I think we are much more safety-conscious; we can't let children just play anything nowadays.'

How many children do you know who have suffered dreadful injuries from conker fights or ingesting Top Trump cards? Our concern with safety has reached frankly barking proportions. Sure, there is the theoretical possibility that little Jimmy might just get a bit of conker in his eye/fall over and break his ankle/get a runny nose from the cold and, for some reason, that seems to be sufficient risk to justify the call for a ban. Our demands for bans (or at least the school's decision to ban it in case of our response to accidents) are triggered by the *potential* risk that something might happen, and not by specific evidence that it has. Frankly there is more danger in driving them to school in your car (instead of letting them walk – but that's another story).

This 'us versus the school' attitude is even more divisive than nasty letters from Sue Them & Win. 'The whole mood has changed,' says one head. 'If something happens in class and I have to tell a child off – sometimes for something quite serious – I get the parents on my back the next morning. What happened to children's accountability? There is always an excuse. Their little darling can't possibly have done something wrong and how dare we tell him or her off? Parents seem to build a defence mechanism around their children and we are always on the back foot. They never seem to be able to say sorry, either, when they have clearly got something wrong.'

Will you join the committee?

You might be the sort of person who would rather have their skull drilled than join a committee of any kind, but it all changes, doesn't it, when there's a chance of getting a closer look at school life and a peek at what other kids are up to. There only has to be a whiff of involvement – make-up for the school play, reading help in class, baking cakes for the fête – and we can get that foot in the door and closer to the coalface.

Until that moment the only insight we had was the school bag of a child who came back with yours for tea. There it is by the front door, crying out for you to have a peek and, unable to resist and while their backs are turned as they watch *CBeebies*, you open it up. If you are lucky you can sit back on your heels in smug satisfaction as you see they have read far fewer books than your child. There are his mother's excuses: 'Dan was tired tonight.' Dan may be seven but, you hope, that one night's missed reading might be the difference between an A and a B at GCSE. The pleasure.

But there's always the risk of the terror. The Superstar stamp from the teacher to congratulate Dan on finishing *War and Peace*. And, worse still, there's the News Book, that most insidious of tomes that reveals all about someone else's family life you never see. Trips to National Trust properties and art galleries. Culture made fun.

Ilana couldn't resist a nose when a friend came over: 'I had a little sneaky peek inside the book bag and sure enough there were the most amazing Miró illustrations of what they'd done at the weekend. My kid does things like go to a car wash and Asda shopping, so there was quite a discrepancy and also in the quality of the work. With my kid each letter was apart and this child was already doing joined-up writing aged four. It wasn't a very happy experience, I must admit, but the problem was I forgot to actually put the book back in the book folder and in fact the mother had to phone me about three nights later and say, "Have you got Xander's exercise book?" '

Get through the classroom door, though, and you can really make comparisons. 'I definitely went in to help with reading so I could see how Katie was doing compared to the class,' admits Hannah. 'You can only find out so much from the book bag, but being in class was brilliant!'

John has a theory about this: 'They're not listening to the child read – they've got the other ear firmly cocked in the direction of the class round the corner, seeing what is being taught; whether their child was left unattended for a microsecond and, you know, all that intelligence is gathered and taken back home and collated, and probably they're gonna be a governor of the school as well so that will be brought up at the governors' meetings. And sometimes there are so many parents going in to volunteer to read in some of these classrooms that there's no chance of any children being left in the actual classroom to be taught by the teacher, because the parents are too busy spying on them!'

Why can't we resist the snooping? Ilana is honest: 'I couldn't accept that another child was so much better than my child,' she admits. Jane, however, justifies her

'*Don't* get little Henry started on the causes
of the First World War . . .'

involvement. 'Of course you want to get in there. My daughter is in a school in Islington where the teacher can't even spell! I know that if I can get myself in the classroom I can have some sort of understanding of what's going on.'

Day Tripping

It doesn't even have to be the PTA committee or the reading help; it could just be the school outing, that wonderful opportunity to see your child in relation to others and you've got the whole day to do it. It's always the same mothers and fathers who go, though, isn't it? The type who like to be right up there on the good egg ratings, turning up in anorak, sensible shoes, with a few treats in their backpack for the children in their group (that'll make them popular with their children's friends). It all looks suspiciously like information-gathering tactics hidden beneath a helpful and altruistic veneer.

So we are nosey and we are controlling. We are also paranoid and, when our children are taken out of school, that safety obsession becomes pure madness. In fact in one Midlands primary school a trip to a science museum had to be cancelled when there were too many parents volunteering to go and not enough space on the bus, but none would yield and back down.

One teacher recently gave up the profession, so exhausted was he by paranoid parenting. He wearily recalls how another school trip to the seaside, planned for a class of five-year-olds, was cancelled because two parents were concerned that the trip would involve their children in a forty-minute journey in a private car. Would the cars be fully MOT-ed? Were they good enough drivers? Who would ensure correct-fitting seat belts? Were these normally non-smoking cars, or would the children be made victims of passive smoking?

One child's parents even booked a holiday cottage down the road from a school trip destination so they could keep a beady eye and another's mother insisted on driving behind her son's coach on a trip to France to ensure that he arrived safely.

'Can you promise,' insisted one mother at a pre-ski trip meeting at school, 'that someone will come down the piste with Olivia each time to check she is okay?'

Prep and homework

If you can't make your way in through the school trip or PTA routes, the most useful clue to what's going on in school is homework. It's also the most stressful.

Children seem to come home with prep – even if it's in the form of a repetitive and tedious reading book – from the moment they start nursery. Then the amount cranks up as expected, but in the primary years it all seems a little *de trop*. Why do schools feel the children need this much?

The truth is they don't. It's parents who demand it and extra work to boot. 'Even when the child is as young as three, parents want to know where the reading book is,' says Margaret, but it's essential. It's vital. Imagine the ignominy if your child is a level behind the rest of his peers on the Magic Key series! Career disaster; and extra work is even more essential when you take him out of school for a week to make the most of the cheap flights to Geneva for skiing before half-term.

Then there's the Project. Don't the very words fill you with horror? At least there's the Internet so you don't have to schlep down to the library to find that someone else from school has already taken out the only book on Victorian childhood.

'I really really try not to help her,' says Jane, pained, 'but, God, I have so much to say.' And it's irresistible sometimes. Your son is flailing about for information on the economy in Spain, switching back to Runescape on the Internet when you leave the room, until you realise the night before the project is due in he's managed bullfighting and sherry, so in you wade, sleeves rolled up and best research and analysis head on.

Darren takes up the story: 'You want your child to do well at school and it's very difficult because you also want them to learn for themselves and it's so hard; it's so difficult because you're sitting there watching them make mistakes. I've spent nights sort of rubbing out her times table and rewriting them and trying to recreate her handwriting, and getting the five round the wrong way and stuff. And you think: What am I doing, what am I doing?'

Teachers aren't stupid. That's why they write WDM very small at the bottom of the page of homework – Well Done Mum. They make their way determinedly across the playground at 3.30 and pin you with a beady eye: well, did you help with the homework, only it seemed a little better than Samantha's usual standard? And, like a shoplifter faced with the store detective, you hold their eye as steady as you can and swear blind it was all her own work.

But isn't it worth it when the merit badges are handed out, though of course it's you who takes the plaudits. After all, you did most of the work. And sometimes it's not about the children at all – it's between the parents. Two fathers were locked in mortal combat over who had done the best seaside project, both producing something resembling a geologist's scale model made from papier-mâché and sand glued to dunes made painstakingly from wire and plaster, both trying to outdo each other on the exoticness of the shells glued to the shoreline, brought back, one can only assume, from competing holidays in the Caribbean.

In some sort of misguided belief that extra work, better projects, or involvement will speed them along the road to success, we persist. This must explain why we feel this urge to interfere with their education. Unless, of course, it is a desire to bask in reflected glory. If they are doing well, then aren't we the clever ones? After all, it must be genetic.

But that's if you find out a project has to be done at all. 'I don't normally get involved in their homework,' says Emma, 'but I remember coming in to collect my daughter from school on the first day back after the Easter holidays. One of the other mothers sidled up to me. "So what did you think of the holiday science project?" she asked. I could feel the cold sweat. Clemmy hadn't mentioned a science project but I couldn't admit I didn't know. I still found myself saying, "Oh that!" and thinking, *What?*'

Could do better

So how did you do? Enter the parents' evening, the most intense five – or if you are lucky ten – minutes of the year during which you have to glean everything you can about how your pride and joy is doing. You have just 600 seconds to find out everything about Hattie or Charlie's progress, and future career prospects.

'I'm like an athlete out of the blocks,' says Fiona. 'If the parents who are in with the teacher before me overstay by even a minute after the bell I start to cough and make myself obvious. They are stealing my time! Then I try to read the grades in the teacher's mark book upside down to see how Josh has done compared to the rest of the class – while the teacher tries to put their hand over the figures. If you are quick and make a mental note of the surname of the brightest boy in the class you can spot his marks pretty quickly on the list. It helps if it begins with an A.'

Simon uses management tactics. 'I try to read the teacher's face, and see what she is really trying to say. Then afterwards I forget anything good and just focus on the bad.'

It's not always obvious what the performance grading system is anyway. You can't get teachers in state schools to tell you how well your kid is doing relative to the rest of the class so you have to deduce. What's all this with the special name code? There you are being told that the children are squares, diamonds, triangles or circles, and when you are told your child is a diamond you think that sounds great – they must be the best! – until someone tells you it's in fact the bottom percentage of the class. And just when you think you've got a handle on the system, the school changes it. Next year they are jungle animals. Panthers sounds good. Don't you believe it.

But relatively speaking it's all pretty upbeat. No more 'This child is the scourge of my class. He will go nowhere in life.' In this modern climate of win, win, win, we now get fed vapid spin. Reports are the same. You can forget: 'Has no interest, makes no effort' (Mr Wolfson, physics teacher, circa 1977). Like a management appraisal, children are now graded for effort and attainment with an S for satisfactory, 2 for middle third of the class. Like GCSEs it's impossible to make comparisons if everyone's a winner. No wonder we find ourselves interrogating the teacher like the Stasi across the desk on parents' evening.

'You have to be so careful about being negative,' says Gail, a form teacher and an old hand at this parental bunfight. 'Even the worst news has to be couched in positive statements. But I don't really know why we aren't honest. It would make no difference. Parents these days have a complete inability to see anything wrong with their children. Even quite serious defects they just won't acknowledge. Staff are on the back foot all the time.'

'It all comes down to trust,' says Keith. 'There isn't as much trust between parents and teachers any more. They don't let us get on with the job. Parents used to be nervous on parents' evening but not any more. It's all guns blazing. We have a system where parents talk in the classroom one to one with the form teacher. Now I have to sit in with some of the younger teachers when certain parents come in because they don't want to be on their own with aggressive parents.'

Fair enough to be angry if we're talking about an under-performing school with unsatisfactory teaching. But Keith heads up the lower school of a £9,000 a year prep school.

Tell us there is something wrong with the child though and we will obsess. It can't be genetic – that doesn't look good on us – so if it can't actually be blamed on the school it must be an 'ic'. The hot favourite is dyslexic, then there's dyspraxic. Yes, that'll be it. Charlie isn't doing so well at maths because he has a difficulty with number blindness, and off we go to throw the best part of two and a half grand having him 'assessed'. It's that car analogy again. If there is something wrong with the product, send it to the garage to have it put right.

It's become a modern disease to find a condition, and diagnosis of an 'ic' is very reassuring. Then at dinner parties we can say, when asked how he's doing at school/rugby/further nuclear physics, 'Well, of course he's mildly (only mildly, mind) ADHD' (an honorary 'ic'). What we suspect in our heart of hearts is that he's just hard going.

'What my wife and I couldn't bear to admit,' says a substantially poorer Larry, 'is that Harry, our son, was simply *not good enough*. In fact it pains me to say it now. He struggled with maths so we took him to a trendy clinic that had been featured on TV and, after hours of tests, which involved him trying to keep his balance on a wobbly platform, they said his cerebellum was under-developed but they could fix it. It was such a relief and we drove home with a great big weight off our shoulders. But

I think both of us knew the level of the problem was negligible and in fact he was just a bit thick at maths!'

But isn't it wonderful to know their strengths and weaknesses? Doesn't it help when it comes to choosing their exam options? If you thought the child and the school do that, you are wrong. More and more of us seem to push the decision so keen are we to 'get it right'. If we could we'd even sit the blasted exams for them.

Fear not. We can. Send them in with a mobile phone and we can be right there with them, answers ready to text when they need them. Much less obvious (and significantly less dangerous) is 'helping' them with their coursework. In fact we can virtually pass the exams for them now that the potential for plagiarism in qualifications from GCSE to university degrees is now unlimited. According to a 2006 report by the Qualifications and Curriculum Authority, there are at least ten websites offering rip-off answers to coursework in every subject from GCSE to degree level.

'Coursework assignments are available on the Internet at any level and in any subject,' the report adds. 'With so much work being completed outside school, the use of such sites cannot be controlled.' A survey revealed that 93 per cent of pupils had access to the Internet at home, and therefore could link to the websites. In addition, the report says, many parents are unaware of the limits to the amount of help they can give their children with coursework, and in some cases are supplying the answers to questions. One in twenty actually drafted their children's GCSE essays.

(We're not going to reveal the websites to you of course in case your child does better than ours . . .)

PPs: Pushy parents

These are the people we love to hear about. You know the ones – the parents who go to ridiculous lengths to ensure their child achieves/gets the best/does their best. It's all the more satisfying because the things they do are perfectly barking. It couldn't be *us*. We *wouldn't* . . .

No one ever really confesses to being a pushy parent. We find ourselves couching any suggestion of over-zealousness in terms like 'helping him to achieve his potential' or 'making sure he gets the best'. Who's actually going to stand up and say, 'My son is damned well going to lick the lot of you at backstroke and we've been up at 6 a.m. pounding the pool every morning for months'? Well, no one is actually going to say it, but it's a rare one who doesn't do a little gentle directional encouragement no matter how low-key.

Overt PPs are irresistible really and you loathe them, until you find yourself signing your child up for extra violin. But you too read the article that said research shows the offspring of pushy parents are much more likely to succeed in life than those with hands-off ones. After that nugget, how can you *not* steer your progeny with a gentle but firm hand?

So you too are sucked into the PP-dom. You might be the private type, the grade one PP who tries to make sure your darling wins (sorry, fulfils his potential) with a little extra tennis coaching or the odd 'How do you spell "indiscreet"?' The grade two and three PP does the pushing in private, hoping that their efforts will pay off when the activity is done in public: the practising for the egg and spoon race on the lawn which will give them the edge on sports day, or a little extra help from a tutor to back up what they are already learning.

Every little helps

Tutoring used to be for toffs who were educated at home, away from the great unwashed. It was also for those of us who ploughed our A levels and hadn't a chance of a university place unless we miraculously converted a D in French to at least a B in re-sits. Now private tutors are everywhere and even Tony Blair is alleged to have hired one for his children. Right from Key Stage 1, we can secure them for reading, English and maths. 'Give your children an extra chance to shine,' coos one private tutor's ad.

'It's essential,' screech both Beth and Jane, north London mothers with children about to move from infants to juniors. 'It's not about outdoing everyone else in their class now. We do it because the education system has let us down. If they didn't have extra help there is no way they would be good enough to get into the best schools. What else are we supposed to do?'

That's fair enough. With teacher to pupil ratios in Britain the lowest in Europe then you need all the advantages you can get. No, we're talking people who engage tutors above and beyond the call of what could reasonably be called sane. 'We had a call recently from a mother who wanted her child to have hours of Italian classes,' recalls one firm of tutors. 'She had heard that if a child is exposed to a language early, it is easier for them to become fluent. The child turned out to be one and a half.'

On the other hand, there's always the grade four and upwards PPs who can't resist the urge to display their conscientious parenting for all to witness and it's never more overt than in the sporting arena. There they are – the mothers with their mobile phone on stopwatch checking Rebecca's time at one length front crawl. They sit in a gaggle and compare notes, explaining away poor performance with excuses about 'being tired after playing hockey for the A team yesterday'. The more single-minded pace up and down the edge of the pool screeching stirring words to the child, who can't hear them anyway over the noise of water inside their swimming cap.

'I see some odd behaviour at the swimming club,' says Ally, 'where one or two parents think their children might be good enough for national or even international level. One poor girl (who actually isn't all that good) is taken to every session: that's every evening and two 6 a.m. swims a week as well – probably ten hours a week easy. Recently she broke her arm but, amazingly, she turned up at training, holding her plastered arm out of the water as she swam!'

Tennis club reveals a rich seam of PPs too. 'We had one girl who played pretty well until she suddenly stopped coming,' says Paul, a tennis coach. 'I saw her a few weeks later and asked her what had happened. "Mummy doesn't want me to play any more," she said, "because I'm not winning." '

Of course this isn't quite as extreme as the Frenchman who drugged his son's tennis opponents but who's to say to what depths some people plunge to ensure game, set and match? Charlene and her fiancé, Mark, were so convinced their eight-month-old son would become a successful athlete that they named him JJ because it sounds like a catchy sports name.

'Did you see the try I scored? Did you, sir?' crows a muddy but victorious boy to his coach, to be reminded there is no 'i' in 'team'. 'It never used to happen before,' observes the coach philosophically. 'Before it was team-work and no one took the glory but it's tougher on kids now. It's hard not to crow when you have your parents baying on the touchline.' Worst of all, though, is sports day because then everyone is there to watch and isn't there a lot to prove?

When once your mother came in a hat and sat on a folding stool with a flask of tea, now it's stopwatches and testosterone. In 2005 *Country Life* magazine, a study of twenty-five schools found that families no longer 'sit back, relax and enjoy the day'. Parents' races had been banned at seventeen institutions because the competitors were 'over-zealous', it said, and some parents were accused of 'spoiling' events by putting too much pressure on children to succeed. Pleasant egg-and-spoon and sack races have become a thing of the past. Says the then editor Clive Aslet: 'Nowadays, some parents have a highly competitive attitude to life and are neurotic about their children succeeding at everything they attempt.' Cheating was even reported to have gone on during some events. Now that's just not cricket.

In the arts, of course, the PP can appeal to teachers to allow our children the opportunity to show what we are so sure they are capable of. 'Choir school parents are the worst,' moans one teacher. ' "My child needs a solo," one mother insisted to me. "It's good for her self-esteem." '

The literature for the National Children's Orchestra asks parents (and children, to be fair) not to complain if they are in the second violins. The seconds, you are assured, play just as important a role in the orchestra. Second? Isn't second place the first loser?

School plays are a minefield of parental performance anxiety. How *can* they have cast Bettina as the third fairy from the left? She's the perfect lead. What are they thinking of? Marianne is an old hand at directing young talent. 'We have to be so careful what we choose for the school play. You have to find one that the whole year group can be in and there aren't many of those. We can't put on anything where there are only a few lead parts because it becomes so difficult with parents asking why their child hasn't been given the main character to play. We have to keep records of who had big parts in the past.'

Well, if he can't play Hamlet then you can make certain his costume will get him noticed. So you sit up till the wee hours sewing on bits of braid and lace, employing long-forgotten skills at chain stitch to ensure it's a work of art. That'll clinch it, you think, as you proudly send off the costume in a carrier bag, only to find that not only has everyone else hired theirs from a shop, one mother has had her son's costume sent up from a West End show.

'We had one girl with university don parents,' explains one teacher. 'If she went out to tea with a friend she had to make up the time with work later. We did a Greek play – Lord knows why now – and the mother went to each performance, never taking her eyes off the text to make sure her child was word perfect.'

So endemic is the PP, there is even support literature for the children of them. So why are we doing it? There has to be an element of 'I never did it so you can do it on my behalf' going on here. You didn't quite make the grade on the football field so you'll make sure your son is centre-half for Arsenal. But there has to be a big dollop of basking in their successes. If Tabitha gets the high jump cup or comes first in the 400m – well, just who created those legs, hey?

Dependent parents

'A new trend I have noticed,' says Margaret, 'is the needy parent, the one who can't make a decision for themselves without bringing it to me first. This isn't just about their child – I'm marriage guidance counsellor, family therapist, I've even been asked what they should do with the mother-in-law over Christmas.'

But isn't there something quite comforting about your children's teachers? With such paucity of sensible support from our elders about, a friendly face at the school gate, especially someone who takes our beloved children under their wing, takes us back to the days when we had teachers and they smelt nice. They tell you how wonderful your children are and you want to hug them and ask them, 'So am I doing it right?' They ought to know, after all.

' "Will damp come up through the buggy wheels?" is one of the more exceptional things I've been asked,' says Alice, who has thirty years' teaching under her belt. 'Though I did have one boy in my class whose mother latched on to me. She clearly did everything for him. He was very overweight and did nothing. He couldn't even dress himself for PE. Somehow she found out where I lived and she used to come over and ask me advice. One day she came to say she wanted to enter her son for a talent contest on TV and the researchers wanted to come to her house to discuss it. Could she borrow some of my furniture to tart her house up a bit?!'

Of course it's the older teachers we turn to. No point asking the young whippersnappers, is there? Not when, like policemen, they look younger and younger. Heavens, you barely trust them to be out of short pants themselves. Teaching has to be one profession where for once experience is respected. They've seen it all, wiped the bottom and worn the aertex blouse.

'I have to say, though, that I have never known a generation of parents that are so needy,' says Alice, 'and yet give in so easily to their children. It's as if everyone has a right to be happy and so do their children. Nothing must upset them.' Was this the rationale behind the father who rang her late one evening, beside himself with worry. 'I persuaded someone I met who knows you socially to give me your home number. I'm so sorry to call you but I am frantic.' It turned out his six-year-old daughter was sitting on the windowsill, legs dangling out, refusing to come in. Could Alice possibly come over and talk her down?

Teacher's presents

You've forged the homework, and forced the odd issue, but the end-of-term present is the opportunity to sink to outright bribery. Might something a little special ease the way? How can Mr Fellows fail to fast-track George if I give him two bottles of Châteauneuf-du-Pape for Christmas?

When we were kids you might go in with a bunch of flowers at the end of the summer term. A few sweet peas nicked from the garden taken in clasped in a sweaty hand was all it took, and a home-made card would earn you a kiss on the cheek.

Now teachers' gifts have reached unparalleled levels of competitiveness, and places like M&S and supermarkets are even offering boxes of chocolates and bath goodies wrapped specially with sugary messages. The whole issue is fraught with anxiety and uncertainty. A bottle of bath oil? Too obvious – they must have loads of the stuff. A voucher for the garden centre? Too impersonal. I know: an Armani scarf. That'll show how grateful you are.

Of course you have already contributed a tenner to the

class present, the purchase of which will be organised by some eager beaver who will hand round a card for you to sign and make a little speech as she hands over the garden bench she bought with the proceeds of the whip-round. (A tenner each for a class of thirty – you do the figures.) But, racked with uncertainty that the teacher won't truly acknowledge your contribution, you get a little something to hand over on the last day, *just in case*.

'It is great to have a real treat, but what I have a drawerful of is the home-made cards and letters from the children. That's what matters,' says one teacher.

Then the relief when they move on to secondary school and the whole thing fizzles out. But, help, you think, how can you influence things now?

One-Up-Parentship: what they say and what they mean

Isn't it exhausting running them from pillar to post?
   (*But when they are as talented as my children, it's a crime not to.*)

It's so hard to find trousers to fit Tommy. They are always long enough on the leg but too big around the waist
   (*because he's so slim and athletic, unlike your porker*).

I'm rushed off my feet
   (*because I have a job and you don't, you loser*).

Lucky you, not having to freeze on the touchline.
   (*Oh, wasn't she picked for the team? Tough.*)

Yes, I've heard the high school's very good now
   (*but I won't have to worry cos mine is bright enough to pass the eleven-plus*).

Oh, I do envy you going to Cornwall *again*
   (because even though we are going club class it will still take us hours to get to Dubai).
You are so sensible not to buy a new buggy for each child
   (but I did because I can).
My children are so busy
   (cos I'm a great mother).
We don't fly long-haul any more, because of the carbon emissions.
   (We've hit hard times.)
You're lucky your daughter eats anything. Amelia is sooo picky
   (but that's because she has a highly refined palate).
He's just tired.
   (He's just not very good at it.)
Your daughter has a lively personality
   (and is a pain in the arse to teach).
Your daughter has a lively personality
   (which is a good thing because she's thick as a brick).
James has had the opportunity to learn to write his own prayers this term
   (but he didn't bother to take it).
Harriet contributes freely in class
   (in fact, she never bloody shuts up).
Your son does not accept authority easily.
   (Is his father in prison?)
Oscar is a solitary child.
   (Could he bath more often?)

6
Food: A War of Nutrition

It's five o'clock on a sunny evening. You have spent the last hour lovingly preparing organic carrots, butternut squash and puréed spinach for your family's dinner. You couldn't add chicken because that might be contaminated. It couldn't be beef because even now you're still a bit iffy about the BSE issue. It couldn't be lamb either because the butcher at the organic farm shop couldn't guarantee that it had been read a bedtime story every night before it was despatched to lamb heaven.

In fact it couldn't be meat at all because a vegetarian diet, so you have read, is far preferable, though you are carefully balancing iron and protein intake and macronutrients with organic free-range eggs and bioflavinoids – though not nuts because . . . well, you just never know, do you. Cheese of course is out because of your son's eczema and milk will only exacerbate his asthma and sinus problems.

Eventually, exhausted, with a glow of self-congratulation about you, you summon them to the table where you like to meet as a family to share news of your day and enjoy the shared pleasure of food together.

Ha! Dream on, sister. What you actually get is 'I'm not touching this' defiance, demands for ketchup or a flat refusal to try even the smallest bit of anything.

Food: A War of Nutrition

Let's face it, food is to being a modern parent what Al-Qaeda is to world security: an ever present terror. And just the mention of the subject can bring out a twitch in even the most level-headed, highly educated person. In fact you can forget education, the quality of what's on TV, the downfall of the civilised world. It's what goes into our children's stomachs that is the ultimate torment and it's like that before a nipple or a bottle (if you can live with yourself) even goes near their newborn mouth.

Ironic, isn't it, that at a time of concern about health, fast food and the time bomb of unparalleled obesity – a third of kids being seriously overweight in the UK according to the latest findings – we, whose children probably enjoy the best diet ever, obsess manically.

For Starters

From the moment a woman pees on the Stick and discovers she is up the duff, we have to question everything that goes in *our* mouths. Never mind that we are the generation who were gestating as our mothers smoked, drank gin and went to cocktail parties. Never mind that for thousands and thousands of years women have procreated successfully without having to read a magazine about what to eat while they are doing it. We dare not put more than 6oz of tuna in our mouths for fear of mercury levels; we find ourselves steering clear of Ardennes pâté and Brie. Potatoes can be dodgy – can't remember why now – and liver is a no-no. Dioxins and PCBs are everywhere, we hear, and, of course, up to the twelfth week we should have our 400 micrograms a day of folic acid.

If you are not in a state of complete nutritional confusion by now – your conscience being seriously pricked by the Twix you are demolishing that you have been craving all day – then take the weight off your varicose veins and take comfort in the fact that these are just the foothills of the massive ramifications the F-word will have in your life as a parent.

The Boob Job

Breast is best as we already know, and when the little mite is born there is the expectation that you will breastfeed. If you can manage it then the world applauds you – unless you try it in a pub – and you find yourself in the most bizarre places exposing a part of your anatomy you have only ever kept for your very nearest and dearest (and that time on St Tropez – well, everyone else was topless). The baby starts to suck and you have to hold tight to the other breast in case you shower the person sitting on the other side of the room, but you look down in glowing satisfaction as your baby suckles, knowing you are giving it the best you possibly can.

Unless of course you had a curry last night. Or oranges. Or a Pot Noodle. Or alcohol. Or a ready meal. So still we obsess about everything that goes in *our* mouths too. We know deep down that the quality of breast milk is only affected in extreme cases of deprivation and that the baby will take everything from you sooner than suffer itself, but still we worry that, unless we are careful, our children will not become the concert pianists they might be. We gobble up greedily the advice about staying clear of pollutants like nicotine and pesticide residue. We fret about insecticides (especially in airborne forms such as aerosols or coils) and seek out citronella. We fill our shopping trolleys with asparagus, cabbage, corn, chickpeas and spinach because we read somewhere that they contain lots of folic acid, and we search the net for foods with vitamin B9. It's the only vitamin that might just be slightly lacking in the diets of Western women so it's best to take a belt and braces approach, isn't it?

But, like the ability to do geometry or card tricks, some women can and some just can't breastfeed. 'I know I'd like to be doing it. I know I should be doing it. I know that formula milk is no substitute,' frets Belinda. 'There's even a political agenda: I know that there are issues about big corporations encouraging mothers in the Third World to feed their babies formula and I shouldn't be putting money in their pockets. So I pretend to everyone that I am – and the real reason I lie? Because I feel ashamed that I'm not doing the *best for my baby*.'

So what do we do? Sit and watch other women whip out their nipples at the drop of a breast pad as we fuss over bottles and warmers and microwaves (Should you? Shouldn't you? What about the hot spots?), trying hard to play down the faff involved. But take heart because even breastfeeding can have its pressures. Try to continue breastfeeding when you go back to work and you spend every waking hour frantically squeezing your boobs until

'You've got to hide those – I'm supposed
to be breastfeeding.'

they ache to produce enough milk for the au pair to give the baby during the day when you are out (and trying not to leak). That bottle in the fridge, waiting to be heated and served, contains all the guilt and all the best intentions in the world.

Ann even hired a pump so she could keep feeding Tom while she went back to her PR job. 'I just couldn't get on with those hand action things,' she says. 'They just didn't seem to fit my boobs but I couldn't bear not to express. One night at about midnight, feeling like a Holstein Friesian on this blasted pump thing, I realised that 3fl oz of breast milk was costing me about a quid!'

Alexis, determined she was going to take the bottle route for newborn James, came across the most bizarre double standard. 'There was the midwife sitting on my bed in the hospital telling me how I should be trying to breastfeed but I told her I didn't want to and that I found the whole thing disgusting. "So you are decided?" she asked finally. "Yup," says I. "Right, that's fine," she replied. "I couldn't stand it either. Stick to your guns, girl"!'

The Body Politic

So where did this war of nutrition come from? When did food become the enemy? The problem seems to be that the chasm between the classes has never been wider than it is today and never wider than it is about food. In the world that is eating worse junk than ever, where obesity is at epidemic proportions, where the first words for most children in the Western world are 'Happy Meal', and where even dinner ladies don't recognise a French bean, the classes-with-a-conscience are more terrorised by food than ever.

'I seem to compensate for the world's ignorance on my own children,' says Sarah, a usually sensible GP with a daughter of eleven and a son of eight. 'I'm manic about making sure they eat the five portions of fruit and veg a day and my children sigh and count them out. Deep down I know they should be having seven but I don't want to push the point.' What she forgets is that her kids have probably the best diet in the whole world even if they only had a couple of extra apples a week!

Food has become the enemy because, in most cases, food is the enemy. Our 'madness' about what we put in our children's mouths might just be justified when it is revealed there is more protein and less fat and salt in dog food than a fast food burger; that every month more than 90 per cent of the children in the United States eat at McDonald's, and a double quarter-pounder with cheese and medium fries is 1,110 calories and 1,330mg of sodium. Even the pap we are told about the value of low-fat foods becomes deeply suspicious when we find out McD's low-fat salad dressing has 730mg of sodium per 1.5 fl oz – and that's McDonalds' own nutritional information.

But let's not bang on about it (oh please, just one more: per ounce, Chicken McNuggets contain twice as much fat as a hamburger). We all know it's junk food and that only a fool would let their children eat it – you *don't*, do you? What's more scary and more likely to drive us to insane levels of eco food terror is that we are trying to raise children in a country where 40 per cent of the population have allergies of some kind – or at least they think they do. You can't take a step without hearing about asthma-related food intolerances, rashes and dermatitis, not to mention anaphylaxis. There is seafood allergy, rubber latex allergy, yeast, sesame and wheat. Milk, gluten and nickel too.

Supermarkets and food producers live in terror of mis-labelled packaging: Kettle sea salt and balsamic vinegar Chips were recently recalled as cheese seasoning had been mistakenly used instead of vinegar flavouring in two batches. Yikes. The implications.

A 'nut check' at a recent residential course for children turned out not to be a medical once-over to see if the wedding tackle was in order, or even a psychiatric assessment. It was so the matron could ensure no one had sneaked in sweets which the 'significant number of nut allergic children on the course might get hold of'.

Feeding Others

Allergies are not funny and, if you are affected, they can be deadly serious, but they are definitely not something our parents had to contend with. Lucy finds it makes a maniac of her: 'The whole thing about food and what you give other children is a minefield. I have been given an epi pen by the mother of a child who came to play and who had a nut allergy and I was absolutely demented. He was almost eating in a sealed area, because I thought, I've got peanut oil. If he inhales the vapours . . . and once upon a time that bowl had cashew nuts in it . . . The burden of responsibility was just unbelievable.'

And it doesn't stop there, does it? We have to take on responsibility elsewhere too, where perhaps others should. We can't relax in the knowledge that the powers that be are feeding our children properly. Once our school meals were made on the premises by a kindly crew of dinner ladies who peeled potatoes and made liver casserole and jam roly-poly and custard, which we'd go and run off afterwards with PE. Now the choice is turkey twizzlers and chips and chips and chips and there is no time for PE because the children have to do the literacy hour.

And it takes a TV celeb to take it in hand and make a political issue of what should be a nutritional one.

Food is political conflict too and everyone knows that in politics, there madness lies. We've already mentioned the formula milk issue but in your shopping trolley are bananas or a jar of coffee or carton of orange juice that aren't just lying there being bananas or jars of coffee or cartons of orange juice. They don't just make a comment about your choice of diet. They represent a war about Third World exploitation, price rigging and child labour that's going on way over your head and beyond Tescos on the South Circular. Crikey – shopping has never been such a drama.

Don't do what I do!

But don't you find yourself laying down one set of rules for yourself and one for your children? In our crusade to make sure that they have only the best of the best, we end up imposing really quite unreasonable limitations and even expectations on them. Claudia is aware she might be losing her sense of reason. 'Fast food joints are a bit of an issue for me, but I need to go there because otherwise my daughter will discover them and spend her entire life in fast food joints sitting over one of those full ashtrays and drinking bad coffee. The messages, though, are completely wrong. My children have to have chewy apricot bars which I wouldn't eat if I was starving.'

These look suitably disgusting and inedible, you think, as you put the cereal bars in your trolley for their school snacks then, at the checkout and feeling peckish, you slip in a bag of Minstrels for you for the journey home.

If it's not one thing . . .

But when you have finished the chocolate and secreted the wrapper, you can take comfort in the fact that never before have parents been bombarded with so much contradictory information. It's not really surprising that we are confused when we are surrounded by a media that is so keen on one hand to impart scary information about food and, on the other, to give us dogmatic advice about what we should and should not be eating

One minute omega 3 is the elixir of life. You see it everywhere – in special cartons of juice, eggs and spread. There are websites about it and you find yourself reading the back of packets and adding capsules of it to the vitamins and mineral supplements your children are already taking. Next thing you know, it's been decided it's not quite as essential as we'd first thought.

'I fell completely for the organic baby food thing,' says Fran, 'and paid well over the odds for the jars because if I was going to do jars then I had to do the organic jars. Then I read that I was better making non-organic home-made food. You can't win.'

You certainly can't. 'Not when supermarkets and food producers are packaging baby foods with the suggestion that they know best,' complains Jenny. 'One is doing quinoa, blueberry and spinach mushed up for babies. Oh, I found myself thinking, I hadn't thought of that. What is my child missing out on? I've never even heard of a bloody quinoa yet I found myself obsessing about it. I surfed the web in a panic about superfoods. What had I done? Millie was twenty-two months and she still hadn't had squash and sweet potato! What's even weirder is that I could so easily have made these foods myself and instead, like an automaton, I found myself buying them ready done!'

So while baby magazines and weekend sections in national newspapers ramp up the pressure, we seem to lose our ability to make informed decisions. We have very strong opinions as to whether the current government is good for the nation but we're stymied when it comes to something as complicated as butternut squash. Instead of using our common sense and cooking for ourselves, we find ourselves surfing chummy websites that are selling 280g of 'proper organic home-made' chicken in white sauce with sweetcorn and carrots for £3.20. Hang on a minute . . .

But don't just blame the media, poor lambs. Even the medics mess with our heads. Now we are told by the World Health Organisation that for the last forty years we have been given the wrong advice about breastfeeding and that weight charts used to advise us on a baby's optimum size have been based on the growth rates for infants fed on formula milk. There you were thinking you were doing the right thing, bucking the national trend and breastfeeding, only to be told your baby was underweight and you should supplement with a bottle or boost his solids. Aaaaargh!

But if only food was about eating

How many times have you heard yourself saying, 'When I was a little girl/boy I ate what was put in front of me and was grateful for it'? Food is a weapon even before it goes in the mouth, and the ones with their fingers on the trigger? The children.

It was all so easy before. You'd invite friends over for dinner and they'd be full of praise about your ceviche, go away asking for the recipe and all would be lovely. Now for your beloved child, the reason for your existence, you do the same. Not quite a Nigella recipe but as much an offer of love (because as we all know, food is love), and you get complete and utter rejection. Nobody warned us, did they? No one said that the subject of mashed carrots and swede would reduce you to tears. There was a conspiracy of silence about the fact that you could sweat for hours over shepherd's pie or chicken and mash only to find yourself faced with a closed mouth. In fact there is a direct connection between the amount of time you spend making it and the likelihood of rejection.

We have control everywhere else, haven't we? We can make them wear a jumper, we can do our best to get them to bed at night, we can decide where they are going to school, but one broccoli floret and we have met the intractable because food is a lethal weapon in the arsenal of the under-eighteens.

And doesn't the rejection make you psychotic? 'I would hold open his mouth and force-feed him like those poor geese in the Périgord,' confesses Kate. 'I had slaved over the stuff and even though he's only two and a half, he somehow *knew*. He was like Damien in that horror film. I felt he had total control and there was nothing I could do.'

'I'd get it in her mouth,' says Maggie, mum to Natasha, 'but then she'd sit like a hamster with it stored in her cheeks. I tried every trick in the book – diversion, bribery, anger – and she'd chew and chew until it was unswallow-able, then I'd watch as she spat out everything on to the plate.'

The pleasure we feel as we watch a child swallow a forkful of vegetables is second only to winning the Nobel Peace Prize in terms of achievement, so in that blob of masticated dinner, regurgitated on to the plate, lies our failure as a parent.

But isn't food supposed to be about pleasure? Isn't it supposed to be an enjoyable experience – I mean, what are restaurants all about otherwise? Why was the Michelin star invented if it was about misery and suffering? Well,

'Can I have some guacamole with that?'

yes, it is supposed to be, but when it comes to children, food is a symbol of all we are trying to achieve. We want to give them good things in a world of bad ones, and they'd sooner have a burger and chips.

Compromise . . . yours!

So what do you find yourself doing? Bending over backwards to keep everyone happy so long as they eat the stuff, and preparing about as many meals as the Ivy on a busy night. Potatoes are prepared in all manner of ways – one won't eat boiled, the other prefers mash – and chicken is being grilled because the tuna bake you so lovingly prepared is simply not acceptable. Mind you, a mother who offers fish in any form is either brave or downright foolish (okay, so yours *love* it. Don't get smug).

Then you read the food pages of parenting magazines. 'Here's a recipe for coconut cakes that are a simple, scrumptious treat that kids and parents can make together.' Oh, crikey, you think, not only have you not made those, you didn't make it a bonding experience by doing it *with your child*.

The Stasi of control, though, is the faddy eater. Now to some children this might just be some emotional response to food and they will probably grow up obsessive compulsive and unable to leave the house without checking three times they've turned off the gas. But to most, refusing to eat anything but Barbie tinned pasta and Monster Munches is downright dictatorial. In fact it makes Stalin look soft. What kind of glee must these faddists experience as they watch us plead, beg, weep until we cave in and heat up a tin. Anything, anything to get the little sod to eat.

What's even more bizarre is good food becomes bad and bad food, good. Claudia sums it up: 'We get the organic box, we go to the organic market, we have risotto. They have all the posh organic stuff they could possibly eat but when they are having a treat, it's tack – it's horrible, pink, sugary, marshmallow, chocolatey horror.' The message seems to be this: Be good and you will be given a reprieve from this healthy diet. You will be allowed to eat sweet rubbish that tastes nice.

Out to lunch

There's another mistake we are making too and that's confusing taking children to a restaurant with a treat. Get it right: restaurants are a treat for *adults*. They are a break from cooking; a place to have a few glasses of wine and a chat with friends; a place to go on a date or for a gourmet experience. To children, if they don't sell chips and large ice cream sundaes, they are pointless. Burger King calls itself a restaurant. So does Le Gavroche. So why doesn't the latter serve ketchup?

When will we ever learn? Gizelle has 'almost given up going out to restaurants now because it is just too difficult to eat with your child. I mean, by the time they have drunk the milkshake you bought them to keep them quiet before the food arrives, they are full and you're like, "Well, wouldn't you like your goujons of fish?" And you end up eating them because you don't want to let it go to waste.'

'When we were kids it was such a big treat – prawn cocktail and a steak at a restaurant the night before we went back to school,' remembers Gill. 'Now we meet friends at lunchtime and we all think, Won't this be nice? All of us out with the kids having a bite to eat. But in fact I always come away vowing I'm never, ever doing that again. The kids get restless and start getting up and throwing chips at each other or bits of torn-up napkin, and you are trying to listen to keep up with the adult conversation with half an eye on the people frowning at you from tables close by.'

For some bizarre reason, we think going out to a restaurant with children is some form of hospitality. A happy get-together. Actually it's a nightmare of stamina and tolerance. Like everything else they want it here and they want it now. It is beyond them that they might have to wait, and you know what's mad? We don't insist they learn how to. 'I have a bag full of tricks,' says Ann-Marie with a laugh, who finds herself out too often with Will, eight, and Charlotte, six. 'Everything in my head is telling me this is bloody stupid and we should have stayed at home, so, like Mary Poppins, I have a bag full of diversionary toys – crayons, Gameboys, you name it – instead of just telling them to be patient. What on earth am I afraid of?'

Ha! Now that's the million-dollar question.

'Oh, but he simply adores squid ink pasta . . .'

We have been programmed since we were cooking roast mammoth risotto over the cave fire that it is good parenting to nourish. If you feed your children well, then you are a *good parent*. And when it gets scary is when your skills are revealed for everyone else to judge.

It's a bit like giving a dinner party and getting into a complete panic that the food won't be good enough. Only a hundred times worse. Never mind that most of the population are popping take-away chips into their off-spring's mouths in the pram. It doesn't even matter that to the majority of the population a microwave beefburger will suffice as nutrition. *What will other people think* if your children are seen to be eating a bag of crisps?

'We went to the planetarium on a school trip,' says Lucy, fretting about the whole issue. 'The hardest part of the day was lunch because everybody just sat down and got out their lunchboxes, and the parents were saying: "He's got Cheese Strings! Have you seen he's got Cheese Strings?" And the effort that other people had put into their lunchboxes that day knowing that other people were going to be looking was phenomenal. Everything has to be organic and free-range this and good for you and healthy that.' So terrified was she that, even at school, she would be judged by lunchbox, Lucy found herself putting to-gether a five-course meal for her son's lunchbox. 'I realised that perhaps I was going a bit far when I peeled a quail's egg. I thought, Hang on, this is just like Henry VIII's banquet here. And he's five.'

Her paranoia is entirely justified. There's an insuffer-
able modern smugness between parents, which didn't
exist before the invention of the organic rice cracker.
Admit it, doesn't it give you a teensy-weensy bit of
satisfaction when your children say, 'Can I have an apple?'
or 'Oh, I do love tapenade,' in front of other people? Ann
has a theory: 'We like to sort of present ourselves and we
can do that through food, can't we? We can show who we
are through what we give our kids and what we give their
kids, but we need to make sure everybody knows. When
we are having kids over, sometimes I get to the stage
where I'm almost throwing a mini dinner party and
they're six! It has got ridiculous.'

'If I provide sausages to a child who comes over to
play,' admits Pru, 'I do worry what the other parents will
think.'

There's a sweet satisfaction, isn't there, though, when
the mother comes to collect the playmate and you say,
'Oh, he ate *really* well. He even had seconds of baby corn/
cottage pie/foie gras,' and you watch the delicious terror
in her eyes as she says, 'He never eats that at home.' Ha,
you find yourself thinking, isn't it lucky then that your
child has had the privilege of lunch with us! You turn into
this hateful person who says things like, 'Oh, I only ever
buy from the farmers' market,' or, 'George is always
nagging me to make my pasta puttanesca.' We don't talk
like this in other areas of our life, so why on earth are we
doing it here?

Of course there is the odd mad one. The parent who
swoops on your house and does a food standards report

on your larder. One woman, whose child shows no allergies whatsoever, is so traumatised by the thought of them, that she insists nothing potentially allergenic is served at parties *her* son attends.

There's an odd sort of reversal here, though, with this food thing. There are the type of parents who try to be so laid back. 'Oh, yes,' they say languidly, 'we don't mind Jocasta having a bag of Hula Hoops.' Yet you know behind closed doors it's a different story. 'I go out of my way to make it known that my kids are allowed chocolate,' says Liz, 'but in fact that's not true at all. I'm really really careful not to let them have junk, but where I live it's not seen to be cool to be super organic and good and healthy because we are all quite geeky so we pretend to be cool!'

Your children come back from a day of ice cream and Coke with the grandparents and you find yourself contemplating colonic irrigation for them to purge them of this muck. Think what it will do to their well-being and intelligence!

Out of the mouths of babes

Scarier though than our own obsessions, scarier than the disapprobation of other parents is judgement by children themselves.

Part of the curriculum seems to be Keep Your Parents in Order. Clare recently bought some organic strawberries grown in some sunny clime for a special treat for her twins in January. 'Look!' she yelped in glee, bringing them out at the end of the meal as a surprise, only to be met by stony silence. The twins exchanged glances. 'Mum, they've been flown here.' 'So?' 'Well, that uses up fossil fuels and that's contributing to global warming.'

So when did food get so wrapped up in everything: rejection of love, control, the downfall of the planet? It's like living with Friends of the Earth.

'My poor child is like a neurotic Woody Allen figure who paces around the kitchen obsessing about whether or not he has had his five portions of fruit and veg that day,' says Lucy. 'And he's so Mc-phobic that every time we drive past McDonald's he is jeering at people; and food's all colour co-ordinated now. You have to have a piece of red food, blue food, yellow food and it gets to the point where he is saying, "Oh, but Mummy I've had lots of red food today, I should be having blue food," and you are going through the cupboards trying to find a blueberry or a prune or something so you can tick it off the list.'

It's that gastro-terrorism again, only now they aren't refusing to eat the good food that you have so lovingly prepared. They are criticising you for not being good enough. At worst, it's horrendous – and ends up with eating disorders and self-loathing. At best it's distressing, but you know they'll get their comeuppance when they have kids themselves. Then we'll get the last laugh.

Until then we cave in. 'It's been more than a year since I've been allowed to consume the froth on my cappuccino,' coos some self-satisfied food writer. 'Screams of rage ensue if my two-year-old is not allowed to skim it all off with a spoon.' Oh, fear not: market forces will out. Costa and Starbucks now do a Babyccino so the little darlings can have their own way.

You've cooked up a little foodie if your child:

- Thinks McDonald's is a farm
- Gives Smarties back to you because she thinks they're counters
- Uses the Playdoh machine to make pretend fresh pasta
- Looks at a picture of a fish finger and has no idea what it is
- Plays pretend games about eating imaginary 'couscous'
- Tries white chocolate for the first time and says, 'This Brie is very nice'
- Wants a juicer for his birthday
- Asks at the chip shop if they have balsamic vinegar
- Goes on a school trip to France and brings you back a Fourme d'Ambert as a souvenir
- Thinks Pizza Express is fast food

7
Family Holidays: Travelling Hopefully

Remember holidays before we had children? Remember relaxing, winding down, doing what we felt like doing? Returning home tanned, restored and revitalised? Well, we can forget all that, because none of it applies any more, once we start going on holiday with kids. And a week in a caravan at Camber Sands, knocking about with a bucket and spade, won't cut the mustard any more.

In fact, what it really needs these days is a new name – one that has no association with relaxation or pleasure – to describe going through the same shit in a new place with none of the customary support around, tacking on an arduous long-haul journey at both ends, and the privilege of paying through the nose for it, cos we're going in the school holidays.

Face facts. Holidays are no holiday, but since we persist in pretending they are, we have to play the game and all convince each other (and maybe ourselves) that we're actually enjoying our two weeks in the sun. Whereas the truth is that we generally can't wait to go back home. It rapidly becomes clear that what we and our children want from a holiday is completely incompatible – like matter and antimatter. If we are having a good time, they'll be whining. If they are enjoying themselves, we'll be counting the seconds until it's over. And this is something that will go on until the day we can go our separate ways.

The Expense!

Do you too get a sense of panic as term draws to a close? How could they do that to us? Leave us on our own with all those children to look after? And the expense! Because, let's face it, school holidays are expensive now – and that's even before we go anywhere. If we're working, there's childcare. If we're not, we've got to take them places. When we were kids, we'd cycle up to the sweet shop, go and dig holes on the golf course, climb trees and practise whistling, then hiding when somebody looked around. Ah, happy days! Now, kids out on their own are targets of suspicion and resentment, and run the risk of getting ASBOs for not tucking their shirts in or breathing too loudly. So we have to keep them gainfully employed at all times. And that costs.

Lisa fumes, 'We've got to take them places in the car, feed them – cos they want feeding all the time – take them to the cinema, theme parks, day trips, swimming. If we can find somewhere for them to let off some energy on a sports course, we'll pay through the nose. And on top of all that, they'll need extra credit on their phones so they can text each other about what a boring time they're having! It's six weeks of me not being able to do anything I want to do. And when I said that to my daughter one time, she said, "Well, now you know how I feel when you make me go to school." As if it was a choice!'

Despite all the money and time we're throwing at our kids, 24 per cent of parents expect their children will complain of being bored at least once a week during the holidays. Only 24 per cent? These people are not doing right by their kids! If we deny our children the pleasure of whining, 'You're totally ruining my life!' at regular intervals then we are depriving them of a right we all enjoyed as kids. Come on, slackers! Toughen up! Take some pride in your role as parents!

Planes, trains and automobiles

Of course, the first problem with holidays is that we have to get there and, whatever mode of transport we choose, we're going to suffer. A survey commissioned by the games-maker Ravensburger reveals that children squabbling is the biggest cause of holiday stress. No shit, Sherlock! Well, no doubt a bracing game of draughts would sort that out. Or maybe soundproof glass between the front and back seats of the car. Now why don't the manufacturers think of these things? Why don't they ever ask us?

Cram our family into a little tin box for hours on end, and we're bound to have trouble. Particularly when the very first, 'Are we nearly there yet?' generally comes about eight miles from home.

Ginny shakes her head in disbelief. 'Despite the fact that the kids get really car sick, we decided to drive to the south of France. How crazy is that? We had a car full of wet wipes, bottled water and empty carrier bags and we just went for it. It became some sort of twisted macho compulsion to see how many miles we could cover without stopping. And when we got back, that was virtually all we talked about to other parents – how many miles we covered between stops.'

So if driving is hell, we take to the air. Or not. Next time someone tells you their kids will 'probably sleep through most of their transatlantic flight', just do them a favour and slap them hard at once. They need to be brought to their senses. Long-haul flights may be tedious for adults but for kids they're fantastically exciting. What could be better: strapped into a nice bouncy seat, with a tray to open and slam shut repeatedly, captive adults to pull faces at, regular if inedible food with sachets of salt and pepper to shake over everyone, then the promise of portable games consoles and in-flight movies if they get too restless. What possible reason could they have for sleeping?

Flying – progress? We've made ourselves victims of our own success by being able to access the whole world on a whim and a 747. Travel had to be easier when you were restricted to a week in Skegness.

Steve shakes his head at the memory. 'The kids made themselves sleep in the car to make sure they'd be awake for the whole ten hours. We were completely zonked after the long drive to the airport and in no mood for quality time with the little sods, but we had to take it in turns to stay awake with them to make sure they didn't drive everyone else on the plane crazy. I counted up the number of times they each went to the loo during my watch. Twenty-five.'

'Are we enjoying ourselves yet?'

We get into a particular grimly determined mindset when we're travelling with kids, and it's nothing to do with enjoyment or leisure. When we've got everything booked, it becomes an imperative to make it all go according to plan, despite misadventures. Defeat is simply not an option – particularly when we've saved up our air miles and everything is 'non-transferable'.

Roger shudders as he remembers the worst twenty-six hours of his life, travelling with his wife and eighteen-month-old daughter from Auckland to Fresno via Los Angeles by plane and rental car – all pre-booked. 'Little Julia had a gippy tummy in New Zealand and if we'd been even a tiny bit sane, we'd have stayed put. But all we could think about was the tickets, the reservations. It was hideous. She vomited all over us, then diarrhoea would leak out of her nappy. We'd change that and then she'd vomit again. We left the flight with a quarantine bag stuffed with soiled clothes – ours and Julia's. The flight staff even had to replace the seat cushions mid-flight because they were too awful to be used any more. Everyone must have hated us, but we were too stressed out even to notice.'

And baby came too

Travelling light is simply not an option any more. Because, obviously, if our baby doesn't have everything just the same as at home, he's going to be traumatised for the rest of his life. So in goes the nightlight (and an adaptor plug), in goes the musical cot mobile with the fluffy bunnies, in goes the cot bumper. And your case is full already. And then there's food.

Jenny remembers her first family holiday. 'As we all know, they don't have babies in Greece. So we decided we'd better take all Safia's food with us, just like at home. Because if we didn't, she'd cry, she wouldn't sleep, it would be a disaster. So we bought fifteen jars of her favourite banana mush. It weighed a ton, but we couldn't risk her eating foreign bananas – no, she had to have British bananas. And so I ended up taking almost no clothes. And all we took were nappies, factor squillion sun block and banana mush. Some holiday!'

Shared holiday, shared misery

Why is it that, when we've got kids, we suddenly think it would be a good idea to spend two weeks cooped up with another family, just because they've got kids too? What kind of madness is it that makes us think it's going to be somehow easier? Holidays are stressful enough as it is, with the whole dynamic of suddenly having to spend all day every day with your partner and your children; it's like a great big long weekend – and we all know how hellish those are. Add another family, going through the same agony and do it in a house with paper-thin walls and terrible plumbing, and Alcatraz would have been more of a laugh. At least there you had the option of being put in Solitary. Really, it couldn't be less relaxing, because we feel constantly on show so we're trying our hardest to present our family at its best and the whole thing turns into a competition.

Laura recalls, 'We thought we were the best of mates and the kids always got on so well. Now I realise it was only because we all had our own homes to go to, and we never had to have *breakfast together*. From the first morning, when their kids had croissants from the local boulangerie and our two wanted Shreddies, I knew we were in for trouble. The other dad kept laughing and saying our kids were wimps, in a really sneery way. I remember trying to force my daughter to eat this really garlicky pâté, just to show him. It ended up with an ugly showdown over some bouillabaisse.'

There were some upsides to Laura's holiday, though. 'The best thing was that our kids were much better swimmers than theirs and, since we had a pool at the villa, it was blatantly obvious. So to make up ground, my husband was nudging the kids, whispering, "Go on, do another length and a tumble turn, go on. I'll pay you!" It brought out the worst in us all. We've barely seen the other family since.'

Long-haul competition

The very best bit of the holiday, of course, is when we're back at home, all the misery behind us, and we give our (carefully revised) version of events to our friends. There's a definite hierarchy of holiday destinations but it's not all that obvious to the unwary. As time goes by, you'll catch on, but you'll have several years of polishing your anecdotes and buffing your tan, only to be trumped by a more experienced holiday boaster, before you get it quite right.

It's important to be detailed, of course. There is no point in saying, 'Oh, we went to Provence,' because any fool can do that. We have to find a hitherto barely known region of France or, alternatively, have a 'little place' there. If we can't manage that, a villa with a pool and preferably a cleaner is bound to wipe the smile off a few people's faces. And so it goes on, with the ante being upped and upped until we're spending the equivalent of the GDP of a small Eastern European country to take our kids to the Caribbean for island-hopping by private plane in the high season. Then, just when we think it can't be bettered, we'll meet someone who completely takes the wind out of our sails.

'I was so pleased with our holiday,' says Melanie. 'Well, smug would be more accurate. I was telling a woman who has a boy in the class above my son's. She listened politely and nodded but I know something was up. Then, when I'd finished going on about how brilliant Madagascar was, she just said, "We try not to fly long-haul any more. The damage to the environment is just so awful, isn't it? We just went to the Outer Hebrides for three weeks, in the most heavenly cottage with its own beach. We all just swam and sailed and canoed and windsurfed all day long, and the weather was perfect. We caught our own fish most days and cooked them on an open fire." And that was it. I was completely deflated. It had been *Swallows and Amazons*, she'd spared the environment *and* they'd saved money.'

See the genius of that woman? 'We try not to fly long-haul any more.' She not only has the moral high ground now, but she was taking her kids to exotic climes before we even thought about it. You have to admire a put-down like that.

Another useful ploy is to downplay our current holiday, along the lines of, 'We're just camping this summer. A couple of weeks in Cornwall,' then, when the person we're talking to has relaxed and admitted they're only going to poxy Normandy, we hit them with, 'because Whistler in spring is so expensive.' Game, set and match to us!

Ticking the boxes

If we really want to rate in the holiday game, we'll have to cover all bases: culture, adrenalin, something apparently unpretentious, luxury and something no one has thought of doing at all. And we must book it all up at least a year in advance, so we've got plenty of time to tell everyone: Easter in Seville, half-term on a sailing course in Antigua, summer hols in the Scillies, October in Mauritius, and the following February on a camel-riding course in Marrakech. Just think of the round robin we'll be able to make out of *that* next Christmas!

Children, of course, are mostly unaware of the relative costs of holidays and what they represent. Lucy was horrified when her kids came home from school on the first day of the autumn term: 'We'd been flotilla sailing in Croatia, then we spent a week on a gorgeous island. It really had been a fantastic holiday but, when the children got home from school that day, they kept going on and on

'That's not how you spell Mustique.'

about some kid in their class who'd been to Blackpool, and how much fun it sounded, and could we go there next year. Over my cold, lifeless body!'

The pressure works both ways, of course, with children asking to go to Mexico, like their friends, as if the decision were as simple as choosing a pizza topping. Often this is just due to lack of geographical knowledge. One seven-year-old said, 'Josh got his new football boots in South Korea.' And when his mother had picked herself up off the floor, he corrected himself, 'I mean South Kensington.'

A head teacher sighs, 'We had to put an end to holiday diaries because the differences in what the children had done over the summer were so huge. And we couldn't help thinking the parents were using the diary as a showcase for how fantastic they were. There were business-class plane tickets stuck in, pressed exotic flowers from Caribbean islands, photos of the villas they'd stayed in. And then we'd have the other extreme, with bus tickets and stories about going to the leisure centre for a swim.'

As long as it's educational . . .

So if children are at school for roughly thirty-nine weeks a year, that leaves just thirteen weeks for all these holidays. And don't the tour operators know it! Despite the efforts of the government, holiday prices zip up and up in the high season – it's simply supply and demand. No wonder parents want to take the kids on holiday during the school term – it's cheaper and quieter. Yes, but . . . er, what about their education?

Now that the DfES has come out so strongly against holidays in term time, we have to be able to justify going in terms of something other than a cost-saving exercise. So off we go, cap in hand to the head teacher, begging for our ten days out of the academic year, or even more if we can swing it. And it's entirely at the school's discretion – another reason to suck up to the head. If the head teacher won't agree, and we've booked the holiday already, we're in trouble. Our children will be considered to be truanting, just as surely as if we were letting them roam the streets sniffing glue, and, under the recent anti-social behaviour legislation, we could have to pay a fixed penalty. The shame of it!

Luckily for us, there are now plenty of holiday companies around who understand our needs. In recent years, the trend for more adventurous family holidays has really taken off, and we can always find a way of justifying these as 'educational', particularly when the tour operator throws in a bit of trekking and some ancient ruins. For example, on one tour we can travel down the Nile on a felucca, take in the Great Pyramid, a museum or two and find time for a little snorkelling in the Red Sea – all in the cosy company of like-minded, right-on people with children just like ours (we hope).

'After a day whale-watching in the bay of Algeciras, we had all gone up to a nature reserve in the hills of Andalucía to see vultures in their natural habitat. The parents were all being terribly right-on and taking photos, but the kids found some bones the vultures had stripped bare – apparently the farmers leave carcasses out for them. It was like something from *Lord of the Flies*! The kids made a huge pile of bones with skulls on top all facing outwards, then started leaping around with these horns held to their heads. They were all doing it, and all the parents looked terribly uncomfortable and embarrassed, but they didn't really want to bust it all up. In the end, one of the children tripped over and cut his knee and the whole thing ended. But it was a strange moment. I can't imagine what the tour guide must have thought.'

Think of the holiday diary we could have turned in after a trip like that! Trouble is we know the educational credentials of the 'adventure holiday' are bogus and a feeble excuse just to save on our holiday budget, but doesn't it make it so much easier when we go grovelling to the head? We can even take the brochure to prove its relevance to Key Stage whatever (printed on recyclable paper, natch).

Result? Happy head teacher and happy parents. And we can bet ours will be the only kids in the school to have done Costa Rica by the age of seven. Trouble is, they'd still probably prefer Blackpool.

Souvenirs that last and last

So why are we travelling to more and more far-flung regions with our children? Well, you can't expect rugged individualists of the Lonely Planet and Rough Guide generation to make do with a couple of weeks on the

Costa Brava once we have kids of our own, can you? We take long-haul travel so much for granted – indeed, it is usually a major strategy for defining ourselves as 'interesting' – that we would sooner fit the kids into our holiday plans than fit our holiday plan to the kids. The more unusual the destination, the better.

Yet with more exotic holidays come more exotic diseases. Travel clinics are reporting significant increases in the number of children being brought in for a full armful of inoculations. A nurse specialising in the field says, 'My nightmare client would be a pregnant woman with toddlers turning up and saying, "Oh, we're off to the Gambia the day after tomorrow. Can we have our jabs now?" If they took as much time looking into the health risks as they do trying to shave a few pounds off the price of their holiday, they'd be far better prepared. And there must be people who don't bother to see the doctor at all – until they come back from their holiday with amoebic dysentery or worse. And it's all so they can show off to their neighbours about the holiday they've had.'

Amoebic dysentery! What fun! A quick flick through one of the many brochures reveals a trip to Peru, recommended as suitable for children from the age of seven. And the health notes are as follows:

Disease	Vaccination
Diphtheria	Recommended
Malaria	Recommended**
Poliomyelitis	Recommended
Rabies	Recommended

Typhoid	Recommended
Yellow Fever	Compulsory*

*A Yellow Fever vaccination is highly recommended, even if arriving within 6 days from or via an infected area.

**Malaria: At time of writing there have been reports that a strain resistant to choloquine and sulfadoxine pyrimethamine has been identified.

Wouldn't that be enough to scare off the bravest? The idea of having those jabs as an adult, quite apart from having to drag a seven-year-old to the travel clinic to have them would end all holiday spirit in most families. Dr Lisa Ford, a lecturer in travel medicine, says, 'I would not take my young children to chloroquine-resistant malarious areas. I am very keen for them to experience the world soon, but for the time being what's wrong with Northumberland?'

Quite.

Everybody happy?

We know, don't we, that we can't please all the people all of the time. So why don't we stop trying? Taking teenagers on holiday – or in fact anywhere – is nightmarish at the best of times. But when we have to combine their interests with those of our younger children, let alone ours, we know we're heading for trouble. Time was teenagers just had to lump it and sulk for the statutory two weeks until they were old enough for an Interrail card and a backpack. Now their expectations are altogether higher.

The problem is that we would run a mile, clutching our ears, from the kind of resort they would enjoy and, equally, just the sight of a cathedral or (God forbid) a glass-blowing works sends them into a catatonic state that nothing but Bacardi Breezers, trip-hop and scantily clad members of the opposite sex will rouse them from.

Mandy remembers, with a shudder, their last family holiday. 'We'd hired a villa in Umbria and it cost an arm and a leg. The little ones were perfectly happy splashing about in the pool but my fourteen-year-old was furious with us for dragging her out there. She stayed in bed until lunchtime every day, and when she did get up, she complained constantly. She spent every night in her room playing music on her iPod. We'd have done better leaving her at home. Fortunately she stayed out of all the photos, so we didn't have to explain why we appeared to have a member of the Addams family with us. She went back paler than when she arrived. But when we got back, we still pretended we'd all had the jolliest time. Well, you've got to, haven't you?'

The final solution: holidaying together but apart

What's the point in flying halfway across the world to unwind in the lap of luxury if we have to spend our precious leisure time entertaining our own children? Where's the fun in that? If the worst part about the family holiday is the family part of it, then the solution is clear. Split up when you reach your destination and see as little of each other as you can until the flight home. Yes, this is the Kids' Club but five-star! And now parents have discovered how fantastic it is barely to see their kids at all during their holidays, clubs are springing up at luxury resorts everywhere. It's Butlins with palm trees.

Cathy sighs as she remembers her perfect holiday: 'I knew I was in heaven when a uniformed flunky from the hotel approached my sun lounger with a little cloth and a bottle of spray, offering to polish my sunglasses. And what was more, there were no shrieking children, no babies wailing, no sandy footballs landing on my tummy. It was almost spooky. All the kids were occupied for most of the day. I even started to miss mine but not all the parents were like me. We could see the strain for the hour or so they had to spend together each day. But that's what we pay for – someone else to keep our kids out of our way!'

But when children are welcome as long as they're somewhere else, what happens if we actually want to spend time with them? Come on! It could happen! 'I realised we weren't the typical clientele,' she continues, 'because we actually quite wanted to do things with our kids, but bringing them to the beach with us was very uncomfortable because they were just about the only children there. All the others were in the clubs, and there was plenty of tutting and eye-rolling going on when our two started to play ball in among the sun loungers. After that, we consigned them to the clubs, like everyone else.'

Closer to home, there's a burgeoning market for hotels that are child-friendly but we're not talking three-star properties in Bournemouth. These are the height of luxury, offering relaxation for stressed-out mummies and daddies so there's usually a spa attached. But also tagged on is a nursery (all Ofsted checked, of course) where their little darlings can be entertained morning till night (and out of sight), and you don't have any nasty feelings of guilt spoiling your hot stone massage. It's the best of both worlds – for the parents at least.

A Child's Right to Ski

Remember when a week on the piste was fancy? The preserve of royals and glamorous weather-beaten foreigners in fur hats? Those were the good old days, weren't they? When we could get away with not taking a skiing holiday every year, without permanently compromising our family's honour. Now, if we don't book into the Trois Vallées at February half-term, along with the majority of Western Europe, our kids are likely to place a call to ChildLine.

Harry wrings his hands, a shadow of the man he once was. 'I hate skiing,' he moans. 'But the kids insist so we have to. I'm terrified, broke and knackered from the moment we get to wherever we select each year. It's crowded, we have to queue with French people for good-ness sake, it's noisy, it's cold, everything costs a fortune. There's always a chance of permanent disablement and, wherever we go, the snow's always better somewhere else. But the kids have to go, so I have to put up with it.'

Part of the problem, according to a ski instructor, is that no one will admit to being a beginner so they're always trying runs that are, frankly, too difficult for them.

Jenny remembers a late afternoon run when her nine-year-old daughter came with her. 'She'd been in ski school all week and I thought she was probably doing all right. My friend's daughter was quite good and I wanted Becky to keep up, so we all went together. It started out as a blue run, then there was a bit of red, then we were going to finish on a blue near the hotel. Well, I don't know what happened. We must have missed the sign for the blue and we ended up on a black. There was no way Becky could manage it and I could see she was starting to panic. I wasn't doing too great either. Then these stewards appeared with a sledge they use to pick up all the rubbish at the end of the day. They gave me such a look, as if I was the worst mother in the world, and took Becky down on the sledge. Thank goodness I don't speak French too well. I heard some people talking about it in the queue for the ski-lift the next day and I had to pretend it wasn't us.'

But even if we love skiing – and plenty of us do – there is one unpalatable truth we all have to understand. Tim puts it succinctly: 'I've just had to accept that my kids are far better at skiing than I will ever be. Now, they just regard me as an embarrassment. Basically, I'm the wallet and that's all I'm here for and as long as I keep providing the money but stay far enough away that they can disown me, we'll all have a good time.'

Latch-key effect

So are we any better off for the world being a global village? Isn't there something awfully wrong with our children not knowing where Yorkshire is while being totally au fait with the Yucatan Peninsula?

But you must have noticed how delighted your kids are when they get back home. What is it? The telly? The computer? The cat? No, in most cases, it's the plumbing. Sharon has noticed it too. 'We got in, unloaded the car and the kids were nowhere to be seen. We thought they'd slipped out without our noticing. Then we found each of them had locked themselves in the loos, one upstairs and one downstairs. When we asked them why – cos there was no sound of flushing or anything – they both said, "We just wanted to be alone for a bit." And, do you know, I knew how they felt.'

Family Holidays: Travelling Hopefully

Why you need to be mad to have children . . .

	Then	Now
Average income	1970: £1,400 pa	£27,000
House prices (average)	1970: £4,480	£178,992
Week in a hotel in Cornwall for a family of four in summer	1972: £98 for seven nights	£3,080 for seven nights
Family estate car	1975: Austin Allegro 1500: £1,500	VW Touareg from £28,600
Fridge	1975: £79	£900
Pair of school shoes	1975: £5.50	£40
Pocket money (weekly)	5p	£7.24 average for 11–14-year-olds
Boarding school fees	1970: £640 per year	£20,000 (plus) per year
Pop music	1975: vinyl album £2	CD £13.99
Comics and magazines	1975: *Beano* 4p per week	*Warhammer* magazine £4 per month
Sweets	1975: Creme Egg 6p	Creme Egg 36p

Sources: Clarks Shoes, Nationwide, Halifax, Norland, *The Lady*, Nannypaye.co.uk, DC Thomson

8

Slaves to the Schedule

You've occupied them for the statutory vacation period by trekking in Nepal; now what are you going to do to fill up the rest of their spare time?

Activity 24/7 is a disease that seems to affect us modern parents. Like doing Sudoku, it becomes a compulsion. And there is less time left unused. Shooting the breeze is not an option. Boredom? Utterly verboten. Imagine the dangers in leaving them to fill their own time! It's no coincidence that the number of children who end up in A&E with injuries from home-made bows and arrows has taken a noticeable dip. And when was the last time you heard about someone falling out of a tree (excluding Keith Richards of course)? They've all been cut down anyway in case they grow conkers. When we were kids we could spend hours with just a stick and our imagination. Now our kids will get repetitive strain injury from opening the car door.

This need to account for every waking moment is partly a result of the same anxiety that stops them being allowed to do skipping in the playground: the perception of danger. We can't let them play in the woods after school or during the holidays, or go over to the village shop (if there still is one) because they will undoubtedly be run over, kidnapped or abducted by aliens, when in fact children are statistically safer now than they have ever been. The bigger danger they face is from having over-developed thumbs from texting or over-use of the game console.

Another reason we can't let our children just fill their time with nothing in particular is because we wouldn't really know what to do with them. 'I get quite incensed if they are watching TV,' admits Lily, 'even if we have been out for the day doing wall-to-wall activities or even if they have been at school all day. I know they are tired and deserve the downtime, but I become convinced it will just rot their brains. But the problem is, what will I do with them when they turn it off?' The prospect of a whole day with nothing planned seems to fill us with terror and we become convinced that time not taken up with construc-tive activity is time wasted because . . .

. . . the real reason we fill every waking moment of their young lives is that they must have an advantage, an edge over other children. Some sociologists have a theory that we pursue this inane timetable of extra-curricular activity because it is in some way making up for what was missing in our own youth.

Poppycock. It's all about improvement and being the best, isn't it? Getting one over on the Opposition. We don't seem to be satisfied unless every possible talent, however faint, is being exploited, and any possible hidden talents are being uncovered.

John shares the pressure: 'You find out that all these classes are going on at the weekend and gradually you

Lara found quality time for herself and
Millie at 4 a.m, before the gym.

think, Oh, maybe our children should be, you know, stretching themselves a bit more. Our children always have to be stretched – I don't know why! It's like some sort of medieval torture, but suddenly you feel a bit guilty that they're not doing ballet, football, fencing, architecture, glass blowing at the weekend and you start to sort of get swept up in this madness and start to go along to some of these things.'

First of all, of course, we have to improve the essential parts. We're not talking the basic coaching that is needed to give children a leg up to a good school, nor are we talking about sports activities for kids whose school curriculum (and lack of playing fields) allows for a negligible amount of PE.

Oh no, the schedule we refer to and to which we are slaves is the hysterical round of *improving* activities that will gives *us* the gold medal in the parenting Olympics.

Skills, skills, skills

Being tutored is like being coached but for the brain. How can we resist a sales pitch that promises 'the opportunity to realise their full potential . . . We can work to give your child the best chance of leading a happy and successful life . . .' Only the brave or certifiably insane would pass up the guarantee of a better skilled child – it would be negligent to really – and that's why so many sign up for after-school Kumon maths and English tutoring.

The whole ethos behind this, and other similar learning schemes, is the suggestion that a child's life will be more successful if they join up. Well, you can't be too caring, can you?

Gizella had a friend who wanted her son to be well rounded, 'so it wasn't enough that he was accomplished at sports and music and everything that he did at school, but he had to speak very well and so she took him to drama classes but the idea of drama at that age is very much, "ooh, let's be trees, and let's now be a river" or whatever – I mean it's meant to be very kind of creative and that's not the kind of drama she was after. She wanted her child to be able to not just speak well but to project well, as BBC broadcasters train to do. It wasn't enough that he had this extensive vocabulary and could spell all the words and could do his six times table. So in the end she actually got private tuition, once a week. He's three and a half.'

The weirder the better

The important thing is to choose an activity that has a whiff of the unusual about it. There are two reasons for this.

First, the more unique the activity, the more innovative and, frankly, inspired a parent you'll appear. Mandarin Chinese is a hot favourite, especially among children in university towns, and London, of course, where everything is available. Well, the Far East is such an emerging culture, you hear yourself say when quizzed about it by envious friends (envious because they didn't think of it first), and it will be so useful on Rory's CV. You, in turn, though, feel a flutter of panic when a friend says, 'Must dash,' and whisks her daughter off to coaching in some niche sport like racquets or real tennis. Then you are told another child is county standard, which sounds a terrifyingly high achievement and, in your panic at your own failure, you forget that there may actually not be that much competition to be county standard in croquet.

Of course we are all dedicated followers of whatever happens to be in fashion. Children's yoga – now there's an idea, especially when the literature says it 'stimulates children's imagination' *and* 'is a fun way to exercise' *and* 'helps them relax and learn to have balance in their lives'. Result: ticks all the boxes.

'I do remember trying to become one of those calm and beautiful-looking yoga mums and went for several weeks to this mother and baby yoga class,' says Fran. 'Harvey and I turned up for our weekly lesson in trying to look relaxed, lying on the floor of some woman's living room in Crouch End with a bunch of other women and babies. The hour for us was largely filled with me doing continual breast feeding and feeling most unrelaxed while everyone else managed to have such yogatastic babies that they had advanced to foot massages and chi baby breathing exercises. I finally decided I didn't have to keep putting Harvey and myself through this ordeal of smelly feet and chilly floorboards when the yoga teacher said, apologetically, that the session would have to end early as the yoga mats appeared to have some form of parasite, termites I think she said. I'd been trying to pluck up the courage to get off the whole treadmill. Oh, joy, the relief at not having to be a perfect yoga mummy.'

Circus skills is another fave. My kids are having fun, it says, and juggling is *so* good for cerebellum development – or so I read somewhere.

Second, the choice of odd options and niche sports gives your child the chance to shine at something because there is no competition. It's easy to boast about Henry's ability at the viol when he is the only one for a hundred square miles playing it. It's also a good way of getting him a place in the orchestra, which is always good for a boast because music sounds so brainy.

'I just know Hector is not a team player,' says Liz. 'He hates football – which I know is because he isn't very good at it – but it makes me feel a bit hopeless when all the other mothers in the playground are looking at the noticeboard and complaining in that oh-how-tiresome voice that their little darling is in the team on Saturday and they'll have to get them to the back of beyond. Oh, the sacrifices talent brings! So I suppose I consciously have looked for things he can do that will sound impressive and wipe the smug smiles off their faces.'

Oh, Liz. So it is she takes Hector along to fencing for an hour after school on Fridays. Touché!

The really determined among us find ourselves looking for sports that are *emerging* so, when the rest of the universe catches up, our progeny will have an edge. Have you thought of footvolley? Oh, you haven't? Well, it's going to be played during the 2012 Olympics at Horse-guards Parade, you know. George, explain the rules, will you . . . ?

Of course a solitary activity is preferable, which cuts out synchronised swimming as an option – it involves relying too much on others. Archery would be okay, though you don't want people to think your child is a saddo, but it's so much nicer to spend the time talking to other parents while he is improving himself.

The Price of Success

And it is during that time when you talk to other parents, while your children are learning breast stroke or doing a David Beckham Football Skills Course, that you get the chance to share the pain of this punishing schedule.

'Isn't it exhausting,' you hear yourself sigh. 'I've got to take Izzy to ballet after this – she's practising for her grade 2 – then, while she's doing that, I'll drop Louis at tennis. He'll have to have a snack after all these lengths up and down the pool. Then tomorrow it's his drumming lesson of course, after his cello lesson and mini rugby the day after.' You see your companion's eyebrows rise in surprise and you go in for the kill. 'Oh, you don't do that? I seem to be going through petrol at an alarming rate and sometimes I think I might as well put a taxi sign on top of my car!' Because, the words hang in the air, my children are doing more than yours so will inevitably be *better*.

There is the awful worry in your head, of course, that Louis will never improve on the cello because he is never home long enough to practise.

The most popular after-school activity, though, is competitive boasting, as you find yourself trying to outdo other people about just how complicated your schedule is. Of course you've been juggling this tortuous regime since Bump 'n' Bounce when your children were toddlers, through Let's Make Music, Tumble Tots and then, when they were three, cookery classes. You were way ahead of Jamie Oliver. You're now hoping very much to get them to La Petite Ecole at Le Manoir aux Quat' Saisons, which seems a really fulfilling idea.

'It's some sort of hyperactive parenting,' says Marylin. 'Some of my pupils – all five and six – are doing activities after school four nights a week. And on the fifth evening they go out for tea. They come to school for a rest and I've had lots fall asleep in class.' The record we heard was a child doing nine activities in a week. We tried to talk to the parents but there was never anyone in to answer our calls.

There is always the danger of mutiny in the ranks – one friend's son told her it was a violation of his human rights to make him go to orchestra on a Saturday morning – and you can hear the resignation in their voices as they complain that they are fed up with doing homework in the back of the car, but what's the option if their sister doesn't finish trampolining until half past five and there's no time to get home?

Meanwhile the dog is in the boot, desperate for a walk. It will all be much easier in the summer when they have cricket nets and you can use the time to walk her round the park during the session.

You lean over to the glove compartment and pull out the contents – all easy-to-eat food like Pepperamis and Frubes (how did our parents cope without them?) – and offer them to the sulking child on the back seat. A picnic tea. What fun!

Totting up the Parent Points

While brownie points are something men get for putting out the bins or bringing tea in bed, parent points are awarded for Excellence in the Field of Schedule Juggling. You rarely see your spouse at weekends as you both head off in opposite directions to deliver offspring to football/rugby/swimming/golf/orchestra/ theatre studies (or all six), and by Sunday night, once the whip has finished being cracked over homework, you both collapse in a heap and complain that the time has just *gone* and you've got nothing done. You don't have dinner parties any more because one of the children is at Saturday swimming galas until 9 p.m., and you can't afford to go out because you are getting through tyres and petrol like Jenson Button at Monza. Not to mention the cost of all these club memberships, and the equipment doesn't come cheap.

There's another danger too. One couple had two sons with different personalities and they never took two children out together. One would go to rugby with the father, one to museums with their mother. Result? Siblings with nothing in common at all.

The point we've missed, though, is that this relentless schedule-chasing is parenting by proxy. We're conveniently leaving the improving to someone else and, as we sit outside the piano teacher's house, flicking through a magazine or phoning our mothers on the mobile to complain how exhausting it all is, we omit to acknowledge to ourselves that this feeling of smug satisfaction of parenting well done comes as a result of someone else's skills and our cheque book.

Then there's parenting at even greater arm's length when it is the nanny who delivers and fetches the children.

'I get nannies who barely speak English delivering these children to my door,' says Caro, a cellist who gives private lessons, 'and I have barely any contact with the parents unless they phone to insist on knowing why their five-year-old isn't on grade eight. I'm exaggerating, but only about the children's ages. They might be nine or ten!'

There is something alarming about the fact that we are doing all this remotely while still congratulating ourselves on being good parents. In fact the more extreme we are in terms of the amount and type of activity, the better we think we are doing.

And what brings it to an end? The children themselves, who are either old enough to refuse point blank or who are so tired they can no longer function.

You get home one evening from hang-gliding, harpsichord and further nuclear physics, with just enough time to do homework, wash their hair and do their Kumon maths sheet, and your child is asleep on the back seat. 'They're waif-faced,' says John, 'and have bags under their eyes and you think, Actually, why don't we just give them Sunday off? I know, you can go to a museum or something.'

Ooops, there you go again.

'So, now you're in Butterflies.
Is that better than Snails?'

Glove Box Menus: a balanced diet

Fruit: Sunmaid sultanas, Winders and Jaffa Cakes

Dairy: Frubes, Cheese Strings and Cheddars

Carbohydrate: Dippas, Pringles

Protein: Pepperami, Dairylea Lunchables

Fibre: The cardboard it came in

Serve in a traffic jam with a warm Fruit Shoot, wet wipes
   and times tables.

9

Consumerism: Can I have one too, pleeeese? Can I?

Take a look around your house. Did you ever dream that having a child would result in so much clobber? It would be tempting to get a big bin liner and throw it all away, but how would we survive without the musical potty or the travel cot? Of course we all know a baby would be quite happy wrapped in swaddling clothes and laid in a manger, but aren't sippy cups sooo useful? And dishwasher-safe too!

Trouble is we're drowning in product these days but what a way to go! The retail opportunities are almost endless. Some of it we really, really need. Most of it we just really, really want. And of course, it's not real spending when you're buying it for them, is it?

Forty shopping weeks to go . . .

It all starts deliciously early. Pregnancy is now *the* prime retail opportunity. Now that mummies have to be yummy, you have to look the part, don't you? You can go with two opposing looks here. In one you can start drifting around in voluminous cambric smocks long before your

188

first midwife appointment. You could even get a T-shirt printed to announce the happy news. In the other (and slightly more irritating) you can do like the celebs and lay in stocks of designer black Lycra and just let that scrumptious little bump push its way into the open air, while claiming you haven't had to buy any maternity clothes. (Failing that an elastic band wrapped around the button of your jeans works for a while!)

These days even the traditionally boring purchases, like maternity bras, have been given the glamour treatment. Instead of the sturdy boulder holders that comprised the full range only ten years ago, you can now select maternity lingerie from Agent Provocateur and Elle McPherson. Not so much a balcony bra as a grandstand. Of course, nothing will ever make paper pants and nighttime pads an exciting purchase, but even stretch-mark prevention creams have been given a makeover, with emu oil, shea butter and a price tag to match. So that's you pretty much taken care of. But nine months is a long time – even longer than people spend on the waiting list for an Hermès Birkin bag, so the high-spending mamas need something to divert them. But don't worry, there's plenty more they can be buying before the baby actually arrives. And plenty of advice out there on how to spend their money.

Spending has never been so painless

For most of us, getting baby stuff is an excursion into uncharted territory. What do we need? Why? When? Back in the good old days, of course, our mums would dig out the stuff we had as babies and we'd use that until it fell apart. But that's not good enough any more. We're a generation who turn up our noses at the highchairs and cots she's been carefully storing in the attic all these years. We don't listen to our mothers' advice, because what do they know about children? So we get all our knowledge from TV and magazines – and they're all out to sell us something. The pressure's on to have new and to have the best. But with all the choice available now – did you realise there are over sixty-four three-wheeler buggies on the market? – where do we even start?

You've guessed it. There are people out there who will do it all for you. Like a fitted kitchen, you can now have a fitted nursery, designed, stylish, practical – and all taken care of by someone else. There are even bespoke baby shopping companies, conveniently located in quiet streets near the King's Road or in Primrose Hill, that will thoughtfully tell you what you need to buy in the way of equipment, from buggies, cots, linen to clothes, bathing products and gifts. You pay a joining or consultation fee – yes, really – and your 'nursery consultant' will take you through it, step by step, order it for you and have it all delivered. It will all be perfectly suited to your lifestyle and the statement you want your baby to make (other than 'waaaah'), because after all it's so difficult to choose between the FrostFrench papoose and the Bill Amberg baby sling. All you have to do is hand over your credit card – and they probably offer an epidural to take away the pain of that.

'Surely we can get an upgrade?'

Does my nappy look big in this?

When you're feeling a bit blobby but you have an overwhelming urge to shop for some lovely designer clothes in
tiny sizes, what's easier? Go on a diet or start buying
clothes for your children? Well, thank heaven the de-
signers have seen sense and created baby ranges, or it'd be
back to the grapefruit for most of us. High spenders can
now dress their infants in Ralph Lauren, Gucci, Baby
Dior, D&G, Young Versace and Kenzo; they can take
their first steps in tiny Tods, and sleep the night away in
their hand-made cherry wood cot, wearing Shanghai Tang
silk pyjamas. For the super-rich, the sky's the limit. But
even we ordinary mortals can get sucked in – albeit at a
lower level.

'I don't think we went over the top,' says Lucy, looking
back over her bank statements in horror. 'But we'd spent
the best part of two grand before Thom was even born.
It's absurd, because really a baby doesn't need much at all
– I mean, look at how little most babies in the world have.
But it all seemed so *vital* at the time.'

Didn't you feel, once you had a child, somehow different about your place in the world – simultaneously
humbled and entitled? It has this weird effect on your
wallet. We either resist the calling of the Visa and go and
lie down in a darkened room until the urge passes, or we
give in and go and buy a huge great car.

Clare chose the car option. It's the stamp of the yummy
mummy.

'For the first time I feel vulnerable and exposed to the

world. Suddenly, my values have all changed and I want to protect my child so the best way to do that is to get a huge 4 x 4. So now we're elevated off the road, at a safe distance from the rest of the world. Of course, it's a gas-guzzler and I can't reverse in it, and it's ridiculously over-specified when we only have one child. Actually, it would be over-specified even if we had four. But it makes me feel *safer*. I've done the responsible parenting thing.'

Battle of the buggy

Funny how things sometimes come full circle. As a child, did you ride high in a stately Silver Cross pram, sheltered from the elements and snug as a bug? Or did you hang loose in one of those newfangled lightweight, high-speed Maclarens that could take corners on two wheels and folded up to nothing to slip into your mum's Renault 4?

Well, the tide of fashion has well and truly turned and supersize baby strollers are now the benchmark of chic baby transport. But why? The Silver Cross made sense when stay-at-home mums set the trends, and took long healthy walks to the shops and back. It even had a momentary return to popularity in the Diana Years. Then, when mobility became essential, and every mummy had a little run-around, the minimalist buggies were perfect for babies on the move. So why go back to huge unwieldy strollers when families are more mobile than ever?

It has to be a prestige thing, doesn't it? The rise and rise of the SUV stroller can be dated almost exactly to the guest appearance of a Bugaboo Frog on *Sex and the City*. Now they're everywhere. And so big! Jenny is apologetic about her huge buggy. 'I wish I hadn't bought it now. It's really very inconvenient and I'm always running over people's toes with it, or bashing their shins. Matt looks so tiny in it too. I only got it because I thought it would protect him but he rattles around in it like a dried pea. Oh, all right then, I admit I did get it because I'd seen pictures of celebs with it, so I thought it must be the best.'

'I don't like it,' says Jenny's mother, 'because I can't see Matthew at all when I'm pushing it. He could have fallen out for all I know. Or have a bee in his hair. A baby should be able to see his mother when they're out. It's ridiculous making fashion out of these things.'

Jenny's mother wouldn't be impressed at all, then, with a recent offering from Bugaboo: a limited-edition line of only 1,000, of which only 150 would ever be available in the UK. The price? A mere £1,100. 'Bugaboo is like the BMW of baby buggies,' the publicity gushes. 'In other words, your bambino will really know he or she has arrived in the world when you step out with your cutie in one of these state-of-the-art strollers . . . And then there's the added plus that you'll be turning heads wherever you go. If this is the bit that appeals most of all to you, then you'll love what comes next. Bugaboo have created a limited edition line with Bas, which takes the notion of pushchair posing to a whole new level.'

Pushchair posing? So that's what it's all about, and maybe that's why we have to buy a huge car – to fit the huge buggy in!

Toys: a serious business

'I was a thirty-eight-year-old, first-time mother,' explains Jess. 'I didn't have a network of friends with babies – all their kids were school age – so I didn't have anyone to ask. It was going to be my only shot at it, so I was desperate to get it right. When I look back on it, I was a sitting duck for advertisers. They must have seen me coming.'

So with this captive market of us vulnerable new parents, why do children's toys have to look so ghastly and tasteless? Sadly, because children seem to like them that way. Children are not known for their innate good taste so for those parents who have agonised over the interior décor of their homes, suddenly having all this plastic tat around is a big shock to the system. But then, we reason, why should we be so precious? It's the baby's home too and at least it's educational (in some obscure way we haven't worked out yet). When we get to that stage in our reasoning, we might as well raise the white flag and just hand over our credit cards to the nice people at Toys'R'Us.

Of course, occasionally we come across people who seem to have got a handle on this whole toy thing. Their calm woody homes contain a choice few calm woody toys and we think, That's how it should be. That's all I'll buy from now on, sensible toys from sustainable forests with vegetarian trees. That's until *their* little girl comes round to play and she flings herself at the revolting purple dinosaur that we were browbeaten into like a starving man on a loaf of bread and we think, Hmm.

When we were growing up, toys meant sensible things like wooden jigsaw puzzles, Animal Snap, sweet wholesome Sindy (not those whorish Bratz), chess and Meccano. A Sasha doll and Lego for the posh kids up the road. We got toys at Christmas or on our birthday, we looked after them and they lasted for years (unless you gave Sindy a bath, resulting in her head falling off). Playrooms didn't exist – they weren't needed, because all your toys fitted in a single wooden chest in your bedroom.

So it's all the more shocking the first time your child gets a surprisingly sophisticated plastic toy free with a fast food meal or inside a chocolate egg. And not at all surprising that kids have no interest in looking after their toys, or even picking them up off the floor or bringing them in from the garden. There will always be more and more. And the galling thing is, they're absolutely right.

The next fifteen years are going to be a nightmare of backache from picking up and tidying in our children's bedrooms, illuminated for a few years in the middle by the searing agony of stepping on Lego with bare feet. It culminates in them slamming the door and forbidding you to go in because you were careless enough to step on a CD, filed on the floor, while trying to manoeuvre the Dyson (but of course!) round the teetering piles of discarded clothes. At this stage, it's easier to give in and just fumigate the place once they leave for university – hopefully taking some of their possessions with them.

Consumers in training

'When I do the proper parent thing and take the kids to a museum or art gallery,' fumes Kris, 'all they want to do is get the cultural bit over and done with and go to the shop. And what do we get? What do we always get? A shiny pencil with the name of the place on it, a keyring – and a bloody great tantrum because I won't spring for anything else. I actually think they feel more comfortable with the shopping experience than they do with the educational one. They have more practice at shopping, don't they?'

There's no doubt our kids are very savvy consumers. They check their change, they pore over the Argos catalogue and spend hours mooching round the shops with their pals. For kids of ten and up, shopping is a form of entertainment. They probably even know what Statutory Rights are.

'My daughter and her friends live like middle-aged divorcées, meeting each other for coffee (well, hot chocolate) then spending the day trying on lip gloss and jewellery, looking at clothes they can't afford on their allowance,' muses Caroline. 'They're old before their time. At their age, I'd be out climbing trees or at home playing pretend games. They're almost scarily sophisticated but very naïve at the same time.'

Of course, there's a marketing term for the way our kids are. It's called 'age compression' or 'KGOY' (kids getting older younger) and it means that their childhood is truncated and they take on adult interests earlier than ever before. This means that eight-year-olds are craving mobile phones and if you haven't got an iPod by the time you're twelve, you daren't show your face on the street. 'Pester power' is no longer a cliché, it's a fact of life, and it's no coincidence that the expression that something is 'so *yesterday*' is so twenty-first century. Nothing is allowed to be 'old'. And if it is, it's pants. Everything has in-built obsolescence, doesn't it?

'I really dread my daughter's birthday coming round because I just don't know what to get her,' admits Teresa. 'She's going to be twelve and she's got everything she wants – apart from boobs. Bike, iPod, rollerblades, CD player. What's left? Only things she doesn't want, like game consoles. She's too young for jewellery, too old for toys, so what's left? More clothes? I wish they'd invent something new, so I could get it for her and she'd be the first of her friends to have it.'

Boys seem even more switched on to consumer trends than girls, according to Steph. 'My ten-year-old reads Jeremy Clarkson's column every Sunday. It's hard going for him, but he's desperate to know about cars so he sticks with it. When we go out, he knows every make and model. To tell you the truth, he's a bit of an anorak. And he's like that with trainers, mobile phones, music download software. How does he know this stuff?'

So if our kids have everything they need, why are we getting so worked up about finding something new for them? Haven't we given them enough already? Christmas panic sets in some time around September, according to Kevin. 'Christmas presents seem so pointless. I feel as if I'm trying to prove something. It's almost like I'm going through an exercise just to show how much I love them – do I love them £40 or £80 or even £270? And if I get an expensive present for one, does that mean I have to spend the same on the others too? I'm sure the perfect present is out there somewhere, and I'm damned if someone else is going to find it before me.'

Shame on you, Kevin, for breaking ranks from that unspoken don't-surrender parental cartel. Okay, so we all caved in and got our children those micro-scooters when they were all the rage – we probably crumbled from the pestering – but then, blow me, someone else goes and buys their little darling an electric one. They should be flogged as traitors – and for thinking of it first.

What not to (let your children) wear

Buying clothes for children is utter pleasure – when they're too young to have their own opinions. They look gorgeous in everything we put them in, we can indulge our daftest impulses and deck our daughters out in buttons and bows, our sons in cute little dungarees.

For the really imaginative, there's cashmere from top to tiny little toes (best keep them off the mashed banana though), organic cotton rompers and, wait for it, faux fur nappy covers. Whatever the fashion, it's like having your very own walking, talking doll, but regrettably it doesn't seem to last.

Ella sighs, 'My husband used to freak out at our credit card bill when the children were small but I couldn't resist anything! But I'm so glad I couldn't, because it was fun for me and now they're ten and twelve they just look ghastly all the time. If I get them clothes I like, they just refuse to wear them, so there's no point. They dress like . . . well, like chavs, frankly.'

Chavs is not the worst it could be either. Margot remembers collecting her daughter from a school disco: 'Fortunately, my daughter and her friends were all into those long cotton skirts – it was the tail end of the boho thing – and they all looked lovely. But there was this little girl there who couldn't have been more than nine, and she was up on the stage dancing, well gyrating like those girls on the rap videos, in a short denim skirt and a little crop top. Nobody knew where to look.'

The weird thing is for a brief spell – all too brief – we can dress like our little girls, thanks to the current quirk of fashion and the Boden catalogue. Don't you just love that trimmed cardigan and shift dress look, cropped trousers and floral T-shirt, with ballet pumps or flip-flops. If you're a teeny-weeny yummy mummy you and your daughter can both get your T-shirts from H&M children's department and be like twins!

'Oh, for the days when we were in sync and used to browse the catalogues together,' says Cathy, 'but that was long ago. Now she wants to look like – God help me – Paris Hilton.'

As a role model for young girls, Paris Hilton does leave something to be desired, but she features constantly in the pages of tween magazines, such as *Shout* (with its regular free gifts of make-up) and *Mizz*. A quick flick through the pages only serves to raise the blood pressure: Posh,

Charlotte Church, Lindsay Lohan and, incredibly, Pete Burns! Please, no!

Maggie is spluttering with indignation over this: 'Why do our pre-teen daughters need to know about a tattooed, cosmetically altered transvestite? Make-up tips? How to disguise five o'clock shadow? What message is *that* giving them about the world?'

Come back *Jackie* with your sweetly chaste fashion – all is forgiven.

Boys, once they manage to escape the indignity of having their mother as their stylist, are just as much victims of fashion (see later), but it's the grooming issue that makes us smile. Maggie's husband takes up the story: 'What his fourteen-year-old sister spends on make-up and perfume, our son easily spends on hair gel and Lynx deodorant. I think he must have seen the advert and be hoping for scantily clad girls to throw themselves at him. At his age, I'd cross the road to avoid a girl.'

And who's to blame for all this? Well, apart from us, of course, for giving in. The media, fair and square. We grew up with one commercial channel, and Channel 4 was only launched in 1982. Now there are an obscene number of channels all jostling for a piece of the advertising action. With tweens one of the fastest growing consumer markets, it's gloves off and not just on TV. Magazines and the Internet are just as keen to suck out your children's pocket money (and your savings). Ten-year-olds surf eBay to satisfy their insatiable appetites for consumer goods. We've trained them to be good little shoppers. Must have it all. Must have it now.

When Claudia asked for a Goldfish,
she meant the credit card.

And aren't they so savvy? It's like living with a mini-independent financial adviser. They watch TV so much of the time, our kids even know that if they go into debt someone will lend them the money to go on spending. 'We were chatting the other night about how we could afford a new car and Harry, our eight-year-old, suddenly piped up: "Just go to Ocean Finance." Now we're thinking of asking him to advise us about an ISA!'

Mobile madness

Those scares about brain tumours didn't last for long, did they? Now virtually every child at secondary school has a mobile phone – and they're trickling down to younger kids too – and all because of free upgrades. It makes perfect sense for the mobile phone companies to get more phones out there, because few of us have any qualms about handing on an old phone when we've got a nice new one. And it has introduced a whole new generation of eight-year-olds to the wonders of being constantly in touch. But hang on – when they're at primary school, they shouldn't really be out of adult supervision anyway. What's going on? Do eight-year-olds really need phones at all, let alone ones with streaming media?

'A six-year-old at my children's school had her own mobile phone,' seethes Gaby. 'Immediately all the other children wanted one. I could have killed her parents. Anyway, none of her friends have phones, but that doesn't stop her whipping it out every two seconds to check if she's been texted – is that a verb?'

If you're worried about any health dangers, there's always the Teddyfone, specially aimed at pre-schoolers with emissions much lower than those of conventional phones. Oh, and since it's for toddlers, it only has four buttons that you can pre-programme with approved contacts, and no screen either.

Excuse me, but what the hell is that all about? Under what circumstance could a toddler need a mobile phone? To call you from his cot to say he needs his nappy changing? Call me cynical but this wouldn't have anything to do with grooming ever younger kids to hop on the mobile bandwagon, would it perchance? Since many parents pay as much as £20 a month for their children's mobile bills, you've got to suspect underhand tactics.

But how about this? Mattel in the US, in conjunction with its content partner Single Touch Interactive, for example, launched the Barbie My Scene phone, aimed at girls between the ages of eight and fourteen. The phone is activated by parents, who can go to a designated website and list chores they want their children to perform to earn extra minutes. At the end of each month, parents can buy extra minutes if their children have behaved.

Surprise, surprise, children will then trade them in for the 'real thing' – they don't want to have stuff that looks . . . er, childish. Lee is resigned to coming a poor second to his technocratic son: 'I told him he could have my old phone when I trade up. But he keeps darting into the phone shop to look at the upgrades I could get, and I just know he's going to try to charm me out of the new one, so he can have it instead. And frankly, he'd make far more use of it than I do. I've got no idea about streaming media and uploading MP3 stuff. All I use my phone for is calls and the occasional text. The new one will be wasted on me. And I expect I'll let him have it, in the end. Grown-up toys are wasted on grown-ups.'

And this is exactly how our children have managed to get us where they want us. By growing up so fast that by the time they reach their early teens they are surpassing us in virtually every area of modern life – except in earning money – and money is really all they need us for now.

Beware. 'When I asked my soon-to-be-teenage daughter what she wanted for her birthday, she said a goldfish,' remembers Gary. 'How sweet, I thought. Until I realised she meant the credit card.'

Twenty things you've probably had in your house . . .

- *What to Expect When You're Expecting*
- *Toddler Taming* by Christopher Green
- Flashcards
- A GameBoy
- Inserts from a Kinder Egg
- An unfinished box of Cinnamon Grahams (minus free toy)
- Free toy from a cereal packet
- A receipt from the Rainforest Café
- *The Big Hungry Caterpillar*
- A Dorling Kindersley Eyewitness guide or CD-ROM
- A Burger King paper 'crown'
- An untouched SATs coaching book
- An unopened guide to activities for children around the UK

- Wax crayons
- An Early Learning Centre carrier bag
- *Guess How Much I Love You*
- Child-sized chairs
- A nightlight
- Anything that plays Brahms' *Lullaby*
- Fairy Non-Bio
- Gina Ford or Penelope Leach but not both (obviously)
- Ribena
- A baby gym
- A pencil from a museum gift shop
- A lollo ball
- A book by Steve Biddulph
- Playmobil
- A Thomas the Tank Engine pillow case
- Something with added omega 3
- Petit Filous
- A forehead thermometer

10
Teenagers: The Hormone Himalayas

It's 3 a.m., and you are in the kitchen on your third pot of tea, one hand poised over the malt whisky bottle, the other over your mobile phone. You didn't want to get one at all – heavens, you've survived your life this far without one – but that was before your children became teenagers.

Your ears strain for every noise that might be her boyfriend's car bringing her back from the party. Why hasn't she called? Perhaps she's in a bad area for coverage – a basement nightclub? Please, God, no. Perhaps she's run out of credit. Perhaps she's been run over.

Nobody warned us, did they, that parenting teenagers would be the single largest challenge of our lives. Now we understand why, when our children were younger and we moaned about things like bedtimes, the parents of teenagers just smiled knowingly and kept quiet. What is the wrangling about a nine or nine thirty bedtime curfew compared with the anxiety of them not coming home at all?

Now we also know what our parents meant by all the things they said (especially when we find ourselves saying the same things). They tried to warn us, but when you are faced with the arms crossed, sullen impenetrable face of a fourteen-year-old in a stand-off about whether or not she can go to a nightclub, suddenly the memory of your own teenage years disappears like the dawn mist.

Everything we ever said, every parenting plan we ever made, goes right out of the window as we struggle to keep up with an age group for whom 'because I say so' doesn't wash any more. Requests, which sometimes, if challenged, could be escalated into orders, used to be effective when they were smaller. Now orders are about the worst thing you can issue. Why should I? Whatever. D'ya think I'm bovered?

And if you lose your rag completely you know you have blown it, because there is nowhere else you can go.

If the madness of modern family life comes from the issue of control, then when they reach teenage we've lost it completely – in all senses! In the quieter moments, before we enter the theatre of war, we do remember our own childhoods. We did what we were told, didn't we? So where have we gone so wrong?

Problem number one: our children think we are hip. No, really. Our parents – raised by Edwardian parents themselves – listened to Radio 2 and Mantovani. We had to wear white socks with our sandals and dresses to go somewhere important. We, however, listen to Radio 1 while driving them to school (natch), buy the same fashions as our daughters, and can text with the best of 'em. Have you noticed how punk and the Brit sound of the eighties are making a comeback? Kids are downloading the Who, the Jam, Hendrix. Bands like the Arctic Monkeys would have fitted right in with Johnny Rotten. Instead of refusing to let them go to a rock concert, we find ourselves asking, Can you get me a ticket and can I borrow that CD?

Your daughter moots the idea of a tattoo and instead of flying off the handle, you wonder if you are too old for a discreet and tasteful little rose on your lower back. How can our children possibly know what the boundaries are if they are working out how to stop their mother borrowing their jeans and their dad from listening to their hiphop albums on his MP3 player?

Which brings us to problem number two and it's not unrelated to number one. Because we have so much more in common with our children, we are terrified of flexing our parenting muscles *in case they hate us*. Everything in our heads tells us to stand firm against unacceptable behaviour or demands. We've all read the advice that says teenagers and rebellion go together like a Big Mac and large fries, because it is all about learning to 'stand on their own two feet'. And yet and yet . . . when they scream at you that you are sad and old and they hate you and slam the door, you are racked with anxiety. How can you be 'sad'? You like Will Young.

It's that which makes us decide to go away for the night so they can have a 'few friends over for a bit of a party'. Who's to blame then when we get home, the house has been totalled, the cat is in the tumble drier and the neighbours have issued legal proceedings?

'My daughter has been grounded until July!' shrieks one yummy mummy. 'She's fifteen and she said she was only going to have a few friends round. Well, of course people found out and *she* couldn't cope with the gatecrashers. The mess! They even took the keys to the Maserati!'

What's so disappointing is that we thought we'd be so good at it, didn't we? We'd be understanding and in tune. We'd rolled a joint with a Rizla so we'd be on the same wavelength, wouldn't we? Not like our parents were. Oh, no. What we didn't realise is that the one thing teenagers hate but want is boundaries. They want parents not mates.

Problem three and not unrelated to problem two: there's less and less there for them to rebel against. The boundaries have dissolved when everything is there for the taking. There is every kind of sex and perversion you can imagine on the Internet; TV reality shows display adults they are supposed to respect in the most tacky light imaginable; the nine o'clock watershed means nothing when the contents of the programmes are trailed well before nine; the mothers of women who win *Big Brother* announce on the front of tabloid newspapers that they bought them sex toys when they were sixteen. What's left to discover?

'My eight-year-old seems perfectly at ease with the fact that Elton John has married a bloke,' says Lynn. 'He asked me the other day why celebrities married other celebrities and then, when he read about another big Hollywood wedding, I heard him say: "I wonder how long that one will last"!'

Problem four: we are far too busy with our own lives. 'There doesn't seem to be any strategic planning in being a parent these days,' says David, another teacher in the state sector. 'We are so busy juggling work and financial demands on us, even our own emotional issues, that we miss a lot of what is going on in our children's lives. What we don't realise, and indeed refuse to accept, is that in having children you have to make sacrifices. You have to be selfless. Parenting brings no rights – it's a life choice and brings responsibilities of selflessness with it.'

Crikey! That's something to think about when you are trying to sort out the latest crisis in your teenager's life. And what do you end up doing? The crisis has happened by the time you get to the scene and all you can do is put out the fire. Can't somebody out there help me?

No, but then we are parenting in a vacuum. Our parents may raise their eyebrows about the crazy decisions we make, but they have no idea what we are contending with and we have no previous examples to use as a guideline. Did they have to warn us about Rohypnol in our drinks and date rape? Did they have to discuss with us how a fatal virus is passed from person to person via anal sex? Did they have to explain to us why it is not right that you can see pictures of people having sex with animals on the PC in your own front room? We, however, find ourselves having incredible conversations about such things with our children. To paraphrase Talking Heads, how did we get here?

No wonder we look for help in our droves. You can't move for parenting know-it-alls, but their answers never quite match our questions.

Carly prided herself on sharing her
daughter's interests and tastes.

Keeping it between friends

In the category of teenage issues that have parents pacing the house in the wee small hours, the peer group may not seem like a priority, but it is. Despite the fact that we are meeting our kids on a leveller playing field than ever before, our influence is but nothing compared to that of their mates and other kids at school/on TV/ in Internet forums.

Teenagers today don't want to be different any more than they did when we were young. Remember the pain of wearing the wrong trainers? At worst we were square. How much worse to be a 'geek' or 'gay' or a 'loser'? The trouble is this peer group is now global, isn't it? What hope have you got when your child can go into a teen Internet chat room any time of the day or night and discover just how horrible a parent you are because someone in Seattle is still allowed to be sleepless till midnight?

Our kids *have* to watch the crap on TV because if they don't know what happened on '*St*enders or *Strictly I'm a Pop Idol* last night then they will have nothing to talk to their friends about tomorrow, and, 'Francesca says like that I've *got* to be on MSN like *tonight* because she wants to tell me what's happening like about the *party* at Bianca's on Saturday.'

One withering look from them confirms your suspicion that they think you know nothing.

'I think peer pressure has always been there but the difference is children are more exposed to it than ever,' says Michael, a housemaster at a leading public school.

One advantage he has is he can keep an eye on kids in that dangerous after-school period which day schooling throws up. But what else are you supposed to do? Your kids will have to knock about with their mates because you don't get back from work until seven, and then there's the dinner to cook.

It's funny, isn't it, that we whinge about children not communicating with each other, yet they are probably communicating more than ever before. They ask each other out (and dump each other) by text; they bully by text and My Space and Bebo (come on, keep up, Lewis); they chat on web forums and MSN; they tell everyone which parties to gatecrash via the Internet. They can even talk to other players on the X-Box. Teenagers may not be able to write full words, but they are writing more words – no matter how abbrviatd – than they have since they sent letters to each other with the footman in Victorian times. Rabbit, rabbit, rabbit . . . and as they do so they are sharing how miserably deprived they are, how their mother is a witch and their dad is tight with their pocket money. They start to learn about rights – they've always got blasted rights (they've been threatening you with ChildLine since they could talk) – and quote the United Nations Convention on the Rights of the Child. With rights come responsibilities, you say, but something stops you laying down the law in case you are accused of infringing them. Heaven forbid.

You are running to keep up. Just when you thought you'd worked out the rules for something, the goalposts move. Oh, that's so last week.

But what they don't have is common sense. That still comes with age and experience.

And seems to leave you again when you become a parent.

Money and Mobiles

Perhaps the issues haven't changed, it's just how we handle them. But one thing that has changed is the ramifications of the mobile phone with teenagers simply because they didn't exist when we were their age. We weren't allowed to use the phone until after 6 p.m. because it was cheaper, and the phone was in the hall so everyone could hear your conversation anyway. Who would have imagined that you'd be able to take a picture, listen to music, go online, send an email – oh, and talk – on a phone while wandering along the road or hiding under your bedclothes!

Mobiles are not an accessory, they're a must have, an irritant – we've talked about them before – but where they have particular relevance with teenagers is that they enable plans to be made without your knowledge and they *cost money*. Money, mobiles, mobiles, money – the two are linked.

'My younger son, who's eleven, is on pay-as-you-go because he only has a phone in case he misses the bus from school,' says Gail. 'But what did I do with my fifteen-year-old daughter? I got her on a contract so if she got stuck somewhere she'd always be able to get hold of us. Next thing I know she's racked up £150 in one month on texts!'

And text they do – all day long. It's as if someone you are talking to is having a private conversation in front of you that you aren't part of. Beep beep. Beep beep. Out it comes from the pocket or the teensy handbag so they can see who's sent a message. They even take it out when it hasn't beeped to check they haven't missed anything. And what do the texts say? Lord only knows (and you probably wouldn't understand even if you read them, which of course you haven't . . .), but you can't help thinking it would be cheaper simply to dial the phone and speak to the other person. Lol. Cu l8ter.

Despite concerns regarding the side effects of mobile phone usage on children, it is us who are responsible for the increase. Ninety-five per cent of under-fourteen-year-olds have received their mobile phone from their parents. The average age when a UK child will now obtain their first mobile phone is down to just eight years. They need it in case there's an emergency in the unlikely event that they are ever allowed out on their own, don't they? Or at least that's what you grit your teeth and remind yourself as they download yet another polyphonic ring tone that is so irritating it makes you want to flush the damned thing down the loo.

And what does it matter if they use them to film each other slapping some poor unsuspecting passer-by? *So long as you know where they are.*

They are a double-edged sword, aren't they? We rationalise the decision to give our children one because of the security issue but, truth to tell, mobiles are an umbilicus. You can keep tabs on your children (when they

'Dad, are you downstairs? I'm nearly out
of credit, can you phone me back?'

choose to answer) and a 'Where the hell are you?' message will get to its destination, even if the little sod decides to ignore it. But have you heard? Several companies have launched a service that enables parents to monitor how their children use their mobile phones. Isn't that great? You will be able to track voice, text, video and picture messages and set limits on your children's calls. But best of all, the phone will also allow you to locate where your children are via a global positioning system. The power!

The only possible advantage of this phone addiction is that teenagers are apparently spending less on cigarettes so they can fund their mobile phone habit. But they won't be able to hold cigarettes soon, anyway, because of the RSI they'll get from all that texting.

Image, and the nip and tuck

Not sure our parents had to deal with this either: the growing demand for plastic surgery. Do you remember asking your mum if she'd mind stumping up for you to have a boob job, only the size of your breasts is interfering with your happiness and it is imperative that something is done? No, we don't either.

'Thousands of teenage girls are turning to plastic surgery in pursuit of bodily perfection,' goes a news report. 'Increasingly, it's seen as a totally acceptable way of improving their image – and more and more parents are willing to come up with the cash.'

There are no official statistics apparently – though over 40 per cent of teenagers say they'd like to have something done – but many cosmetic surgeons and clinics admit they are seeing greater numbers of young women under twenty asking for procedures ranging from bigger breasts to better noses. The average price of a 'boob job' is around £3,000. A nose op or liposuction slightly less, and though some teenagers go into debt to finance the surgery by taking out a bank loan or other credit, most of them have mummy or daddy to come up with the money.

It's one thing to want surgery to correct deformities or accident scars; quite another to see girls as young as eleven undergoing surgery for purely cosmetic reasons. But it isn't so much that teenage (and younger) girls are willing to go to such lengths to create the perfect image, it's the fact that many parents are willing to pay for it.

And why do they do it? Anything to make their princess happy. 'I know it's wrong and she's too young,' says Hailey about her daughter who's just sixteen. 'But I am terrified that if she doesn't have the tummy tuck she wants, she will be miserable.'

There seems to be such an obsession with the right to happiness that some schools are introducing courses on the pursuit of it as part of the curriculum. If we think that looking like a member of a girl band is the answer to all life's woes, then bring on the men in the white coats.

Drugs, booze and smoking . . . and money

There's some correlation between growing older and starting to read the *Daily Mail*. Against your better nature – well, you've been a *Guardian* reader since college, haven't you? – a headline about teenage excesses catches your eye and you find yourself agreeing with it. You are middle-aged, probably Middle England (even if you live in Hackney), and when it comes to drugs, drink and fags you are totally mystified.

'They are a massive problem,' says Michael, who confirms that it is not just among the richer children who are pupils at his school. Of course it doesn't help that they all seem to have so much disposable income.

'It really is a case of too much, much too young,' says Alice, who is coping with two teenagers. 'I can't believe how much money my children's friends have on them. Fifty pounds for a night out! With money like that burning a hole in your pocket you can afford a packet of fags, a few rounds of alcopops and change for an E. My children rail at me about how unfair it is, but holding back cash is the only control I have.'

That's music to Michael's ears – a parent who's exercising control! 'At school our boundaries are often different than at home – they are tighter. I wanted to suspend a boy for drinking and smoking, and his parents said, "But he does that at home." There are definitely parents who come home from a hard day at the office and light a spliff. What does that say to a child?'

'I wish I could have had parties like they do,' complains Clive. 'If I've got some extra cash in my pocket, then I'll bung some his way and tell him to have fun with it.' Thanks, Clive. Tempting though it is to live life through our children, that doesn't really help any.

School work, computers and er . . . money

As we all know, thanks to Margaret Thatcher, we can now climb the greasy pole. We can better ourselves regardless of where we come from. And if we didn't manage it then we still have another shot at it through our children. Isn't that reassuring?

That must explain why we put the pressure on them to get A*** for their GCSEs. Why we nag them about their coursework and then spend every evening tweaking it and adding to it so it's really really good. Competition is never as harsh as it is at the secondary level and it's partly thanks to parents who push from behind.

'Frankly, I chose his options for him,' says Giselle. 'He was in Neanderthal mode at the time and I said, why don't you do this and that and he just grunted. I just hope he doesn't throw it all back in my face afterwards.'

The scary part about this stage of their education is that suddenly you are not in the equation at school. Stay in touch, advise all the advisers. Keep up with what your children are doing. That's all very well, if you can get to the teachers, and you'll be lucky if you can get anything out of your children. Sometimes it comes as quite a surprise that they get any qualifications at all.

Secondary schools, to be honest, hate interference. We keep being told by other knowing parents, who are older and wiser, that we should just mind our own business and not get involved. You'll only be talked about in the staffroom. But it's impossible not to. Not being allowed to get involved means we've lost control completely.

Instead, you watch your children as they slump in front of the PC, which naturally is in their bedroom, because everyone else has one in their bedroom, and just hope to goodness they are doing what they are supposed to do. Then off they go on the school bus, shoes not done up properly, tie askew and hair fashionably ruffled, and you have no idea whether they have done homework to hand in or not. Until the report arrives.

Of course when it comes to the computer, you've even less clue what they are doing.

Shall we talk about computers? They're another thing, like mobile phones, that our parents never had to contend with. Let's face it, we're pretty new to them ourselves, and not only are our teenagers up to speed, they leave us behind on the starting blocks. You feel a bit like a superpower who knows the 'enemy' has more advanced weaponry and has already found ways to scupper yours. MSN – like texting – is a sort of private conversation that you have no part of and even throws up its own excluding language. GTG – got to go. POS – parent over shoulder. Of course, like we should, we invest in cyber-nanny software to restrict what they view, until the little bugger downloads a progam that bypasses everything else so they can browse bigknockers.com.

If only it were just big knockers though. 'I got all "well, it's like this, son" and tried to explain to him that I wasn't a prude,' says Steve, 'but how in our day we bought mucky magazines from the corner shop, but the newsagent was the first line of censorship. He'd draw the line at tits and bums. The Internet – well, it's all there, isn't it? Pervs, animals, even children; how in heaven's name can you keep up with the censorship?'

You can't. It's a damage-limitation exercise, fire-fighting at its most extreme. 'I hate it, that blasted box in the corner of the room,' screams Gillian. 'It seems to dominate their lives and sucks them in. And what do they expect you to do! First the screen's too small, then it doesn't have enough memory, then we need broadband. And now my daughter is nagging that she has to have a laptop because *everyone* takes notes in class on them at school and she needs to as well. Never mind the cost.'

Of course we have to eat our words when they go off on a gap year and we can email them when they are canoeing up the Amazon, in real time, and talk to them on Skype without it costing money. You see, Mum, computers are pretty cool really.

Clothes and . . . money

With teenagers the clothes issue is subtly different than just a consumer issue. This is another area where your control slowly slips away. Suddenly (and the term teenager applies here to anything over nine) they sense another area, like food, where they can flex their muscles. They can smell your frustration in the air and, boy, do they exploit it.

It's also another area where choice has become a rod for our own backs. Way back in the mists of time the choice was corduroy from Laura Ashley and something from M&S that didn't look too frumpy. Oh, yes and C&A.

Rebellious was black lipstick, but you wouldn't dare go the whole hog and do the punk look, though the New Romantic movement (Duran Duran and floppy fringes) was okay because you didn't think you looked *too* stupid (oh yeah?), but you could be sure your mother wouldn't wear it.

Now there's a whole high street of shops aimed at your daughter and which are okay with your daughter because you don't shop there – you know you'd look like mutton dressed as lamb (or at least, you *should* know that). Or she has the cheaper end of the designer labels, the prices for which still make you gasp.

'I thought I could fool my daughter with the designer range at Debenhams,' says a confused Lily, 'but she was having none of it. It wasn't the real thing apparently. She saved up for a pair of jeans for £180! Even her pants have to be some chic label – though I don't think it's chic to say chic any more, is it?'

Of course, there's the other temptation for them too: charity shop 'chic' which we conveniently forget we used to indulge in (remember the excitement of finding a granddad shirt for 50p?), but who wants their daughter looking like a hobo or a hooker?

Teenage boys are no better when it comes to sartorial terrorism. 'What's wrong with a pack of three T-shirts from Tesco?' wails one mother of two boys. 'Why does it have to be some over-priced surfing label – which racks up the price – when we live about as far from the sea as you can get? He has to have some snowboard or surfboard connection, when he's never done those things in his life!'

It makes you yearn for grunge when a ripped T-shirt and torn jeans were the height of cool.

Once the clothes are bought comes the dressing and, as any parent will vouch, this is a time-consuming process designed to drive you nuts. In fact so time-consuming that, with most girls, you can tell them it's time to leave for wherever, then go and mow the lawn, make bread, and have a cup of tea before they will emerge from the bathroom, fragrant and looking like Barbie (they all look like Barbie). And it is irrelevant where you are going – the supermarket or Stringfellows.

Then of course teenagers grow and they grow and they grow. Yes, yes, they always have but not quite at the rate we are now having to contend with. Stats show that our children are growing faster than any previous generation. Bob Hardy, the foot fitting manager at Clarks, says, 'Each range we do is getting bigger by a size or two. Our boys' shoes go up to a ten, girls' to a nine, and there are some twelve- and thirteen-year-olds who have grown out of our boys' ranges.' Then they have to wear adult shoes, which makes the whole problem worse because it increases the choice. Again.

Sons (or daughters) and Lovers

We purposely kept this little gem until last because, for once, this is a timeless issue and the emotions that surround it haven't really changed. The parents in Jane Austen went on about it: Elizabeth Bennett's dad wasn't too chuffed about Darcy. D.H. Lawrence took the subject to an almost incestuous level. Basically, once our children start having relationships, that last little vestige of them we had control over slips away. They fall in love, they start having sex with someone; they start having sex with someone before they fall in love – either way, it's the beginning of the end.

There are telltale signs. They go all secretive and coy. Phones (yeah, them again) get slipped out under the dinner table as they text Him or Her. Hair begins to be washed and deodorant used. Your favourite top disappears out of the cupboard (and that's just your son). You find yourself resorting to subterfuge as you use cleaning their room (you never did that before) as an excuse to try to find out details. Then they bring them home, with a casual 'Oh, this is Miles' as they slink off upstairs, and you are dying to find out where he lives, what his parents do. And you HATE yourself for it, because it is just the way your parents behaved when you were bringing home boys or girls.

The bit that *has* changed, though, is that they'll start having the sex earlier. 'I think those of us who were teenagers in the 1970s, we were the ones who changed things,' says Michael. 'We were cutting edge, so in many respects being a teenager now isn't that different – except when it comes to sex. Now there is barely a virgin doing A levels.' Wishful thinking we say. There's probably barely a virgin doing GCSEs.

Terry is blunter: 'The instant gratification that children demand these days seems to apply at the basest level. Waiting to lose your virginity doesn't have the same relevance it used to have – even we thought sixteen was worth holding out for, and even that was a little on the young side, but they can't wait at all. They have the mobile, the iPod, the TV and computer in their room. They probably have a double bed because we want them to have it all – so they think, Right, I'll have it all. They think they are all grown up, so now they want the sex.'

We did our best to dissuade them, didn't we? Of course we didn't want to come down all draconian and say, 'You are far too young to have sex, young lady,' because that's not the way we do things, is it? No, instead we sat down face to face, reminding ourselves about all the advice we'd read up on, and talked about 'mature relationships' and having sex in the context of a 'loving relationship', even how pleased we were that *we* waited, and they look at us but not at us, and we know it's gone in one ear and out the other.

So – damage limitation again – we fill the bathroom cabinet with condoms (and keep counting them), and keep our fingers and toes crossed, and hope they keep their legs the same way.

Of course an added complication is that we might also be dealing with a relationship issue. 'I'm a single mum,' says Fiona, 'and I struggle with the real double standard: trying to tell my daughter how to handle her relationships when I am trying to be drop dead gorgeous for my new boyfriend. I know I should be wearing prim clothes, like my mother did when I was trying to be a teenage vamp, and I find myself wearing short skirts and high boots because that's what he likes me to wear.'

So what do you tell them? With boys there's now the

added issue of being accused of rape. That's a tricky one that we don't remember being mentioned as our mother or father, pink with embarrassment, told us the facts of life in the car (always a good place for a talk, the car – no escape). And STIs need a mention too. They've forgotten about Aids – that's something that affects Africa – but chlamydia is a real concern. But why should they care – they're only fourteen.

'What I'm only just realising,' says Lucy, 'is that for all their posing and grown-up attitudes they are still very, very immature. They think they know everything because it's on TV, in the soaps, in the papers, but actually the fundamental messages aren't getting though. Pregnancy – and the risks of unprotected sex – for example get taught to them when they are ten or eleven, when they are still more interested in their bikes and the PlayStation, and then it isn't mentioned at the critical time, when they are about fifteen. And it's all very well teaching it as part of the National Curriculum, but they don't listen to anything else they are taught, so the last place they are going to learn about it is from a teacher.'

'I know in my heart,' says Anne, 'that I am older and wiser and I know better than they do, but when it comes to confronting the issues I have a crisis of confidence in my experience, my ability as a parent. Where's my conviction gone? It seems to disappear when I am faced with a "whatever, minger" attitude from my teenagers. I had the boundaries from my parents, and accepted them. Why am I too weak to put them in place for my own children? Why can't I just say "no"?'

Therein lies the madness of modern parenting.

And just as they come out the other end of childhood and become rational, sensible adults who you enjoy being with, what do they do? Leave home.

The Ten Most Irritating Things Teenagers Say:

- Calm down, dear. It's only a commercial
- Can you come and collect me?
- Yeah, whatever
- Can I borrow your car?
- I ran out of credit
- It's my life
- The party is at Gemma's house but we might go on somewhere else later . . .
- You're so *sad*
- Promise I'll pay you back
- Yeah, but nothing did happen, did it?

II
And then I woke up . . .

So what have we concluded out of all this? That, frankly, it's all terribly stressful. That it's all about being competitive, being the best and it's about other people. In fact, come to think of it, other people are the main problem. If it weren't for other people, the whole thing would be a piece of cake. We'd all procreate like rabbits and make quite a good job of it, but because, more than ever, we are judged by the quality of our families, we get in a tizzy about it: 'What *will* people *think*?!'

The difference now is *we* judge our own performance as people by our children too and worry ourselves into a frenzy about it. Parenting gets us tied up into the most awful knots that have us behaving in a totally different way than we did when we were childless, rational beings.

And to resort to cod psychology, these seem to be the factors:

Controlling Interests

Having children has far more of an effect on *our* lives than it did for our mothers' generation. Those were the days when *Good Housekeeping* was about good housekeeping, and they took pride in baking and washing in the new twin tub and hanging the terry nappies on the washing line to dance in the wind. They had the Pill, of course, but once they had gone up the aisle in damask silk they settled down and got on with the serious business of having babies. Some had jobs, some had good careers, but, when babies came along, it was okay to be a full-time mother. And, to get all sociological about it, likely as not their mother/aunt/granny lived up the road to help out and tell them how to do it. The difference is our mothers didn't want everything or believe they were entitled to it.

We, the Choice Generation, make babies part of a grand life-plan. We get the degree (in the days when a 2:1 meant something), find the career, find the alpha partner, buy the house in the right area, accessorise it, buy the car with the lowest mpg and emissions. Now, we decide, let's do the baby thing.

The result? We expect babies to fit into the balance of our lives. Everything else is within our control and we're damned if this new gadget is going to upset our perfectly ordered apple cart. We approach the whole thing as we might a job: we research it, we take it terribly seriously, we expect returns, and instinct gives way to something much less human. It's an R and D Project, an exercise in box ticking, an inter-personal solution.

Even worse, we've selected everything in our lives to say something about who we are and what we've achieved (the Dualit toaster, the Smeg fridge, the holiday in the Maldives), so it's obvious, isn't it? Our children must be part of our lifestyle statement. They must be clever, beautiful and accomplished. And preferably come with a lifetime guarantee.

The Curse of the Mummy

Pick your team: are you batting for the Full-Time Mothers or the Working Mothers? If we made the decision to put our years of over-education on the back burner (or away for good), then we have to make a career out of being a full-time mother, baking biscuits and making crafty things, to show we are doing it brilliantly. That should work to cover up our deep-seated fear that life is happening somewhere else, away from relentless round of toddler groups and bottom-wiping, and that our brains are slowly atrophying to the extent that we will never function as normal human beings again. FTMs criticise WMs as selfish and uncaring, and hope deep down that their children will come off the rails good and proper, at which point they will be able to sit back and crow about how 'important those early years are'.

WMs of course are well chronicled: permanently knackered, wrinkled before their time, riddled with guilt, and feeling quite nauseous from all that cake they are apparently having *and* eating. But, as they battle their way home from work, trying to put behind them the boardroom struggles and focus on the brief quality-time they are about to impose on their children, they wonder which part of win-win they got wrong-wrong.

Social Engineering

Why is it that wanting the very best for our children brings out the very worst in us? The trouble is it goes a bit beyond just wanting the best, doesn't it? It's about wanting *better than you* and there are no depths to which we won't sink to achieve this. Whether it's sucking up to the teacher, getting our children tutored in Japanese, bribing the admissions secretary, booking the longest-haul holiday, having the biggest best everything, we can't seem to stop ourselves interfering.

It's made us into a pretty nasty bunch and nowhere is it more obvious than at school, the natural parenting habitat. 'When I look out on to the playground these days at picking-up time,' says Margaret, long-time primary teacher, 'I can see the parents as they were as children. In fact, it's like a mirror of the situation I have inside the classroom behind me. The same bullies, the same cliques, the same social manipulation.'

It becomes a bit like a game. You start on the first square and roll your dice. You scan the playground to find people you might be friends with and you form an alliance. Links of course are the only way to make friends, and it can be the most spurious connection. Ooh, she's got a Radley bag, she must be my type. It's like speed-dating by the hopscotch grid. And then shamelessly we try to force our children to socialise with the children of the people we want to get in with.

It can all get pretty nasty though if things get personal. Conflicts and tiffs between children were once sorted out in the classroom. Now they seem to escalate into slanging matches and nasty phone calls and that's just between the mothers. 'I've had to ban one woman from the playground until she calmed down,' remembers Betty, a head teacher. 'She picked so many fights I had no choice. Her daughter was as bad but at least I could put her on the naughty chair.'

Shouldn't we be able to talk to other parents about how hard it all is? Before we spawned we bored each other rigid about our love lives, didn't we, so why are we so reticent now? Do you detect a lack of adult solidarity here? It's hard to admit weakness and uncertainty to the very people we are competing against.

Lyn, experienced mother of older children, puts it succinctly: 'You only 'fess up when they are older. You can't admit you are failing while you are on the job.'

Mixed Media

Thinking about it now, we reckon we've been fairly lenient so far on the media but it has to take a big slice of the blame for creating the generation of Prozac Parents.

Issues, discussion, advice about parenting and how to do it/not to do it/to do it better are everywhere, and everywhere parents are being judged and found wanting. It's all based on half-baked parenting theories and lies, lies and statistics.

Google the words 'parenting advice' and there are over 27 million links. There are books on getting pregnant, thinking about getting pregnant, and thinking about thinking about getting pregnant. There's advice on being positive and not pushy, weaning without tears, getting them to sleep without committing violence, having the perfect relationship with teenagers and, while you are at it, being Nigella Lawson in the kitchen and John Prescott in the bedroom.

We live in a world where we have to find out how to bake a cake; how to plant a garden; how to train a dog; so why not how to raise a child? And it's more than that, it's how to raise the perfect child. There are guides on how to do it as a working mum, a stay-at-home mum and some-times working sometimes staying-at-home mum.

Be under no illusion though: the aim here is not to reassure. It's to create anxiety that can only be allayed by buying the book, reading the article, getting the gadget, eating the vitamins. The overwhelming imperative is to sell product. The other myth we are fed (and we consume greedily) is the pap of celebrity parenting. We see this air-brushed image of effortless mother- and fatherhood in magazines like *Hello!* and *OK!*, *Heat* and the like, and it fuels our paranoia and our anxiety. 'I want to be like her,' we screech as we scan the picture of yummy mummy *du jour*, so we rush out to buy the stretch-mark cream she swears by, the buggy she takes round Central Park, the designer baseball cap her little (ridiculously named) dar-ling is wearing. It's not unlike touching relics – we hope a little of her grace will rub off on us and our miserable lives – and we fail to see that behind this glossy veneer of celebrity lie the same puking babies, haemorrhoids and dissatisfaction that we feel. It's just hidden behind a pink Juicy Couture trackie.

Why do we swallow all this hype? Where on earth did we put our ability to make our own decisions? We must have thrown it out with the disposable nappies. (You didn't use those, did you? Haven't you heard about the planet?) Child-rearing has been going on since Fred and Wilma Flintstone, so why have we, the most highly educated generation ever, become so gullible? We are happy to hold forth on the subject of nuclear proliferation, but we'd rather die than admit we gave our baby a dummy.

The Pol Potty Regime

Following on from this tyranny of fear is the increased perception of danger and jeopardy – all that stuff about why playground games are being banned. And the result is a culture of general anxiety where everything is up for question. In 1971 eight out of ten eight-year-olds walked to school alone. Now fewer than one in ten does, because we've been cranked up to hysteria level that they will be abducted if they step outside the house. We run *Crimewatch* scenarios through our heads every time they are out of our sight. Now they are virtual prisoners in their own homes. Oops, then the media tells us they will get fat. Slap wrist, you shouldn't let them spend so much time on the computer; but hang on, they better had because, we are then told, they are falling behind on their basic curriculum skills. No wonder we are barking.

'Is that them or us?'

We become incapable of absorbing the statistics that in fact children are safer now than they have ever been, because they are hidden behind hysterical headlines and minute by minute of news analysis of the jeopardy that constantly threatens our children: murders, abductions, saturated fats. The media has found the chink in our parenting armour and, boy, does it put in the knife.

The Other Parent

And this is not just any old other parent. Another of those modern issues we have to deal with is the Ex-Parent. The one you used to parent with, but whom you now hand your children over to in the supermarket car park along with an overnight bag and a hiss about unpaid maintenance.

Breaking up is hard to do, but co-parenting when you are not only on a different hymn sheet but in a different house, is virtually impossible. It becomes an exercise in ante-upping. Like the Cold War (not a bad analogy), each side escalates the spoils and cranks up the propaganda against the enemy. One of you buys them a bike, the other makes it a moped. You let them have sweets; he responds with knickerbocker glories.

Even worse, you find yourself parenting someone quite unrelated to you or, conversely, your children can end up with another mother/father who's married to or has shacked up with your spouse. How can you hold any sway when there are three or four of you doing the parenting? Then of course they might have kids, and another set of grandparents and then the whole thing gets horribly complicated, especially at times like Christmas when one day to see the whole family simply isn't long enough. And you thought Father Christmas was busy.

Grand Designs

The last bastion of sanity is our parents, the grandparents, but the madness is we don't listen to them because we know better. Like the way antiques have gone out of fashion, so has the wisdom of their experience. They are the Queen Anne armoire of parenting, but we are the Philippe Starke chair: cutting edge and on the button and not terribly comfortable. But damn, we look good. They'd never have told us that though. Stop showing off, they'd have said when we were children, and Be quiet, I'm talking, dear.

Like those big fridges, self-esteem was something they only had in America in those days.

Anyway, what do our parents know? They must have had the odd concern about us – would we get scarlet fever or measles? Would the Russians bomb us? – but, come off it, they didn't have to cope with crucial decisions like which pull-up pants to use, did they?

Doesn't it drive you mad, though, the way they always tell you what to do; the way they question your lifestyle choices; the way they tell you that parenting should not be about diplomacy but about despotism (less Baby Whisperer and more Baby Doc); the way they poison your children with chocolate then roll their eyes when you

239

show them the latest research from Sweden on how it might affect their fertility? And then, of course, they have to step in and pick up the pieces when your carefully ordered lifestyle falls apart because the nanny has walked out and you have to go to a conference in Frankfurt and pleeeese, Mum, can you have the children?

Of course they won't though, because they are having far too much fun learning the tango in Buenos Aires and spending your inheritance. How selfish is that?

So here's to our Admit-No-Blame Society: next time you find yourself getting your children to play their violin in front of visitors, or putting them on your answerphone message, or sticking a 'Baby on Board' label in the car window because it makes your car so much safer, you can just blame the parents. Yours.

What goes around comes around

And what will we end up with when our over-nurtured, over-protected and over-stimulated progeny reach the age of responsibility? Will they be gibbering wrecks of uncertainty who won't be able to sleep unless they are sung a lullaby, who will be morbidly obese from not being allowed to exercise in case they hurt themselves, and totally unmotivated because they have no idea about aspiration and the effort they need to put into life because you did their coursework for them?

Or will they be level-headed adults who will, like we did with hippydom and flower power, throw all our cock-eyed theories back in our faces and embrace a more laid-back form of child rearing? Will they take pity on us, the poor pilloried generation who were so besieged by advice we didn't know which way to turn, or will they do what we did? Yes, that's what they'll do. Blame it all on the parents. Theirs.

A Thank You Letter . . .*

It's been quite an eye-opener writing this book, and facing up to how we rate as parents. So it's been a comfort to know we are not the only ones who are fumbling our way through. Massive appreciation to all those people who have talked to us, on and off the record. They include Sue Margolis, Marilyn Bunce, Penny Wilson, Alan Beeton, Priscilla Chase, Jane Ross-Macdonald, Beth Elgood, Elaine Townshend, David Arthur, Sophie Campbell, Alison Purchon, Lyn Shone, John Simpson CBE, Steve Hayward, Deirdre Shields, Keith Adams, Helen Gunton, Lucy Horner, Fran Johnson, David Martin, Paula Byrne, Dr Sarah Thomson, Jackie Ciotkowski, Marie Rendall, Lucy Strauss, Peter Robertson, Clare Jervis, Doreen Massey, Dr Lisa Ford, Kate Newton, Sharon Walpole, Alex Fraser, Rachel Burn, Bob Hardy at Clarks, and of course those who wanted to remain anonymous for fear of reprisals! We know who you are! Hope we haven't forgotten anyone. Thanks also to Nicola Doherty, Sam Evans and all at Hodders, Nikki Melluish, Madonna Benjamin, Ian Denyer and all at Maverick TV, and everyone at RDF. Also of course Mary Pachnos, a doberman among agents.

AA and MS, 2006

* Remember them?

DIMENSIONS OF SCIENCE
Series Editor: Professor Jeff Thompson

IONIC ORGANIC MECHANISMS

Charles Went

Coventry Lanchester Polytechnic

MACMILLAN

First published 1986

Published by
MACMILLAN EDUCATION LTD
Houndmills, Basingstoke, Hampshire RG21 2XS
and London
Companies and representatives
throughout the world

Printed in Great Britain by
The Camelot Press Ltd,
Southampton

British Library Cataloguing in Publication Data
Went, Charles
Ionic organic mechanisms.–(Dimensions of science)
1. Chemical reaction, Conditions and laws of
I. Title   II. Series
541.3'9   QD502

ISBN 0-333-39160-8

Contents

Acknowledgements   vii

Introduction   viii

1 Structure and Physical Properties of Organic Molecules   **1**
Structural terminology. Polar molecules. The inductive
effect. Physical properties of polar molecules

2 The Concept of Resonance   **15**
Mesomeric effect. MO description of conjugated molecules.
Limiting forms. Induced polarisation. Manifestation of
resonance. Determination of resonance energy. Bond lengths.
Electric dipole moments. Spectral data

3 Classification of Reactions and Reagents   **41**
Annotated equations. Classification of reactions and reagents.
Mechanistic equations. Use of partial structures

4 Organic Acids and Bases   **58**
General concepts. Measurement of acidity and basicity.
Conjugate acids and bases. Acidity of carboxylic acids.
Acidity of phenols. Acidity of alcohols. Basicity of amines

5 Nucleophilic Substitution   **79**
Reactions of haloalkanes. Unimolecular and bimolecular
mechanisms. Energy profiles, transition states and intermediates. Stereochemistry. The Hammond Postulate.
Unsaturated halocompounds. Reactions of alcohols, phenols,
ethers and amines

6 Elimination   **123**
Haloalkanes. Unimolecular and bimolecular mechanisms.
Substitution versus elimination. Reactions of alcohols and
amines

7   **Nucleophilic Reactions of Carbonyl Compounds**   142
    Addition and addition with elimination. Acidic hydrogen.
    Tautomerism. Condensation reactions

8   **Nucleophilic Reactions of Carboxylic Acids and their**   176
    Derivatives
    Reactions of carboxylic acids. Reactions of acid chlorides.
    Reactions of acid anhydrides. Reactions of esters. Reactions
    of acid amides

9   **Electrophilic Addition Reactions of Alkenes and Alkynes**   193
    Addition reactions of alkenes. Oxidation of alkenes. Hydro-
    genation of alkenes. Reactivity of buta-1,3-diene. Reactions
    of alkynes

10 **Aromatic Electrophilic Substitution**   220
    Mechanism of nitration, sulphonation, halogenation, and
    Friedel–Crafts reaction. Electronic effects of substituents.
    Steric effects

    Outline Solutions to Exercises   257

    Brief Bibliography: some more-advanced textbooks   271

    Index   272

Acknowledgements

I would like to thank the Senior Science Editor, Ms Mary Hoddinott, and the Series Editor, Professor Jeff Thompson, for their advice and encouragement in the preparation of this manuscript.

Introduction

WHY STUDY ORGANIC REACTION MECHANISMS?

There are many possible answers to this question! A teacher might reply that it is an interesting way of introducing what is called 'the scientific method'. He or she might also point to the pleasure which can result from satisfying the natural curiosity that chemists have about the way in which reactions occur.

Of more appeal to the student, perhaps, is that a good understanding of mechanisms provides a means of correlating and rationalising a large volume of otherwise apparently unrelated reactions. It is not intended that a mechanistic study of organic chemistry should replace the traditional approach, but in an integrated course even a simple treatment of mechanisms can help to give 'rhyme and reason' to many of the reactions studied.

It can also be argued, of course, that there are good economic reasons for studying mechanisms. The more that is known about the way in which a reaction occurs, the more successful a chemist is likely to be in designing a new synthesis or improving an existing process.

ABOUT THIS BOOK

Since this is a book just about mechanisms, it will be assumed that you have already made some progress in your study of organic chemistry, and are conversant with basic ideas of structure and stereochemistry, etc. Even so, the first four chapters are devoted to a revision of some of the concepts and terminology considered essential to the study of ionic mechanisms.

The order of subsequent chapters in which particular mechanisms (such as nucleophilic substitution or alkene addition) are discussed, may differ from that of the course which you are taking. If this is the case, you are still advised to read chapter 5 before embarking on other topics, because it is in the discussion of nucleophilic reactions that many of the ideas assumed to be familiar in later chapters are first introduced and explained. Throughout the text there are a number of exercises designed to help you assess your own understanding and progress. It is hoped that you will attempt at least some of these, and outline solutions are given at the end of the book.

1 Structure and Physical Properties of Organic Molecules

ORGANIC STRUCTURES ON PAPER

Two-dimensional drawings which are used to represent three-dimensional molecules are called **projections**. For particular purposes Newman, Fischer and other projections may be employed, but in discussion of basic organic reaction mechanisms at an introductory level, simple **planar formulae** are generally quite satisfactory. These may be full **Lewis structures** in which electron pairs are shown as dots or solid lines

$$
\begin{array}{ccc}
& H & \\
& \overset{..}{\underset{..}{H:C}}\overset{..}{\underset{..}{:O}}:H & \\
& H &
\end{array}
\qquad \text{or} \qquad
\begin{array}{c}
H \\
| \\
H-\overset{}{\underset{|}{C}}-\overset{..}{\underset{..}{O}}-H \\
H
\end{array}
$$

or **condensed formulae**, leaving out the electrons altogether

$$CH_3OH$$

However, *you are strongly urged not to omit the unshared electron pairs when these are present.* For example, the methoxide ion is often abbreviated to $CH_3O^\ominus$, and it is easy to forget that the oxygen atom has *three* unshared pairs of electrons, $CH_3\overset{..}{\underset{..}{O}}:^\ominus$.

The origin of charges is also important. In the methanol molecule, the oxygen atom has a complete octet of electrons in the valence shell, but only six of these actually 'belong' to that atom — two lone pairs and a half-share of two bonded pairs. On formation of the methoxide ion, the oxygen atom takes full possession of the electron pair from the oxygen-hydrogen bond, and so gains *one* extra unit of electron density

$$
H_3C:\overset{..}{\underset{..}{O}}:H \xrightarrow{\;-H^\oplus\;} H_3C:\overset{..}{\underset{..}{O}}:^\ominus
$$

the oxygen atom has a complete octet, but has also gained one unit of electron density

1

Conversely, when methanol is protonated, the oxygen atom has to share an electron pair with the proton which previously it had all to itself; that is, it loses one unit of electron density

$$H_3C : \overset{\cdot\cdot}{\underset{\cdot\cdot}{O}} : H \overset{+H^{\oplus}}{\longrightarrow} H_3C : \overset{\oplus}{\underset{\cdot\cdot}{O}} : H$$

the oxygen atom retains a complete octet, but has 'lost' one unit of electron density

Confusion sometimes arises because the oxygen atom is said to 'donate an electron pair' to the proton. A less deceptive description would be that the oxygen atom donates a *half-share* of an electron pair to the proton. Reaction mechanisms are all about electron exchanges, and if one species donates an electron pair to another species, the two finish up sharing the electron pair between them. As a result, the donor species loses *one* unit of electron density, whereas the receiver gains *one* unit of electron density

the hydrogen atom has gained one unit of negative charge and is now neutral

the oxygen atom donates an electron pair

the proton receives an electron pair

the oxygen atom now has a unit positive charge

This may seem a rather elementary concept, but errors in the 'electron accounting' can easily lead to misunderstandings in writing mechanistic equations.

Exercise 1.1
Use the 'two dot' notation to indicate lone pairs of valence electrons in the following formulae

(a) $CH_3 - \overset{\overset{\displaystyle O}{\parallel}}{C} - O - CH_3$ (b) $CH_3 - N = N - CH_3$ (c) $CH_3 - \overset{\oplus}{O}H_2$

(d) $CH_3 - \overset{\ominus}{C}H_2$ (e) $C \equiv N^{\ominus}$ (f) $CH_2 = \overset{\oplus}{N} = \overset{\ominus}{N}$

STRUCTURAL TERMINOLOGY

Structurally, a molecule such as 2-methylpropan-1-ol can be considered in two portions: the hydrocarbon **skeleton** (which here is an alkyl group) and the hydroxyl **functional group**.

hydrocarbon
skeleton

position of attachment of
functional group

functional
group

The functional group is responsible for the main chemical reactivity of the molecule and also influences physical properties such as solubility and boiling point. As we shall see later, the position of attachment of the functional group on the hydrocarbon skeleton also affects the chemical and physical behaviour, as does the size and shape of the hydrocarbon skeleton.

In a widely used convention, the carbon atom to which the functional is attached is called the **alpha (α) carbon atom**. The adjacent atom is then called **beta (β)**, and so on

$$-\overset{|}{\underset{|}{C}}-\overset{|}{\underset{|}{C}}-\overset{|}{\underset{|}{C}}-G \qquad (G = \text{functional group})$$

$$\gamma \quad \beta \quad \alpha$$

Hydrogen atoms attached to these carbon atoms are referred to as *α-hydrogen*, *β-hydrogen*, etc.

3

Allylic, benzylic and vinyl structures

Despite the wide adoption of systematic (IUPAC) nomenclature, many 'common' names are still in use, particularly in industry, and it is therefore necessary to be familiar with these as well as the systematic names. An important example is the ethenyl group, $CH_2 = CH$ — which is commonly known as **vinyl**. Hydrogen atoms attached to doubly bonded carbon atoms are called **vinylic hydrogen atoms**. Similarly, the prop-2-enyl group, $CH_2 = CH - CH_2 -$, is called **allyl**, and hydrogen atoms on a carbon atom adjacent to a doubly bonded carbon atom are referred to as **allylic hydrogen atoms**.

vinylic hydrogen   allylic hydrogen

The phenylmethyl group, $PhCH_2 -$, is also known as **benzyl**, and so hydrogen atoms on a carbon atom adjacent to a benzene ring are referred to as **benzylic hydrogen atoms**.

benzylic hydrogen

Functional groups such as halogen may have their reactivity considerably modified when in vinylic, allylic or benzylic positions.

POLAR MOLECULES

A normal covalent bond is formed by sharing a pair of electrons between two atoms, each of which contributes one electron. (An exception is the coordinate or dative bond, in which one atom donates both electrons.) When the two atoms are identical, for example the two carbon atoms in ethane, the electron pair is shared equally between the two atoms. No

4

charge separation occurs and the bond is said to be **non-polar**. A molecule whose atoms are linked only by non-polar bonds is a **non-polar molecule**.

However, in a bond between non-identical atoms, the atom which most strongly attracts electrons will have more than a half share of the electron pair. It will thus acquire a partial negative charge (represented by $\delta-$), leaving the other bonded atom slightly electron deficient with a partial positive charge ($\delta+$). The phenomenon is called **polarisation**, and the bond is said to be **polarised**, or a **polar bond**. A molecule containing such a bond will thus be a **polar molecule**.

The ability of a covalently bonded atom to attract the bonding electrons towards itself is expressed quantitatively in terms of its **electronegativity**. Some values suggested by Pauling are given in table 1.1.

Table 1.1 The Pauling electronegativity scale

Atom	H	C	N	O	F	Cl	Br	I
Relative electronegativity	2.1	2.5	3.0	3.5	4.0	3.0	2.8	2.5

It is found that electronegativity is greatest for atoms with nearly complete outer electron levels, and the value decreases with increasing size of atom. Rising values in the series $C < N < O < F$ parallel increases in the positive charge on the nucleus. The influence of size is apparent in the series $F > Cl > Br > I$ where, although the charge on the nucleus increases, the nucleus is effectively 'screened' by additional inner levels of electrons, and electronegativity *decreases*.

Representation of polar bonds on paper

The direction of displacement of the electron pair can be shown by drawing an arrowhead on the line representing the electron pair bond

$$CH_3 \longrightarrow \overset{\cdot\cdot}{\underset{\cdot\cdot}{Cl}}:$$

Note that the arrowhead is placed halfway along the line, and not as an ordinary arrow. The latter is used when writing equations, or to represent a coordinate (dative) bond

$$-\overset{\oplus}{N}\overset{\nearrow \overset{\cdot\cdot}{O}{:}^{\ominus}}{\underset{\searrow \overset{\cdot\cdot}{O}{\cdot}}{}}$$

Here, the $N \longrightarrow O$ arrow indicates that both electrons in the nitrogen-oxygen bond are supplied by the nitrogen atom. Alternatively, charge separation can be indicated by the use of the symbols $\delta+$ and $\delta-$

$$\overset{\delta+}{CH_3} - \overset{\delta-}{\underset{\cdot\cdot}{\overset{\cdot\cdot}{Cl}}}:$$

THE INDUCTIVE EFFECT

Uneven sharing or displacement of electrons in an ordinary sigma bond, leading to charge separation on the two bonded atoms, is called an **inductive displacement**, or **inductive effect**. In assessing this effect, the $C - H$ bond in an alkane is taken as a standard for comparison, and is regarded as being essentially non-polar*. If an atom or group attached to a carbon atom is electron-withdrawing compared with a hydrogen atom in the same situation, it is said to exert a **negative inductive effect**, symbol $-I$. (Negative because it *lowers* the electron density about the carbon atom to which it is attached.)

Conversely, an atom or group which is electron-releasing relative to a hydrogen atom is said to exert a **positive inductive effect**, symbol $+I$. (Positive because it *raises* the electron density about the carbon atom to which it is attached.) Thus

$$-\overset{|}{\underset{|}{C}} - H \qquad \text{non-polar standard}$$

$$-\overset{|}{\underset{|}{C}} \rightarrow X \qquad \begin{array}{l}\text{X is an electron-withdrawing atom or group.} \\ = \textbf{negative inductive effect}, -I\end{array}$$

$$-\overset{|}{\underset{|}{C}} \leftarrow Y \qquad \begin{array}{l}\text{Y is an electron-releasing atom or group,} \\ = \textbf{positive inductive effect}, +I\end{array}$$

Some examples are given in table 1.2.

---

*Carbon is more electronegative than hydrogen, and we should therefore expect a carbon–hydrogen bond to be very weakly polar. The calculated bond moment is about 1.6×10^{-30} C m (0.5 Debye). In centro-symmetric hydrocarbons, the individual bond moments cancel out and these compounds have zero molecular dipole moments.

6

Table 1.2 Inductive effects of some common groups

Atoms or groups exerting a negative inductive effect, $-I$	*Atoms or groups exerting a positive inductive effect, $+I$*
$—\ddot{N}H_2$, $—\ddot{N}HR$	$—\ddot{N}H^{\ominus}$
$—\ddot{O}H$, $—\ddot{O}R$	$—\ddot{\ddot{O}}{:}^{\ominus}$
$—\ddot{X}{:}$ (halogen)	$—C\ddot{\ddot{O}}\ddot{O}{:}^{\ominus}$
$\overset{\oplus}{—N}\longrightarrow \ddot{O}{:}^{\ominus}$, $—C\ddot{H}\ddot{O}$, $—C\ddot{O}\ddot{O}H$ $\underset{{:}O{:}}{\overset{\|}{}}$	$—R$ (alkyl)
$\overset{\oplus}{—NR_3}$	

The negative inductive effect

An examination of the functional groups in table 1.2 shows that the atom by which each group is attached to a hydrocarbon skeleton is more electronegative than carbon; for example, the oxygen atom in $—\ddot{O}H$ and $—\ddot{O}R$, and the nitrogen atom in $—\ddot{N}H_2$ and $—\ddot{N}HR$, etc.

The nitro group exerts a particularly powerful $-I$ effect as the nitrogen atom is positively charged. Thus, nitromethane is a highly polar molecule*

$$CH_3 \rightarrow \overset{\oplus}{N} \diagup \overset{\ddot{O}{:}^{\ominus}}{\underset{\ddot{O}}{\diagdown}} \qquad -I \text{ effect of a nitro group}$$

Likewise, the carbon atom of a polar carbonyl group has a partial positive charge and will therefore exert a strong $-I$ effect in adjacent sigma-bonds. Propanone is a good example

$$\begin{array}{c} CH_3 \diagdown \\ C \overset{\delta+}{=} \overset{\delta-}{\ddot{O}}{:} \\ CH_3 \diagup \end{array} \qquad -I \text{ effect of a carbonyl group}$$

*This is the classical representation; the structure of the nitro group is considered in more detail in chapter 2.

The positive inductive effect

It is clear that groups having one or more negatively charged atoms will tend to be electron repelling, but it may be less obvious why alkyl groups should exert a positive inductive effect. The behaviour of alkyl groups results not so much from an actual *repulsion* of electrons, but rather from the ability to *release* sigma electrons towards a more powerfully electron-attracting atom or group. Consider, for example, the structure of the ethyl carbocation (carbonium ion) in which a methyl group is attached to a positively charged carbon atom

$$CH_3 - \overset{\oplus}{C}H_2$$

Obviously, the positively charged carbon atom will exert a much greater pull on the bonding sigma electrons than will the neutral carbon atom of the methyl group. So the sigma electrons will be displaced towards the $C^{\oplus}$ atom

$$CH_3 \rightarrow \overset{\oplus}{C}H_2$$

Relay of the inductive effect

A carbon atom made slightly positive by the negative inductive effect of a bonded atom or group will in turn be more electronegative than the adjacent bonded atom

$$\underset{\beta}{CH_3} - \underset{\alpha}{\overset{\delta+}{CH_2}} \rightarrow \overset{\delta-}{X}$$

So in a molecule of ethanol, for example (where $X = -\overset{..}{\underset{..}{O}}H$), there will be an inductive displacement from the β-carbon atom towards the α-carbon atom

$$\underset{\beta}{\overset{\delta\delta+}{CH_3}} \rightarrow \underset{\alpha}{\overset{\delta+}{CH_2}} \rightarrow \overset{\delta-}{\underset{..}{\overset{..}{O}}}H$$

The negative inductive effect of the hydroxyl group is thus transmitted or **relayed** to the more remote β-carbon atom. In a longer chain of carbon atoms, there might be a further small displacement in the bond adjacent to the β-carbon atom, but beyond the third carbon atom the effect will have essentially 'died out'

$$CH_3 \overset{\delta\delta\delta+}{\underset{}{—}} CH_2 \overset{\delta\delta+}{\underset{}{\longrightarrow}} CH_2 \overset{\delta+}{\underset{}{\longrightarrow}} CH_2 \overset{\delta-}{\underset{}{\longrightarrow}} \overset{\cdot\cdot}{\underset{}{O}}H$$
$$-I \text{ effect}$$

no observable effect beyond the
third carbon atom

The progressive diminution of the inductive effect along a carbon–carbon chain is referred to as the *'damping out effect'* of methylene (CH_2) groups.

Inductive effects in other bonds

Inductive displacements may occur in sigma-bonds other than those with carbon atoms. For example, oxygen–hydrogen and nitrogen–hydrogen bonds are both strongly polarised

$$\overset{\delta-}{\underset{\cdot\cdot}{—\overset{\cdot\cdot}{O}}} \overset{\delta+}{\longleftarrow} H \qquad\qquad \overset{\delta-}{\underset{}{\overset{\cdot\cdot}{N}}} \overset{\delta+}{\longleftarrow} H$$

SUMMARY

The important features of the inductive effect may be summarised as follows

(1) The effect relates to the unequal sharing of the electron pair in an ordinary sigma-bond.

(2) Although the sigma electrons are displaced towards the more electro-negative of the two bonded atoms, they remain in a bonding position; that is, **localised** between the two atoms.

(3) The effect may be transmitted or relayed along a carbon–carbon chain, but is usually ineffective beyond about the second or third carbon atom.

Field effects

Owing to the presence of bond dipoles in a molecule, coulombic inter-actions (attractive and repulsive) may occur across space or through a solvent. Such interactions are known as **field effects**, and these may be influential both intermolecularly and intramolecularly. An example is given in chapter 3 (see page 69).

9

SOME CONSEQUENCES OF THE INDUCTIVE EFFECT

As a result of their inductive effects, substituents may markedly influence both the physical and chemical behaviour of a compound. We will look first at the effect on physical properties.

Physical properties of polar molecules

(1) *Electric dipole moments*
A molecule with a polar structure is like a mini-dipole, and as such tends to orient itself in an applied electric field. The magnitude of this tendency can be measured and called the **electric dipole moment**, μ (mu), of the molecule or compound. This is defined by the product of the charge and the distance of separation. Formerly, these quantities were expressed in CGS units, where charge is in electrostatic units and distance in cm. The basic unit was the **Debye**, defined as

$$1 \text{ Debye} = 10^{-18} \text{ esu cm}$$

Now that CGS units have been replaced by SI units (Système International d'Unités), charge is measured in Coulombs (C), and distance in metres (m). For convenience, values are often quoted in terms of 10^{-30} C m. There is as yet no special name for this unit. As many textbooks (and all earlier literature!) still state electric dipole moment data in Debye units, the following conversion factor is useful

$$1 \text{ Debye} = 3.34 \times 10^{-30} \text{C m}$$

Some comparative values are given in table 1.3.

Table 1.3 Electric dipole moments of some organic compounds expressed in CGS and SI units

	$-\overset{\displaystyle |}{\underset{\displaystyle |}{C}} - X$ bond		
	$CH_3 - H$	$\overset{\delta+}{CH_3} - \overset{\delta-}{\underset{..}{N}H_2}$	$\overset{\delta+}{CH_3} - \overset{\delta-}{\underset{..}{O}H}$	$\overset{\delta+}{CH_3} - \overset{\delta-}{\underset{..}{F}:}$
μ (D)	0.0	1.32	1.69	1.82
μ (10^{-30} C m)	0.0	4.41	5.65	6.08

Of course, if a molecule contains more than one polar bond, the molecular dipole moment will be the vector resultant of the individual bond moments. This may even be zero in some cases, as can be seen from the examples in figure 1.1.

Figure 1.1 *Electric dipole moments of some organic molecules. These examples also illustrate how dipole moment data can be of help in determining the shapes of organic molecules.*

Exercise 1.3
What can be deduced about the shape of the boron trifluoride molecule (BF_3) from the observation that it has zero electric dipole moment?

(2) *Association*
Polar molecules will exhibit an attraction for one another, owing to electrostatic attraction of opposite charges. Association may occur through **dipole–dipole** interaction, for example in propanone

or through **hydrogen bonding**. This may be **inter**molecular, for example

weak intermolecular
hydrogen bonds

or **intra**molecular, for example

weak intramolecular
hydrogen bond

Hydrogen bonding is stronger than dipole–dipole interaction, but both types of bonding are relatively weak*, and any particular molecule will constantly be dissociating from one neighbouring molecule and reassociating with another.

*The bond dissociation energy of a hydrogen bond in alcohols is about 20–40 kJ mol, compared with 500 kJ mol for an oxygen–hydrogen sigma-bond.

12

(3) *Effect on solubility*

When a solute dissolves in a solvent, the solute molecules separate from one another and intermingle with the molecules of the solvent. Associative forces holding the solute molecules together have to be overcome, and new associations occur between the solute and solvent molecules. For example, when an alcohol dissolves in water, intermolecular hydrogen bonds have to be broken and new hydrogen bonds form between alcohol and water molecules

The lower alcohols, aldehydes, ketones and carboxylic acids are all water soluble, mainly because of the ability of water molecules to hydrogen-bond with molecules of these compounds. Water solubility decreases with increase in relative molecular mass, that is, with increase in size of the non-polar hydrocarbon skeleton. Similarly, non-polar solutes generally will dissolve only in non-polar solvents. Propanone (acetone) is a moderately polar compound and has the ability to dissolve both polar and non-polar solutes (though to varying degrees).

14

2　The Concept of Resonance

INTRODUCTION

There are many compounds for which the classical formula (Lewis structure) is apparently not consistent with the observed chemical behaviour. For example, an aminoaldehyde such as 3-aminopropanal has properties of both an amine and a carbonyl compound, and is well represented by the formula $\overset{..}{N}H_2 CH_2 CH_2 CH\overset{..}{O}$. But propanamide, which also has an amino group and a carbonyl group in its structure, $CH_3 CH_2 C\overset{..}{O}\overset{....}{N}H_2$, is appreciably less basic than an aliphatic amine, and does not react at all with many of the reagents (weak nucleophiles) which attack the carbonyl group in aldehydes and ketones. It would appear that when these two functional groups are adjacent to one another, they are each able to modify the properties of the other in a way which would not be predicted from the Lewis formula*.

Another example is the varying acidity of the hydroxyl group in alcohols, phenols and carboxylic acids, the reason for which is not at all obvious from the classical structures for these compounds. Equally well, of course, the Kekulé (cyclohexatriene) structure for benzene is hardly in keeping with the observed properties of this compound, which typically undergoes electrophilic *substitution* rather than addition which is characteristic of alkenes.

To explain these and many other apparent 'anomalies' between structure and behaviour, we have to take into account another factor which influences the distribution of electrons within a molecule or ion. This is called the **mesomeric** or **resonance effect**. We will begin our discussion of this effect by taking a closer look at the structure of the carbonyl group in aldehydes and ketones.

*The reactivity of ethanamide is discussed in chapter 8. See page 185.

THE MESOMERIC (RESONANCE) EFFECT

In a carbonyl group, the so-called 'double bond' consists of a sigma-bond plus a pi-bond

Because of the difference in electronegativity of the two atoms, both the sigma and pi electrons are drawn more towards the oxygen atom. In order to differentiate between the two types of electron displacement, the shift of a pair of pi electrons is described as a **mesomeric effect**, symbol M, and is shown by means of a **curved arrow**.

Inductive displacement — arrowhead indicates displacement of sigma electrons towards the oxygen atom

Mesomeric displacement — curved arrow indicates displacement of pi electrons to a non-bonded position on the oxygen atom

The tail of the arrow indicates where the pi electrons come from (that is, a bonding position between the two atoms), and the head of the arrow shows the position towards which the electrons are displaced (that is, a non-bonding position on the oxygen atom).

By analogy with the terminology used in connection with the inductive effect, the withdrawal of electrons by the oxygen atom is described as a *negative mesomeric effect*, symbol $-M$. Note that the use of a curved arrow in this context* is not meant to imply an actual movement of pi electrons, but like the arrowhead on a sigma-bond, it shows the *direction in which electron displacement has already occurred* in the pi-bond of a carbonyl group. In other words, both the sigma and pi electron pairs are unequally shared by the two bonded atoms, and as a result the carbonyl group has a polar structure

---

*When writing mechanistic equations, curved arrows may be used to show actual movement of electron pairs believed to occur during the course of a reaction.

$$\overset{\delta+}{\underset{}{C}} = \overset{\delta-}{\underset{\cdots}{O}}$$

polarity results from a combination of inductive and mesomeric effects

the carbon atom has less than a half-share of both the sigma and pi electron pairs and therefore carries a fractional positive charge

the oxygen atom has more than a half-share of the sigma and pi electron pairs and therefore carries a fractional negative charge

Pi electrons are 'more mobile' than sigma electrons, and so polarisation of the pi-bond is greater than that of the sigma-bond.

It is interesting to examine the structure which would result from complete transference of the pi electron pair to the oxygen atom

(I) $\qquad$ imaginary complete displacement $\qquad$ (II)

electrons now shown as a non-bonded pair on the oxygen atom

In structure (II) there is one less electron pair bond, opposite unit charges are shown on adjacent atoms, and the carbon atom has only six valence electrons. A structure like this would be of much higher energy (that is, less stable) than structure (I).

For convenience, we shall refer to the normal Lewis structure (I) as the **classical structure**, and to structure (II) as the **charge-separated structure**. These two structures represent the two extremes of a whole spectrum of possible dispositions of the pi electrons, and are therefore called **limiting forms** or **limiting structures**. Neither structure accurately represents a real carbonyl group, because the pi electrons are not equally shared by the two bonded atoms as in the classical structure (I), nor yet do they reside entirely on the oxygen atom as in the charge-separated structure (II). Clearly, in a real molecule, the carbonyl group has a pi electron distribution somewhere between these two extremes, but is more closely represented by (I) than by (II). The real structure is said to be a **mesomer** of the two limiting forms. The word mesomer means 'between the parts', and implies a structure (pi electron distribution) somewhere between that shown in the two limiting forms. On paper, we draw the classical and charge-separated forms either side of a **double-headed arrow**

classical
limiting form

charge-separated
limiting form

the double-headed arrow
indicates that the actual
distribution of pi electrons
lies somewhere between that
shown in the two limiting forms

In order to indicate that the real structure is nearer to that of the classical limiting form, we say that the latter 'makes a *larger contribution*' to the mesomer than does the charge-separated limiting form. Using this terminology, then, the larger the contribution of a particular limiting form, the more closely does it represent the actual electron distribution in the real molecule or ion, etc.

Another way of showing that a carbonyl group has a mesomeric structure is to replace the full line representing the pi-bond with a broken line

$$\underset{\diagdown}{\overset{\diagup}{C}} \overset{\delta+}{} \overset{\delta-}{=\!=\!=} \overset{\cdot\cdot}{\underset{\cdot\cdot}{O}} :$$

the broken line indicates a
decrease in pi electron density,
and the $\delta-$ sign shows that this
has been displaced on to the
oxygen atom

Relay of the mesomeric effect

When two double bonds such as those in buta-1,3-diene

$$CH_2 = CH - CH = CH_2$$

are separated by a single bond, they are said to be **conjugated** with one another. In the propenal molecule, a carbonyl double bond is conjugated with an alkene double bond

$$CH_2 = CH - \underset{\underset{H}{|}}{C} = \overset{\cdot\cdot}{\underset{\cdot\cdot}{O}}$$

Just as the inductive effect is relayed along a chain of sigma-bonded carbon atoms, so the mesomeric effect can be transmitted along a conjugated system. In propenal, the (negative) mesomeric effect of the oxygen atom induces a displacement of pi electrons in the conjugated alkene

18

double bond. The alkene double bond is not merely polarised, but the pi electrons are drawn towards a new bonding position between the α-carbon atom and the carbonyl carbon atom

(a linear arrangement of atoms is shown for simplicity)

If we imagined that these displacements went to completion, the resulting pi electron distribution would look like this

charge-separated structure

We regard the classical and charge-separated structures as limiting forms, and the actual structure as a mesomer of the two

In order to represent the mesomer by a single structural formula, the basic 'sigma-bonded' structure is drawn first, together with the non-bonded electron pairs on the oxygen atom

sigma-bonded skeletal structure

Then, using the two limiting forms as a guide, distribution of the pi electron density is indicated by inserting the appropriate broken lines and fractional charges

broken lines here indicate loss of pi electron density

mesomeric structure

broken line here indicates gain in pi electron density

19

In principle, the mesomeric effect can be relayed along a conjugated system of indefinite length, and this is in marked contrast to the inductive effect which can only be transmitted over a relatively short distance before it is damped out by the intervening methylene groups

relay of mesomeric effect
along a conjugated chain

limited relay of inductive effect
along a saturated chain

MOLECULAR ORBITAL DESCRIPTION OF CONJUGATED MOLECULES

In attempting to arrive at a more accurate description of pi electron distribution in a conjugated molecule such as propenal, we have used what is known as the **valence bond approach**. That is, we have looked at various possible electron distributions in terms of valence bond structures (limiting forms) and used these as a guide in assessing the likely distribution of electrons in the real molecule. Another way of looking at the problem is by application of molecular orbital theory, known as the **molecular orbital approach**. In this approach, we visualise a structure for the propenal molecule in which the four sigma-bonded atoms — three carbons and one oxygen atom — are further bonded by a pi molecular orbital encompassing all four atoms. You will recall that pi-bond formation takes place by sideways overalp of 'spare' $2p$ orbitals on adjacent carbon (or carbon and oxygen) atoms.

sideways overlap of $2p$
atomic orbitals, each
with an unpaired electron

new bonding pi molecular
orbitals, each with an
electron pair

Further interaction (overlap) between the $2p$ orbitals on carbon atoms 1 and 2 will lead to the formation of a more extended bonding molecular orbital embracing all four atoms

20

additional overlap of
2p orbitals on carbon
atoms 1 and 2

new molecular orbital
encompassing all four
atoms

Because of the greater electronegativity of the oxygen atom, the pi electron density is not evenly distributed, and fractional charges are present at opposite ends of the molecule.

This is, of course, a very simplified description of bonding in propenal, but it does give a picture of a molecule in which the pi electron density is smeared over all four atoms in the main chain, and is closely similar to the mesomeric structure of the valence bond approach

$$\overset{\delta+}{CH_2} = CH = CH = \overset{\delta-}{\underset{..}{O}} :$$

The displacement of electrons away from localised positions shown in classical Lewis structures is referred to as **delocalisation**. Electrons are said to be **delocalised**, and a structure in which delocalisation occurs is called a **delocalised system**. Delocalisation is a characteristic feature of conjugated systems, but the phenomenon is not restricted to neutral molecules, nor yet is it necessarily the result of a mesomeric shift of electrons. In the buta-1,3-diene molecule, for example, further sideways interaction of the 2p atomic orbitals on carbon atoms 2 and 3 leads to the formation of an extended bonding molecular orbital involving all four carbon atoms*

*MO theory shows that interaction between four 2p atomic orbitals results in *four* new molecular orbitals: two low-energy bonding orbitals and two higher-energy anti-bonding orbitals. Each of the bonding orbitals contains a pair of pi electrons. Only the lower-energy bonding orbital is shown in the above diagram.

21

Since the four bonded atoms are identical, the pi electron density is more evenly distributed than in propenal, where, as we have seen, distortion occurs as a result of the mesomeric effect of the oxygen atom.

In valence bond notation, the structure is regarded as a mesomer of three limiting forms

$$CH_2 = CH - CH = CH_2 \quad \leftrightarrow \quad \overset{\oplus}{CH_2} - CH = CH - \overset{\ominus}{\underset{..}{CH_2}} \quad \leftrightarrow \quad \overset{\ominus}{\underset{..}{CH_2}} - CH = CH - \overset{\oplus}{C}$$

which may be abbreviated to

$$CH_2 \ \text{---}\!\!\text{---}\ CH \ \text{---}\!\!\text{---}\ CH \ \text{---}\!\!\text{---}\ CH_2$$

Some other mesomeric structures

Benzene
We may think of the two Kekulé structures for benzene as limiting forms, the true structure being a mesomer of the two

Kekulé structures
= limiting forms

two possible representations
of the mesomeric structure

In an alternative theoretical treatment known as **resonance theory**, benzene is described as a **resonance hybrid** of the Kekulé (and other) structures which are called **canonical forms** or **contributing structures**. For our purposes, the terms 'mesomer' and 'resonance hybrid' may be taken to mean essentially the same thing, and indeed they are frequently used interchangeably in elementary textbooks.

Benzene derivatives
Substituents on the benzene ring influence the distribution of pi electron density. In benzaldehyde, for example, the mesomeric effect of the carbonyl group is relayed to the nucleus, producing an electron-deficient ring in which positive charge is located on alternate ring carbon atoms

Kekulé structures

displacement of pi electrons in
the carbonyl group is relayed to
the aromatic nucleus

further displacements
transfer the positive
charge to other ring
carbon atoms

Note carefully the use of the curved arrow in this context. The tail of
the arrow is joined to a line representing a pair of pi electrons in the
Kekulé structure, and the arrowhead shows the position to which these are
displaced. This is a convenient way of showing on paper how one limiting
form is converted into another, but remember that the arrows do not
express an actual movement of electrons, but indicate the direction in
which electrons have already been displaced in the real molecule. Later we
shall use curved arrows to show the direction of movement of electrons
which occurs during the course of a reaction, or one step in a reaction. For
this reason, and to avoid possible misinterpretation, some chemists prefer
not to use curved arrows for the interconversion of limiting forms.

Only a small contribution is expected from the less stable charge-
separated forms, but the pi electron density and charge distribution is
reasonably well represented by the structure

mesomeric structure
of benzaldehyde

The phenoxide ion is an example where an electron-releasing substituent
is conjugated with the aromatic nucleus. Delocalisation of the negative
charge raises the electron density of the ring, and again the excess charge
appears on alternate ring carbon atoms

23

notice here that the curved arrow is used to show displacement of the electron pair and *not* the negative charge (see page 16)

Carbon atoms accommodate negative charge less readily than the more electronegative oxygen atom, and the three non-Kekulé forms will make a smaller contribution to the mesomer than the two Kekulé structures. Electron distribution in the mesomer may be summarised as

The nitro group

The classical Lewis representation of the nitro group shows the nitrogen atom doubly bonded to one oxygen atom and forming a coordinate (dative) bond with the other

Physical measurements cannot distinguish the two oxygen atoms, and the true structure is a mesomer in which the nitrogen atom is partially doubly bonded to *both* oxygen atoms. The nitrogen atom remains positively charged, but the oxygen atoms each have a half share of the negative charge limiting forms

dispersal of the
negative charge gives
a more stable structure

mesomeric structure

The propenyl (allyl) carbanion

Two limiting forms may be written, showing delocalisation of the negative charge

$$\overset{\ominus}{C}H_2 \!=\! CH \!-\! \overset{..\ominus}{C}H_2 \quad \longleftrightarrow \quad \overset{..\ominus}{C}H_2 \!-\! CH \!=\! CH_2$$

limiting forms

$$\left[\overset{\delta-}{C}H_2 \text{---} CH \text{---} \overset{\delta-}{C}H_2 \right]^{\ominus}$$

mesomeric structure

The propenyl carbocation

Similar limiting forms can be written, showing delocalisation of the positive charge

$$CH_2 \!=\! CH \!-\! \overset{\oplus}{C}H_2 \quad \longleftrightarrow \quad \overset{\oplus}{C}H_2 \!-\! CH \!=\! CH_2$$

limiting forms

$$\left[\overset{\delta+}{C}H_2 \text{---} CH \text{---} \overset{\delta+}{C}H_2 \right]^{\oplus}$$

mesomeric structure

note again that
the curved arrow
is used to show
the change in
position of the
electron pair, and
not the positive
charge

In molecular orbital terms, the two propenyl ions have a common structure, sideways *p–p* interaction giving three molecular orbitals, one of which extends over all three carbon atoms

25

The original $2p$ atomic orbital on carbon 1 is either vacant (in the carbocation) or contains an electron pair (in the carbanion). Consequently, the resulting molecular orbitals have to accommodate either 2 or 4 pi electrons.

Exercise 2.1

For the following compounds, draw the Lewis structures which would result from the indicated electron movements. In each case, show any charges which may develop or change position as a result of such movements.

(a) $\overset{H}{\underset{H}{>}}N \overset{\frown}{-} C \overset{\frown}{\equiv} N:$ (b) $\overset{\frown}{CH_2} \overset{\frown}{=} CH \overset{\frown}{-} \overset{..}{\underset{..}{Cl}}:$ (c) $CH_3 - \overset{..}{N} \overset{\frown}{=} \overset{\oplus}{N} \overset{\frown}{=} \overset{..}{\underset{\ominus}{N}}:$ (d) $CH_3 - \overset{..}{\underset{..}{O}} \overset{\frown}{-} \overset{..}{N} \overset{\frown}{=} \overset{..}{O}:$

RESONANCE STABILISATION AND THE CONCEPT OF RESONANCE ENERGY

The molecules, groups and ions described above as mesomers or resonance hybrids are all more stable than they would be if they actually existed in the classical (or other limiting) structures. The whole point about delocalisation is that it *gives a more stable structure*. The gain in stability, which means a reduction in energy, is referred to as **delocalisation energy, stabilisation energy**, or, more commonly, **resonance energy**. In resonance theory, resonance energy is defined as the *difference in energy between the resonance hybrid (or mesomer) and the most stable of the contributing (limiting) forms*. The most stable contributing form, of course, is usually the normal Lewis structure (the 'classical structure') which we write for the molecule or ion, etc.

Note that although we conventionally speak of resonance energy as a positive quantity, it is a measure of the increased stability of the species concerned, and as such represents a *reduction* in its energy. This idea may be clearer from the qualitative energy diagram, figure 2.1, illustrating energy differences for the propenal molecule.

26

Figure 2.1 *Qualitative energy diagram to illustrate resonance energy in the propenal molecule*

The diagram shows that resonance energy represents the work which would have to be done on a molecule of propenal to force the electrons to stay in localised positions (that is, in alkene and carbonyl double bonds) shown in the classical structure. Later in this chapter we shall discuss how we can actually quantify the resonance energy for compounds such as buta-1,3-diene and benzene, etc.

Contribution of the limiting forms

Resonance theory states that the more stable a particular limiting form, 'the greater its contribution to the resonance hybrid'. What this means, of course, is that if there is not much difference in energy between a limiting form and the resonance hybrid, then there is not much difference in structure; that is, the distribution of electrons in the real molecule is close to that shown in the limiting form. In the case of the two limiting forms representing the carbonyl group

$$\begin{array}{c}\diagup\\ \diagdown\end{array}C = \ddot{O} \quad \text{and} \quad \begin{array}{c}\diagup\\ \diagdown\end{array}\overset{\oplus}{C} - \ddot{O}\text{:}^{\ominus}$$

it is said that the classical limiting form makes a 'high contribution' to the resonance hybrid, and the high-energy charge-separated form makes 'very little contribution'. This is another way of saying that electrons are not very likely to be distributed in the way shown in the charge-separated form, and so the classical limiting form is quite a reasonable representation

27

of the true structure, particularly if δ+ and δ− signs are used to show polarisation of the bond.

Exercise 2.2

State, with reasons, which is likely to be the major contributor in each of the following pairs of limiting forms

(a) $\overset{H}{\underset{H}{>}}C = \overset{\oplus}{\underset{..}{O}} - H$ or $\overset{H}{\underset{H}{>}}C \overset{\oplus}{\underset{..}{-}} \overset{..}{\underset{..}{O}} - H$ (b) $\overset{H}{\underset{H}{>}}N \overset{..}{-} \overset{\oplus}{C} \overset{H}{\underset{H}{<}}$ or $\overset{H}{\underset{H}{>}}\overset{\oplus}{N} = C \overset{H}{\underset{H}{<}}$

(c) $H - \overset{\ominus}{\underset{..}{N}} - C = \overset{..}{\underset{..}{O}}$ or $H - \overset{..}{N} = C - \overset{..}{\underset{..}{O}} \colon^{\ominus}$ (d) $\overset{H}{\underset{H}{>}}\overset{\ominus}{C} - \overset{\oplus}{N} \equiv N$ or $\overset{H}{\underset{H}{>}}C = \overset{\oplus}{N} = \overset{..}{\underset{..}{N}}{}^{\ominus}$
          | H

Significance of the number of limiting forms

According to theory, the larger the number of reasonably stable limiting forms which can be written for a species, the higher its resonance energy. Bearing in mind that limiting forms represent possible (hypothetical) electron distributions, then the larger the number, the more extensive is delocalisation, and therefore the more stable the species.

Ethanamide is a resonance hybrid of two principal limiting forms

$$CH_3 - C \overset{\displaystyle \overset{..}{\underset{..}{O}}}{\underset{\displaystyle \underset{..}{NH_2}}{\diagdown}} \quad \text{and} \quad CH_3 - C \overset{\displaystyle \overset{..}{\underset{..}{O}}{}^{\ominus}}{\underset{\displaystyle \underset{\oplus}{NH_2}}{=}}$$

Exercise 2.3

A third limiting form can be written. Draw its structure and indicate why it is relatively unstable.

As there are only two limiting forms, and these are of unequal stability, the resonance energy of ethanamide is quite small. The classical limiting structure is a reasonable representation of the true structure, but δ+ and δ− signs should be employed to indicate the polar nature of the molecule.

In contrast with this, let us consider the structure of the carbonate anion, $CO_3{}^{2\ominus}$. The classical Lewis formula is but two other structures can be written, differing only by which of the two oxygen atoms is shown doubly bonded to the carbon atom

In resonance terms, then, the carbonate ion would be described as a mesomer or resonance hybrid of three equivalent limiting forms. Compared with ethanamide, the larger number of equally stable limiting forms means that the carbonate ion has a much higher resonance energy. It is much more stable than it would be if it had the structure of any one of the limiting forms. This comes about because in the real carbonate ion, two units of negative charge are shared by all three oxygen atoms. Each oxygen atom has two-thirds of a unit negative charge, and this is a much more stable arrangement than if two of the oxygen atoms each had to accommodate a whole unit of negative charge. 'Spreading the load' gives a lower-energy, more stable, structure. The usual way of representing the actual electron distribution by means of a single structural formula is like this

shows charge distribution

shows total negative charge is two units

Reference to the energy diagrams in figure 2.2 should make clear the difference in magnitude of resonance energy in the two species.

Figure 2.2 *Energy diagrams to illustrate resonance energy in ethanamide and the carbonate anion*

Some guidelines for writing limiting forms

1. When drawing limiting forms for a molecule or ion, begin by writing the classical Lewis structure. The other limiting forms can then be derived from this by changing positions of electron pairs.

2. Remember that only *electrons* are delocalised. Atoms must stay in their same relative positions.

3. Electrons may be displaced from a bonding position between two atoms on to one of the atoms where they become non-bonded electrons, for example

or alternatively, from a non-bonding position on one atom to a bonding position between it and an adjacent atom, where they become bonding pi electrons, for example

Displacement may also occur from one bonding position to a new bonding position with an adjacent atom, for example

4. An atom may be electron *deficient* (for example, a positively charged carbon atom has only six valence electrons), but structures must not be drawn in which an atom has *more* valence electrons than it can accommodate (that is, normally a complete octet).

5. Similarly, although the number of electron pair bonds may vary, the *total* number of valence electrons must not change.

6. The total charge must also remain constant. If, for example, the shift of a pair of electrons in a neutral molecule results in the development of a negative charge on an atom, then elsewhere in the structure another atom must have a compensating positive charge.

7. Limiting forms are separated on paper by double-headed arrows, $\longleftrightarrow$. Equilibrium signs, $\rightleftharpoons$ must *never* be used for this purpose.

8. Finally, when assessing the extent of delocalisation, keep in mind the following generalisations.

   (i) Highly unstable structures (which may happily be written on paper!) will represent very unlikely electron distributions, and should not therefore be considered.

   (ii) The more stable a particular limiting form, the greater its contribution to the mesomer (that is, the more closely it resembles the true structure).

   (iii) The larger the number of reasonably stable limiting forms which can be written, the more stable the mesomer, and the larger the resonance energy.

31

Choice of representations

In writing mechanistic equations, the valence bond representation of structures is normally the most convenient, and is the one we shall continue to use in this book. However, there is generally no need to draw all the limiting forms for a particular resonance structure. Indeed, to do so could be extremely tedious. Even the 'single formula' representation of a mesomer is usually too explicit and for most purposes the normal Lewis formula will suffice. Aldehydes and ketones, for example, are adequately represented by the classical Lewis structure, especially if the polar nature of the carbonyl group is indicated by the use of $\delta+$ and $\delta-$ signs. Keep in mind, though, that a given formula may be only one of several possible limiting forms for a resonance structure. With experience, you will readily recognise when this is the case, and be able, if required, to draw the various other limiting forms which together help to give a better picture of the true structure.

INDUCED POLARISATION

The inductive and mesomeric effects which we have been describing are *permanent* effects, which would exist even in an isolated molecule or ion, etc. As a result of their operation, the molecule may have a **permanent polarisation**. However, during the course of reaction, a further displacement of sigma or pi electrons may occur on close approach of an attacking reagent. For example, the inductive displacement of sigma electrons in the carbon–bromine bond of bromomethane will be increased on close approach to the carbon atom of a negatively charged hydroxide ion

$$\overset{\delta+}{CH_3} - \overset{\overset{..}{\delta-}}{\underset{..}{Br}} :$$

permanent polarisation
due to $-I$ effect of the
more electronegative
bromine atom

$$\overset{\ominus}{\underset{..}{H - O}} : \quad \overset{\delta+}{CH_3} \rightarrow\!\!\!\rightarrow \overset{\overset{..}{\delta-}}{\underset{..}{Br}} :$$

further displacement of
sigma electrons due to
electrostatic repulsion
by negatively charged
hydroxide ion

This is a *temporary* effect. If no reaction occurs, the hydroxide ion will move away and the haloalkane will revert to the normal polarisation. To distinguish it from the permanent effect, this temporary induced additional polarisation is referred to as an **inductomeric effect**.

Similar enhancement of the mesomeric effect, called an **electromeric effect**, is also possible. For example, as an attacking hydroxide ion gets near to the carbonyl carbon atom of a molecule such as ethanal, further displacement of both sigma and pi electrons may occur

| permanent polarisation resulting from $-I$ and $-M$ effects of the oxygen atom | further displacement of both sigma and pi electrons on close approach of a negatively charged hydroxide ion |

Since in reality temporary induced effects cannot be quantitatively distinguished from permanent effects, many chemists feel that the terms inductomeric and electromeric effects are of little practical value.

MANIFESTATIONS OF RESONANCE

Resonance has a profound effect both on the *physical properties* and *reactivity* of molecules. Many examples will be found throughout the text of the way in which resonance influences chemical behaviour, particularly the effect on the rate and course of a reaction, or the position of an equilibrium. The effect on various physical characteristics is often quoted as evidence for resonance, so we will conclude this chapter with a survey of some of these properties, beginning with methods for the determination of resonance energy.

Estimation of resonance energy

Two methods are employed, based on measurements of enthalpies of combustion, and where appropriate, enthalpies of hydrogenation.

1. *Enthalpies of combustion*

By making certain assumptions, it is possible to estimate the enthalpy of combustion of benzene on the basis of the Kekulé structure (that is, if benzene had the cyclohexatriene structure with three carbon–carbon sigma-bonds, three carbon–carbon sigma-bonds, three carbon–carbon pi-bonds and six carbon–hydrogen sigma-bonds). The predicted value is $-3450 \text{ kJ mol}^{-1}$, but when benzene is actually burnt, the observed value for ΔH is 150 kJ mol less than the calculated value

33

$$C_6H_{6\,(l)} + 7\tfrac{1}{2}O_{2\,(g)} \longrightarrow 6CO_{2\,(g)} + 3H_2O_{(l)}$$

$$\Delta H \text{ predicted} = -3450 \text{ kJ mol}^{-1}$$
$$\Delta H \text{ observed} = -3300 \text{ kJ mol}^{-1}$$

Now, if on combustion benzene *evolves* 150 kJ mol^{-1} less energy than calculated for the hypothetical cyclohexatriene, it must *contain* that much less energy. In other words, real benzene is 150 kJ mol^{-1} more stable than it would be if it had the Kekulé structure.

Similar data supports the postulated structure for ethanamide. The calculated enthalpy of combustion is -1318 kJ mol^{-1}, while the observed value is only -1272 kJ mol^{-1}. The difference, 46 kJ mol^{-1}, represents the resonance energy of ethanamide.

2. *Enthalpies of hydrogenation*

Hydrogenation, like combustion, is an exothermic process, and conversion of cyclohexene to cyclohexane liberates 120 kJ mol^{-1}. Thus if benzene simply had a cyclohexatriene structure, it would be reasonable to expect the enthalpy of hydrogenation to be three times that of cyclohexene, that is, -360 kJ mol^{-1}. However, when benzene is hydrogenated, the energy given out is only 210 kJ mol^{-1}. Again, the difference shows that benzene is about 150 kJ mol^{-1} more stable than it would be if it had the localised Kekulé structure. These differences can be shown graphically in the form of an energy diagram, figure 2.3.

Comparison of bond lengths

Bond lengths (internuclear distances) and bond angles can be determined with great precision by X-ray diffraction and electron diffraction methods. In the past, bond lengths were quoted in Ångström units (Å = 10^{-8} cm) and you will still find these units used in some textbooks. The relationship between Ångström units and SI units is as follows

$$\begin{aligned}
\text{Nanometre (nm)} &= 10^{-9} \text{ metre} \\
\text{Picometre (pm)} &= 10^{-12} \text{ metre} \\
\text{Ångström (Å)} &= 0.1 \text{ nm} \\
&= 100 \text{ pm}
\end{aligned}$$

Some useful bond lengths are given for reference in table 2.1.

Figure 2.3 *Energy diagram for enthalpies of hydrogenation of cyclohexene, hypothetical cyclohexatriene and benzene*

The type of bond (single, double, triple) is conveniently referred to as **bond order**. An ordinary single (sigma) bond is thus a **first order bond**, a double bond is **second order** and a triple bond is **third order**. Examination of the data in table 2.1 shows that for bonding between two atoms such as carbon and carbon, an increase in bond order is accompanied by a *decrease* in bond length

$$-\overset{|}{\underset{|}{C}}-\overset{|}{\underset{|}{C}}-\qquad >C=C<\qquad -C\equiv C-$$

154 pm   134 pm   121 pm

increase in bond order
decrease in bond length →

Similar observations are made for carbon–oxygen and carbon–nitrogen bonds.

35

Table 2.1 Some useful bondlengths (picometres)

Type of bond		Length (pm)
$-\overset{\displaystyle \mid}{\underset{\displaystyle \mid}{C}} - \overset{\displaystyle \mid}{\underset{\displaystyle \mid}{C}} -$	(alkanes)	154
$\diagup\!C = C\!\diagdown$	(alkenes)	134
$- C \equiv C -$	(alkynes)	121
$-\overset{\displaystyle \mid}{\underset{\displaystyle \mid}{C}} - O -$	(ethers)	143
$\diagup\!C = O$	(aldehydes and ketones)	122
$-\overset{\displaystyle \mid}{\underset{\displaystyle \mid}{C}} - N$	(aliphatic amines)	147
$\diagup\!C = N -$	(imines)	130
$- C \equiv N$	(nitriles)	116
$-\overset{\displaystyle \mid}{\underset{\displaystyle \mid}{C}} - Cl$	(chloro alkanes)	176

(a) Bond lengths in benzene
X-ray diffraction measurements on crystalline benzene (it does solidify when cooled!) show the molecule has a planar structure, and all the carbon–carbon distances are the same, namely 139 pm. If benzene was simply cyclohexatriene, we should expect two different bond lengths, 154 pm and 134 pm, for each of the three single and double bonds

cyclohexatriene   benzene

The fact that all the bonds are the same, and the bond length is intermediate between that of a single and double bond, is strong support for the postulated resonance structure.

(b) *Bond lengths in ethanamide*

The 'expected' and observed bond lengths in ethanamide are as follows

expected values in
classical structure

observed values in
the real structure

The carbon–oxygen bond is longer (128 pm) than a normal carbonyl double bond in an aldehyde or ketone (122 pm). This is consistent with the loss of pi electron density, resulting in a shift from a 'pure' double bond towards a single bond. We say that the carbonyl group has 'lost some **double bond character**'. Conversely, the carbon–nitrogen bond is a little shorter (138 pm) than in an aliphatic amine (147 pm), and has 'gained some double bond character'.

It should be noted that from a molecular orbital point of view, some change in bond lengths is to be expected whenever there is a change in the state of hybridisation of one or both of the bonded atoms. Consider, for example, the carbon–hydrogen bond in ethane, ethene and ethyne. The change in hybridisation of the carbon atom from sp^3 to sp^2 to sp is accompanied by a progressive shortening of the carbon–hydrogen bond lengths

37

The contribution from the 2s orbital in an sp^3 hybrid orbital is 25 per cent. This increases to 33 per cent in an sp^2 hybrid orbital and to 50 per cent in an sp hybrid orbital. Since a 2s orbital is smaller than a 2p orbital, a proportional increase in 's content' leads to a smaller, more compact hybrid atomic orbital. Consequently, overlap with a hydrogen 1s atomic orbital results in a slightly shorter bonding molecular orbital.

A similar argument is used to account for the observed reduction in carbon–carbon bond lengths in the following compounds

Interestingly, the same carbon–carbon distances are observed whether the multiply bonded carbon atom is linked to carbon, oxygen or nitrogen

$$: O = CH — CH_3 \qquad \ddot{N} \equiv C — CH_3$$
$$sp^2 \quad 150 \text{ pm} \qquad sp \quad 146 \text{ pm}$$

Exercise 2.4

Account for the observation that the carbon–nitrogen bond in urea (137 pm) is shorter than that in dimethylamine (147 pm)

$$\overset{137 \text{ pm}}{\ddot{N}H_2 — \ddot{C}O — \ddot{N}H_2} \qquad \overset{147 \text{ pm}}{CH_3 — \ddot{N}H — CH_3}$$

Electric dipole moments

Some care is needed in the interpretation of dipole moment data, but the following example illustrates the way in which such data can be used to support a proposed resonance structure.

Electric dipole moments in butanal and but-2-enal

Butanal has a polar carbonyl group, and the partial positive charge on the carbonyl carbon atom induces smaller positive charges on adjacent carbon atoms (−I effect). Although the molecule is constantly changing conformation, it is essentially linear in shape and there will be a resultant moment roughly in line with the carbon–carbon axis

$$CH_3 \overset{\delta\delta\delta+}{-} CH_2 \overset{\delta\delta+}{\rightarrowtail} CH_2 \overset{\delta+}{\rightarrowtail} CH \overset{\delta-}{=} \ddot{\underset{\cdot\cdot}{O}}$$

resultant moment

$$\mu = 8.91 \times 10^{-30} \text{ C m (2.70 D)}$$

In but-2-enal, the moment increases to 9.90×10^{-30} C m (3.0 D), and this is consistent with a mesomeric structure in which displacement of pi electrons in the carbonyl group is relayed to the adjacent alkene double bond

$$CH_3CH = CH - CH = \ddot{\underset{\cdot\cdot}{O}} \quad \leftrightarrow \quad CH_3\overset{\oplus}{CH} - CH = CH - \overset{\cdot\cdot}{\underset{\cdot\cdot}{O}}: ^\ominus$$

$$CH_3\overset{\delta+}{CH} \equiv\!\equiv CH \equiv\!\equiv CH \equiv\!\equiv \overset{\delta-}{\underset{\cdot\cdot}{O}}$$

greater charge
separation than in
butanal

Evidence from ultraviolet and infrared spectroscopy

Ultraviolet spectra

Absorption of radiation from the ultraviolet region of the electromagnetic spectrum involves the 'promotion' of electrons from their low-energy groundstates to higher-energy 'excited' states. Such a process is called an **electronic transition**. The position and intensity of energy absorption is related to the ease with which such transitions can occur. Very high energy is required for the promotion of sigma electrons, and this may be accompanied by bond fission. The more mobile pi electrons are less tightly held, and excitation of these requires absorption of energy from the instrumentally more accessible region of the ultraviolet spectrum between about 185 nm and 400 nm wavelength. Excitation of pi electrons in the carbonyl group of a molecule such as propanal (known as a $\pi \rightarrow \pi^*$ ('pi to pi starred') transition) occurs at about 188 nm. This is normally expressed as $\lambda_{max} = 188$ nm, where λ_{max} ('lambda max') is the wavelength of maximum absorption.

When the carbonyl group is conjugated with an alkene double bond, as in propenal, absorption *shifts to longer wavelength*, λ_{max} = 217 nm. Delocalisation of pi electrons means that they are held a little less tightly, and so slightly less energy is required for their excitation. Absorption is also *more intense.*

With more extensive conjugation, each additional double bond shifts the position of maximum absorption to longer and longer wavelength. Eventually, the compound absorbs in the visible region (about 400–750 nm) and so becomes coloured. An interesting example is the molecule of β-carotene, whose structure has 11 conjugated double bonds

This compound has a very intense absorption at λ_{max} = 450 nm and is responsible for the orange colour of carrots.

Infrared spectra
The individual atoms in a molecule are not still, but are in a constant state of vibration. This results in stretching, twisting and bending motions in the constituent bonds. Absorption of energy from the infrared region of the electromagnetic spectrum causes an *increase in the amplitude* of these vibrations. For example, butanal shows a strong absorption at λ_{max} = 1735 cm^{-1}, which corresponds to the stretching vibration ($>C = O_{str}$) of the carbonyl group. (Spectroscopists find it convenient to express the position of absorption in terms of **wavenumbers**, cm^{-1}, which are reciprocal wavelengths, $1/\lambda$. Wavenumbers are directly proportional to frequency, and inversely proportional to wavelength. Thus, a decrease in wavenumber means a change to longer wavelength, that is, lower energy.)

When, as in but-2-enal, the carbonyl group is conjugated with an alkene double bond, the carbonyl stretching frequency shifts to λ_{max} = 1637 cm^{-1}, and is more intense. With both ultraviolet and infrared spectra, then, *conjugation leads to more intense absorption at longer wavelength.*

3 Classification of Reactions and Reagents

ANNOTATED EQUATIONS AND CLASSIFICATION OF REACTIONS

When iodoethane is warmed with aqueous sodium hydroxide solution, the main product is ethanol. The reaction may be summarised in equation form as

$$\overset{\ominus}{\text{HO}\!:} \ + \ CH_3CH_2\overset{..}{\underset{..}{I}}\!: \ \longrightarrow \ CH_3CH_2\overset{..}{O}H \ + \ :\overset{..}{\underset{..}{I}}\!:^{\ominus}$$

$$\text{reactants} \qquad\qquad \text{products}$$

The molecule attacked, iodoethane, is referred to as the **substrate**, and the species doing the attacking, the hydroxide ion, is called the **attacking reagent**. Sodium ions are also present, but since they are not directly involved in the reaction, they are often called **spectator ions**, and are normally omitted from the equation.

Equations summarising organic reactions are usually written with an arrow ($\longrightarrow$) rather than equilibrium signs ($\rightleftharpoons$). The arrow indicates the direction of reaction and implies that equilibrium lies well to the right. Conversely, the symbol $\nrightarrow$ means that no appreciable reaction occurs under the given conditions.

Frequently, reaction conditions such as temperature, solvent, catalyst, etc., are shown above and below the arrow. Application of heat is indicated by stating the temperature, by the word **reflux**, or by the use of the symbol Δ. Oxidation by an unspecified agent is shown as [O], and reduction likewise by [H]. An equation labelled in this way is called an **annotated equation.** For the above reaction, the annotation might be

$$\overset{..}{\underset{..}{\text{HO}}}\!:^{\ominus} + \ CH_3CH_2\overset{..}{\underset{..}{I}}\!: \ \xrightarrow[\text{50°C (323K)}]{\text{dil. aq. NaOH}} \ CH_3CH_2\overset{..}{O}H \ + \ :\overset{..}{\underset{..}{I}}\!:^{\ominus}$$

In the iodoethane substrate, the reactive **functional group** is the iodine atom, and in the product ethanol this has been replaced by a new functional group, the hydroxyl group. The iodide ion is therefore called the **displaced group**, and the overall reaction is a **displacement reaction**, or a **substitution reaction**. This particular example, involving replacement of the halogen atom by a hydroxyl group, is called **hydrolysis**.

Although ethanol is the **main product** of this reaction, its formation is always accompanied by the production of a small amount of ethene

$$\overset{..}{\underset{..}{HO}} : \overset{\ominus}{} \ + \ CH_3CH_2 \overset{..}{\underset{..}{I}} : \ \longrightarrow \ CH_2 = CH_2 \ + \ H_2\overset{..}{\underset{}{O}} \ + \ : \overset{..}{\underset{..}{I}} : \overset{\ominus}{}$$

Ethene formed in this reaction is a **by-product** and is said to be produced by a **side reaction**. In some reactions there may be more than one by-product, and the removal of such by-products is an essential part of the purification of the main product. Overall, then, we have

$$\left.\begin{matrix} \text{substrate} \\ + \\ \text{attacking} \\ \text{reagent} \end{matrix}\right\} \ \text{reactants} \ \longrightarrow \ \text{products} \ \left\{\begin{matrix} \text{main product} \\ + \\ \text{by-product(s)} \end{matrix}\right.$$

Many reactions occur in a series of steps, involving the formation of relatively unstable **intermediates** which subsequently further react to give the final products (and by-products). In the side reaction referred to above, involving the formation of ethene, $H^{\oplus}$ and $: \overset{..}{\underset{..}{I}} : ^{\ominus}$ are removed from the substrate without being replaced by other ions or molecules. The process is therefore called an **elimination reaction**.

Under different conditions, it is possible to reverse the above process and add a molecule of hydrogen iodide to a molecule of ethene, forming a molecule of iodoethane

$$CH_2 = CH_2 \ + \ H\overset{..}{\underset{..}{I}} : \ \longrightarrow \ CH_3CH_2 \overset{..}{\underset{..}{I}} :$$

This is called an **addition reaction**.

Sometimes, during the course of a reaction there may be a change in the arrangement of atoms in the carbon skeleton of the substrate molecule, or a newly introduced functional group may occupy a different position in the product molecule. An example is hydrolysis of 1-bromo-2,2-dimethyl-propane (neopentyl bromide), where the main product is not the expected 2,2-dimethylpropanol, but 2-methylbutan-2-ol

This kind of reaction, involving a change in molecular structure in the product, is called a **rearrangement reaction**. Sometimes an initial rearrangement may be followed by further substitution, elimination or addition steps, giving rise to more stable final products.

The whole range of organic processes, including esterification, condensation, polymerisation, cyclisation, oxidation and reduction, etc., can be classified in terms of the four basic reactions. More than one of these may be involved in a particular process; for example, condensation may require both addition and elimination steps.

Exercise 3.1

For the following processes, (1) state which species is the attacking reagent and which the substrate, and (2) classify each reaction as substitution, addition, etc.

(a) $CH_3CH_2Br : + CH_3\ddot{O} :^{\ominus}$ $\longrightarrow$ $CH_3CH_2\ddot{O}CH_3 + : \ddot{Br} :^{\ominus}$

(b) $CH_3CH_2\ddot{I} : + CH_3CH_2\ddot{O} :^{\ominus}$ $\longrightarrow$ $CH_3CH_2\ddot{O}H + CH_3CH = CH_2 + : \ddot{I} :$

(c) $CH_3\ddot{O}H + CH_3C\ddot{O}CH_3$ $\longrightarrow$

(d) $(CH_3)_3C\ddot{O} :^{\ominus} + CH_3C\ddot{O}\ddot{O}CH_3$ $\longrightarrow$ $CH_3C\ddot{O}\ddot{O}C(CH_3)_3 + CH_3\ddot{O} :^{\ominus}$

CLASSIFICATION OF REAGENTS

All organic reactions involve breaking and reformation of covalent bonds. For example, in the substitution reaction

$$\overset{..}{HO}\!: {}^\ominus + CH_2CH_2\overset{..}{I}\!: \longrightarrow CH_3CH_2\overset{..}{O}H + :\overset{..}{\underset{..}{I}}\!:{}^\ominus$$

the bond between the carbon and iodine atoms has to be broken and a new bond formed between the carbon and oxygen atoms in the product. In principle, there are two ways in which a covalent bond between two atoms X and Y could be broken, depending on the relative electronegativities of X and Y

$$X:Y \quad \begin{array}{l} \longrightarrow X^\oplus + \overset{..}{Y}{}^\ominus \quad (or \; \overset{..}{X}{}^\ominus + \overset{\oplus}{Y}) \\ \longrightarrow X^{\textstyle\cdot} + Y^{\textstyle\cdot} \end{array}$$

In the first process, the covalent bond is cleaved in such a way that both electrons go to one or other of the two bonded atoms. This is called **heterolysis** (= uneven splitting). If Y is the more electronegative atom, then *it* receives both electrons to form an **anion**, $\overset{..}{Y}{}^\ominus$, leaving the other atom as a positively charged **cation**, $X^\oplus$. When X is more electronegative than Y, displacement of the electron pair occurs in the opposite direction to give the ions $\overset{..}{X}{}^\ominus$ and $Y^\oplus$.

In the alternative process, the two atoms X and Y are of comparable electronegativity. They each receive one electron from the bonding pair to produce two neutral species, X˙ and Y˙, each with an unpaired electron. Such species are called **free radicals**, and are formed by **homolysis** (= even splitting) of a covalent bond.

In representing the process of heterolysis on paper, movement of electron pairs is indicated by means of a symbol widely known as a **curved** (or **curly**) **arrow**. These should be carefully drawn so that the *tail* of the arrow clearly shows where the electrons *come from*, and the *head* of the arrow indicates the position *to which the electrons are displaced*

$$X\frown Y \longrightarrow X^\oplus + \overset{..}{Y}{}^\ominus$$

Make particular note of why it is that the movement of a *pair* of electrons results in the formation of *single* positive and negative charges. In the original sigma-bond, each atom has a half share of the electron pair. Thus, during heterolysis, Y actually receives only one additional electron, giving it one unit of negative charge. Similarly, X only loses one electron (half a shared pair) and so acquires one unit of positive charge.

Curved arrows should only be used to show *movement of electrons.* Recombination of the ions $X^{\oplus}$ and $\overset{..}{Y}{}^{\ominus}$ would be represented as

$$\overset{\ominus}{\underset{Y}{\overset{..}{}}} \quad X^{\oplus} \quad \longrightarrow \quad Y-X$$

and *not* as

$$\overset{\ominus}{\underset{Y}{}} \quad X^{\oplus} \quad \text{or} \quad \left(X^{\oplus}\right) \rightarrow \overset{..}{Y}{}^{\ominus}$$

Movement of individual electrons in homolytic displacements is indicated by the use of **half-headed curved arrows**

$$Y \!-\! X \quad \longrightarrow \quad Y^{\cdot} + X^{\cdot}$$

Reactions in which bonds are broken and formed homolytically are called **radical reactions.** When heterolysis is involved, the process is described as an **ionic reaction.** Radical reactions may occur in the gas phase or in solution; ionic reactions normally are only carried out in solution, where they may be markedly influenced by the nature of the solvent.

In the process

$$\overset{\ominus}{\underset{Y}{\overset{..}{}}} \quad X^{\oplus} \quad \longrightarrow \quad Y-X$$

the anion $\overset{..}{Y}{}^{\ominus}$ reacts by donating an electron pair to the cation $X^{\oplus}$. Such electron-donating species are known as **nucleophiles** or **nucleophilic reagents.** A nucleophile may be defined as *a species one of whose atoms contains an electron pair which can be donated to form a sigma-bond with another species.* It follows that a nucleophile is also a Lewis base. In organic reactions, the recipient of the electron pair is normally a carbon atom, and *a species which reacts by receiving an electron pair from a nucleophile* is known as an **electrophile** or **electrophilic reagent.** As electron acceptors, electrophiles are also Lewis acids.

Nucleophiles are frequently negatively charged anions, but they may also be neutral molecules one of whose atoms has an unshared electron pair. For example, $H\overset{..}{O}:^{\ominus}$ and $H_2\overset{..}{\underset{..}{O}}$ are both nucleophilic, but the negatively charged hydroxide ion is a stronger nucleophile than the neutral water molecule. Note that not all anions are necessarily nucleophilic, however. The anion $\overset{..}{\underset{..}{B}F}:_4{}^{\ominus}$ exhibits little, if any, nucleophilic character.

Alkenes, alkynes and aromatic nuclei are all nucleophilic*: they all contain multiple bonds from which pi electron pairs can be donated to form sigma-bonds with electrophiles. Many, but not all, electrophiles are cations. A few electrophiles are polar molecules with an electron-deficient centre, for example, bromic (I) acid

$$\overset{\delta-}{\underset{..}{\overset{..}{H}O}} \leftarrow \overset{\delta+}{\underset{..}{\overset{..}{B}r}}: \underset{\text{deficient, that is, electrophilic}}{\overset{\text{bromine atom is electron}}{\rule{3cm}{0pt}}}$$

Some non-polar, but polarisable molecules such as $\overset{..}{\underset{..}{B}r}:_2$ may generate an electrophilic centre as the result of temporary induced polarisation on close approach to a region of high electron density in a substrate molecule

pi-bond in the alkene is a region of high electron density

$$\begin{array}{c} H \quad H \\ \diagdown \diagup \\ C \\ \| \\ C \\ \diagup \diagdown \\ H \quad H \end{array} \quad \overset{\delta+}{:\overset{..}{\underset{..}{B}r}} \rightarrow \overset{\delta-}{\overset{..}{\underset{..}{B}r}}:$$

electrons in the sigma-bond are repelled by the pi electrons, and the bromine atom nearest the double bond becomes electron deficient

Similar polarisation may result from coordination of a bromine molecule with a Lewis acid — see chapter 10, bromination of benzene.

Characteristics of nucleophiles and electrophiles, together with some representative examples are given in table 3.1.

In the hydrolysis reaction considered earlier

$$H\overset{..}{O}:^{\ominus} + CH_3CH_2 - \overset{..}{\underset{..}{I}}: \longrightarrow CH_3CH_2 - \overset{..}{\underset{..}{O}}H + :\overset{..}{\underset{..}{I}}:^{\ominus}$$

*Molecules such as these, and indeed all nucleophiles are frequently described as 'electron rich' species. This term is best avoided as it somehow implies that the molecule has an *excess* of electrons.

Table 3.1 Some nucleophiles and electrophiles

Nucleophiles	Electrophiles
Species which react by donating an electron pair to form a bond	Species which react by receiving an electron pair from a nucleophile
Anions or **neutral molecules** having an atom with an unshared electron pair or **molecules** with **multiple bonds**	**Cations** or **polar molecules** with an electron-deficient centre, or **polarisable molecules** which can develop such a centre

Examples include

$\overset{..}{H\overset{..}{O}} {:}^{\ominus},\ R\overset{..}{O}{:}^{\ominus}$
(hydroxide and alkoxide ions)

$H^{\oplus},\ R^{\oplus}$
(protons, carbocations)

$H_2\overset{..}{\underset{..}{O}},\ R\overset{..}{\underset{..}{O}}H$
(water, alcohols)

$:\overset{..}{\underset{..}{Cl}}{}^{\oplus},\ :\overset{..}{\underset{..}{Br}}{}^{\oplus},\ :\overset{..}{I}{}^{\oplus}$
(halogen cations)

$\overset{..}{\underset{..}{N}}H_2^{\ominus},\ R\overset{..}{\underset{..}{N}}H^{\ominus}$
(amide ions)

$\overset{..\ \delta-}{HO} \longleftarrow \overset{..\ \delta+}{Cl}:$
(chloric(I) acid)

$\overset{..}{N}H_3,\ R\overset{..}{N}H_2$
(ammonia, amines)

$:\overset{..\ \delta+}{Br} \longrightarrow \overset{..\ \delta-}{Br}:$
(polarised bromine molecule)

$:\overset{..}{\underset{..}{Cl}}{:}^{\ominus},\ :\overset{..}{\underset{..}{Br}}{:}^{\ominus},\ :\overset{..}{I}{:}^{\ominus}$
(halide ions)

$ArN_2^{\oplus}$
(diazonium cations)

$\overset{....}{C}N^{\ominus}$
(cyanide ion)

$NO_2^{\oplus}$
(nitryl cation)

alkenes, alkynes, benzene

$NO^{\oplus}$
(nitrosyl cation)

the attacking reagent is a nucleophile, and so the reaction is classified as **nucleophilic substitution**. As we shall see later, *all simple ionic reactions involve both a nucleophile and an electrophile.* Whether a particular reaction is described as electrophilic or nucleophilic depends on which of the species involved is regarded as the attacking reagent, and which the substrate.

Exercise 3.2

Decide whether each of the following species could behave as (1) an electrophile, (2) a nucleophile (3) both, or (d) neither.

(a) $CH_2 = C \big\langle{}^{CH_3}_{CH_3}$ (b) $CH_3 - CH \big\langle{}^{CH_3}_{CH_3}$ (c) $CH_3 - \overset{\oplus}{C} \big\langle{}^{CH_3}_{CH_3}$ (d) $CH_3 - \overset{\ominus}{\underset{..}{C}} \big\langle{}^{CH_3}_{CH_3}$

(e) $\overset{H}{\underset{H}{\big\rangle}} C = \overset{..}{\underset{..}{O}}$ (f) $CH_3 - \overset{\oplus}{\underset{..}{N}} \equiv \overset{..}{N}$ (g) $\overset{..}{\underset{..}{O}} = \overset{\oplus}{N} = \overset{..}{\underset{..}{O}}$ (h) $CH_3C \equiv \overset{..}{N}$

STRUCTURE AND TERMINOLOGY OF SOME COMMON ORGANIC INTERMEDIATES

For a hypothetical derivative of methane, $CH_3 - X$, the following dissociations are theoretically possible

(1) *Heterolysis*

$$CH_3 \overset{\frown}{-} X \quad CH_3^{\oplus} + \overset{..}{X}{}^{\ominus}$$

$$\text{or} \quad CH_3 \overset{\frown}{-} X \quad \overset{..}{C}H_3{}^{\ominus} + X^{\oplus}$$

and (2) *Homolysis*

$$\overset{\frown}{C}H_3 \overset{\frown}{-} X \quad \dot{C}H_3 + \dot{X}$$

Note carefully the structures of the three species $\overset{\oplus}{C}H_3$, $\overset{..}{C}H_3{}^{\ominus}$, and $\dot{C}H_3$. Organic cations such as $\overset{\oplus}{C}H_3$, $CH_3CH_2^{\oplus}$, etc., have for a long time been called **carbonium ions**, and this term is still commonly used. However, it is not considered systematic, as in these ions the positively charged carbon atom has only six electrons in the outer (valence) shell

$$
\begin{array}{ccc}
\text{H} & & \text{H} \\
\text{H} : \ddot{\text{C}} : \text{X} & \longrightarrow & \text{H} : \ddot{\text{C}}^{\oplus} + \ddot{\text{X}}^{\ominus} \\
\text{H} & & \text{H}
\end{array}
$$

six valence electrons
in three sigma-bonds

In analogous inorganic 'onium' ions such as hydroxonium, $H_3\overset{\oplus}{\ddot{O}}$, and ammonium, $\overset{\oplus}{N}H_4$, the positively charged oxygen and nitrogen atoms each have a complete octet of valence electrons

$$
\begin{array}{cc}
\text{H} & \text{H} \\
\text{H} : \ddot{\text{O}} :^{\oplus} & \text{H} : \ddot{\text{N}} :^{\oplus} \text{H} \\
\text{H} & \text{H}
\end{array}
$$

complete octets

Thus for positively charged carbon ions, the term **carbocation** is to be preferred, and is the one which we shall use in this book. Carbocations have a *planar* structure. The carbon atom bearing the positive charge is sp^2-hybridised and able to form three coplanar sigma-bonds at $\sim 120°$ to one another. The 'spare' $2p$ atomic orbital lies at right angles to the plane of these three bonds, and it is this vacant $2p$ orbital which receives an electron pair when a carbocation reacts with a nucleophile.

vacant $2p$ atomic orbital

The methyl **carbanion** has a complete octet, and is *tetrahedral* in structure. The sp^3-hybridised carbon atom forms three sigma-bonds with hydrogen atoms, and the non-bonded electron pair is contained in the fourth sp^3 orbital

sp³ hybrid atomic orbital
with an electron pair

Physical measurements indicate a structure for the methyl **free radical** in which the sp^2-hybridised carbon atom forms three *coplanar* sigma-bonds with hydrogen atoms, and the unshared ('odd') electron is contained in the 'spare' $2p$ orbital

$2p$ atomic orbital with
an unpaired electron

However, it appears that some organic free radicals may have a shallow pyramidal structure, in which the carbon atom bearing the odd electron is in an intermediate state of hybridisation between sp^2 and sp^3. Exceptionally, the trifluoromethyl free radical $\overset{..}{\underset{..}{C}F}:_3$ is tetrahedral in shape.

STABILITY OF INTERMEDIATES

The methyl carbocation is the least stable of such ions, one carbon atom having to sustain the whole positive charge. Replacement of hydrogen atoms by alkyl groups helps to partially dissipate the positive charge, and so stability increases in the series

(methyl)　　　　(1°)　　　　(2°)　　　　(3°)

This increase in stability is most simply attributed to **inductive stabilisation** by the alkyl groups. The carbon atom bearing the unpaired electron in alkyl free radicals is also electron deficient, and the order of stability follows the same pattern, methyl $< 1° < 2° < 3°$. Alkyl carbanions show less variation in stability.

50

When the atom carrying the positive or negative charge, or the unpaired electron, is conjugated with an alkene double bond (or an aromatic nucleus), delocalisation leads to a more stable structure. Such **resonance stabilisation** is more effective than inductive stabilisation. Thus for carbocations and free radicals, the overall order of increasing stability is

$$\text{methyl} < 1° < 2° < 3° < \text{allyl, benzyl}$$

and for carbanions

$$\text{alkyl} < \text{allyl, benzyl}$$

See chapter 2 for details of the resonance structures.

MECHANISTIC EQUATIONS

Hydrolysis of iodoethane involves replacing a carbon-iodine bond with a carbon-oxygen bond, and the electron pair for this new bond is supplied by the attacking hydroxide ion. However, although the α-carbon atom is electron deficient, it does have a complete octet, and can only receive electrons from the hydroxide ion if at the same time it releases an electron pair to the departing iodine atom

Formulations like this, in which curved arrows are used to show electron movements during the course of a reaction or one step in a reaction, are called **mechanistic equations**.

In writing such equations, try to arrange the reactants so that electron movements (and hence curved arrows) always flow from left to right. This may sometimes require structures to be drawn 'back to front', and molecular shapes to be simplified, but you will find that the resulting gain in neatness and uniformity is a great help in understanding and memorising mechanisms.

Mechanistic equations are a useful way of summarising the pathway of a particular reaction, but they also highlight the mechanistic similarities between apparently diverse reactions. For example, neutralisation of ethanoic acid with sodium hydroxide solution

$$CH_3COOH + Na^{\oplus} : OH^{\ominus} \longrightarrow CH_3COO^{\ominus} Na^{\oplus} + H_2O$$

might at first appear to be quite different from the nucleophilic displacement reaction of iodoethane with hydroxide ion. But if we look at the electron movements involved, we can see that the two processes are mechanistically very similar

| attacking nucleophile | electrophilic substrate | | product | displaced group (by-product) |

| attacking base (nucleophile) | acidic substrate (electrophile) | | 'product' | displaced group 'by-product' |

The only real difference is one of terminology. When the hydroxide ion attacks carbon it is described as a nucleophile. When the electrophilic centre is hydrogen rather than carbon, the hydroxide ion is a base. But there is no difference in principle between the two processes.

Although we tend to think of organic reactions as quite different from those we study in inorganic chemistry, the similarity between the above processes and neutralisation of an inorganic acid by a base is apparent from the equation

base	acid
= electron donor	= electron receiver
≡ a nucleophile	≡ an electrophile

As you know, the reaction is more complicated than this. In an aqueous solution of hydrogen bromide, most of the molecules dissociate in a preliminary acid–base reaction

$$H_2\ddot{O} \quad H - \ddot{Br}: \qquad H_2\overset{\oplus}{O} - H + :\ddot{Br}:^{\ominus}$$

Neutralisation of this solution with aqueous sodium hydroxide solution involves reaction between hydroxide and hydroxonium ions

$$H\ddot{O}:^{\ominus} \quad H - \overset{\oplus}{O}H_2 \quad \rightleftharpoons \quad H\ddot{O} - H + \ddot{O}H_2$$

Proton transfer is common in organic reactions, and many processes are acid or base catalysed. The usual role of an acid catalyst is to protonate some atom (such as oxygen or nitrogen) in the substrate molecule, whereas a base catalyst frequently initiates reaction by removing a proton from the substrate molecule.

You might find it helpful to summarise each of the mechanisms that you study in terms of the nucleophile–electrophile interactions involved. The examples set out in table 3.2 show how this can be done. Many of the equations shown may be unfamiliar to you at this stage, but you can refer back to the table as you study each new reaction.

Table 3.2 Summary equations for some characteristic ionic reaction mechanisms, arranged so as to emphasise the nucleophile–electrophile interaction in each step (N = nucleophilic species, E = electrophilic species)

Type of reaction	N E	Product(s)
Nucleophilic substitution	$-\overset{|}{\underset{|}{C}} - X \quad \rightleftharpoons$	$-\overset{|}{\underset{|}{C}} + \ddot{X}^{\ominus}$
(1) *unimolecular*	$^{\ominus}\ddot{Y} \quad \overset{|}{\underset{|}{C}}{}^{\oplus} - \quad \longrightarrow$	$Y - \overset{|}{\underset{|}{C}} -$
(2) *bimolecular*	$^{\ominus}\ddot{Y} \quad \overset{|}{\underset{|}{C}} - X \quad \longrightarrow$	$Y - \overset{|}{\underset{|}{C}} - + \ddot{X}^{\ominus}$
Elimination (1) *unimolecular*	$-\overset{H}{\underset{|}{\overset{|}{C}}} - \overset{|}{\underset{|}{C}} - X \quad \underset{\rightleftharpoons}{slow}$	$-\overset{H}{\underset{|}{\overset{|}{C}}} - \overset{|}{\underset{|}{C}}{}^{\oplus} + \ddot{X}^{\ominus}$

Type of reaction	N E	Product(s)

$$\overset{\ominus}{Y}\!:\!\curvearrowright \overset{H}{\underset{-C \overset{\curvearrowleft}{-} C^{\oplus}}{\Big|}} \longrightarrow \begin{array}{l} Y-H \\ + \quad \Big\rangle C = C \Big\langle \end{array}$$

(2) bimolecular

$$\overset{\ominus}{Y}\!:\!\curvearrowright \underset{X}{\overset{H}{\underset{-C \overset{\curvearrowleft}{-} C-}{\Big|}}} \longrightarrow \begin{array}{l} Y-H \\ + \quad \Big\rangle C = C \Big\langle \\ + \; \ddot{X}^{\ominus} \end{array}$$

Nucleophilic addition

$$\overset{\ominus}{Y}\!:\!\curvearrowright \Big\rangle C \overset{\curvearrowleft}{=} \ddot{O}\!: \overset{slow}{\rightleftharpoons} Y-\overset{|}{\underset{|}{C}}-\ddot{\underset{..}{O}}\!:^{\ominus}$$

(addition may be completed by protonation of $-\ddot{\underset{..}{O}}\!:^{\ominus}$ and/or may be followed by elimination)

Electrophilic addition

$$\Big\rangle C \overset{\curvearrowright}{=} C \Big\langle \quad X \overset{\curvearrowleft}{-} \ddot{Y} \overset{slow}{\longrightarrow} \Big\rangle \overset{\oplus}{C} - \overset{|}{\underset{|}{C}} - X + \ddot{Y}^{\ominus}$$

(essentially a nucleophilic displacement reaction)

$$\overset{\ominus}{Y}\!:\!\curvearrowright \Big\rangle \overset{\oplus}{C} - \overset{|}{\underset{|}{C}} - X \longrightarrow Y - \overset{|}{\underset{|}{C}} - \overset{|}{\underset{|}{C}} - X$$

Electrophilic substitution

(benzene ring) $\curvearrowright E^{\oplus} \longrightarrow$ (cyclohexadienyl cation with $\overset{\oplus}{}$, E, H)

$\overset{\ominus}{Y}\!:\!\curvearrowright$ (cyclohexadienyl cation with E, H, $\oplus$) $\longrightarrow Y-H +$ (substituted benzene with E)

54

Proton transfers which accompany many of the processes shown in table 3.2 are essentially nucleophilic substitution reactions, for example

$$
R - \underset{\substack{\|\\ :O:}}{C} - {}^{\ominus}\ddot{O}: \quad H - \overset{\oplus}{N}H_3 \quad \rightleftharpoons \quad R - \underset{\substack{\|\\ :O:}}{C} - \ddot{O}H \ + \ \ddot{N}H_3
$$

$$
\quad\quad\quad (N) \quad\quad (E)
$$

You will find that you can fit various other reactions into the same scheme. For example, in the reduction of carbonyl compounds with hydride ion, the nucleophile supplies an electron pair from the metal-hydrogen bond, while in the electrophile, a pair of pi electrons is transferred from the carbonyl double bond into a non-bonding position on the oxygen atom. The parallel in electron movements with those shown in table 3.2 is obvious

$$
\underset{\substack{|\\ H}}{\overset{\substack{H\\ |}}{H - \overset{\ominus}{Al}}} - H \quad \underset{\substack{|\\ CH_3}}{\overset{\substack{CH_3\\ |}}{C}} = \ddot{O}: \quad \longrightarrow \quad \underset{\substack{|\\ H}}{\overset{\substack{H\\ |}}{H - Al}} \ + \ H - \underset{\substack{|\\ CH_3}}{\overset{\substack{CH_3\\ |}}{C}} - \ddot{O}:^{\ominus}
$$

Of course, the equations in table 3.2, however useful as an *aide-mémoire*, are only a *summary* of the electron transfers necessary to change the structure of the reactants to that of the products. As you expand your knowledge of mechanistic chemistry, so you will be able to supplement such equations with more and more detail about the timing of the electron movements, the spacial arrangement of the various species, the role of the solvent, and the effects of changes in structure, etc. We shall discuss many of these factors in the following chapters.

THE USE OF PARTIAL STRUCTURES IN MECHANISTIC EQUATIONS

A specific reaction such as the oxidation of propan-2-ol to propanone by heating with dilute aqueous alkaline potassium manganate (VII) might be formulated in the following way

$$\underset{\substack{\text{specific} \\ \text{substrate}}}{\underset{CH_3}{\overset{CH_3}{\diagdown}}CHOH} \quad \xrightarrow[\substack{60°C\ (333K) \\ \text{specific} \\ \text{reaction} \\ \text{conditions}}]{KMnO_4,\ HO^{\ominus}} \quad \underset{\substack{\text{specific} \\ \text{product}}}{\underset{CH_3}{\overset{CH_3}{\diagdown}}C=\overset{\cdot\cdot}{\underset{\cdot\cdot}{O}}}$$

However, many other oxidising agents achieve the same result, so a less specific formulation is sometimes more useful

$$\underset{CH_3}{\overset{CH_3}{\diagdown}}CHOH \quad \xrightarrow[\Delta]{[O]} \quad \underset{CH_3}{\overset{CH_3}{\diagdown}}C=\overset{\cdot\cdot}{\underset{\cdot\cdot}{O}}$$

oxidation by
heating with an
unspecified reagent

Since most secondary alcohols are similarly oxidised, a **general equation** for the reaction can be written

$$\underset{\substack{\text{any }2°\text{ alcohol}}}{\overset{R}{\underset{R'}{\diagdown}}CHOH} \quad \xrightarrow[\Delta]{[O]} \quad \underset{\substack{\text{corresponding} \\ \text{ketone}}}{\overset{R}{\underset{R'}{\diagdown}}C=\overset{\cdot\cdot}{\underset{\cdot\cdot}{O}}}$$

R and R' are alkyl groups which may be the same or different. The only part of the molecule directly involved in the reaction is the $\diagup\!\!\!\!\overset{}{C}H - \overset{\cdot\cdot}{O}H$ group, so we may further generalise the equation by using **partial structures**, that is, by showing only that part of the structure actually involved in the reaction

$$\diagup\!\!\!\!CH - \overset{\cdot\cdot}{\underset{\cdot\cdot}{O}}H \quad \xrightarrow[\Delta]{[O]} \quad \diagup\!\!\!\!C=\overset{\cdot\cdot}{\underset{\cdot\cdot}{O}}$$

We now have the general statement that a primary or secondary alcohol group can be oxidised to a carbonyl group. Details of reagents and conditions employed will vary with the nature of the alcohol, but the general statement will be true for all primary and secondary alcohols, including structures such as cyclohexanol

Some care is necessary when using partial structures to ensure that normal valence requirements are satisfied. Structures with trivalent or pentavalent carbon atoms are not allowed! Partial structures are particularly useful when discussing the chemistry of complex molecules where it would be inconvenient (and unnecessary) to write out the whole structure each time. For example, one step in the synthesis of the sex hormone estrone involves dehydration of an allylic alcohol

The use of partial structures both simplifies the representation and draws attention to the particular operation involved

By including the numbering, the partial structure is readily related to the full molecular formula.

Exercise 3.3
Use partial structures to simplify and generalise the structural changes occuring in the following equilibrium

57

4 Organic Acids and Bases

SOME GENERAL CONCEPTS

You will be familiar with the simple Brönsted–Lowry definition of acids and bases. An **acid** is a *substance which can donate a proton*, and a **base** is a *substance which can accept a proton*. Thus, when hydrogen chloride dissolves in water, an HCl molecule acts as an acid and donates a proton to a water molecule functioning as a base

$$ HCl + H_2O \rightleftharpoons \ :Cl:^{\ominus} + H_2O - H $$

Organic carboxylic acids react in a similar way

$$ R - C - OH + H_2O \rightleftharpoons R - C - O:^{\ominus} + H_2O - H $$

However, many acid-base equilibria do not involve the transfer of a proton, and for this reason a more general concept of an acid and a base was proposed by Lewis. In the above equilibria, the water molecule accepts a proton by *donating an electron pair* to form a sigma-bond

$$ H_2O \ \ H - Cl: \rightleftharpoons H_2O^{\oplus} - H + :Cl:^{\ominus} $$

$$ H_2O \ \ H - O - C - R \rightleftharpoons H_2O^{\oplus} - H + :O - C - R $$

Thus the Lewis definition of a base is a *substance which can donate an electron pair*. It follows that a Lewis acid is a *substance which can accept an electron pair*. In order that an HCl: (or RCOOH) molecule can donate a proton, it must receive an electron pair from a water molecule, so a Brönsted acid is also covered by the Lewis definition.

In organic chemistry, some of the most important Lewis acids are anhydrous metallic salts such as FeBr:₃ and AlCl:₃ which are used as catalysts in aromatic electrophilic substitution, and other reactions. The transition metal atoms have unfilled electron shells capable of accepting an electron pair. Iron(III) bromide, for example, forms a **complex** with bromine which involves polarisation or even complete ionisation of the bromine molecule

:Br : Br :   FeBr:₃   ⇌   :Br : Br : FeBr:₃

Lewis base donates   Lewis acid has
an electron pair   accepted an
                                                       electron pair

: Br : : Br — FeBr:₃

If the complex does dissociate,
the two ions remain in close
contact as an **ion pair**

Another Lewis acid catalyst is the so called 'boron trifluoride etherate'. This is a complex formed when boron trifluoride is dissolved in ethoxyethane (diethyl ether)

The process of forming a complex in this way is referred to as **coordination**.

Of course, the proton is itself a Lewis acid — it has an unfilled orbital able to receive an electron pair. But it is such a strong acid that it normally only exists in coordination with another molecule. In aqueous solution this is a molecule of water. If a strong mineral acid such as HCl: is added to an ether (for example, ethoxyethane), the ether is protonated in what is essentially a Lewis acid–base equilibrium

Lewis acid receiving
an electron pair

The most common organic bases are the amines. These may be regarded as molecules of ammonia in which one or more hydrogen atoms have been replaced by alkyl or aryl groups. Like ammonia, amines are weak bases which react reversibly with strong mineral acids such as hydrochloric acid, or even to a limited extent with water

Acidity and basicity are, of course, *relative* properties of molecules. A compound may behave either as an acid or as a base, depending on the nature of the compound with which it is reacting. Water is the prime example of this: it is readily protonated by even weak acids, but will itself protonate bases such as amines

As we shall see later, compounds which are normally regarded as essentially neutral may exhibit both acidic and basic properties when treated with strong enough bases or acids. As an example, propanone may function as a base and is protonated by strong acids

60

But in the presence of a strong base, propanone is weakly acidic

The acidity of carbonyl compounds is discussed in chapter 7.

Measurement of acidity

When we refer to the 'strength' of an organic acid in aqueous solution, we are speaking not of its concentration, but of the extent to which it undergoes ionisation, that is, the extent to which it protonates water molecules

$$RCOOH + H_2O \rightleftharpoons RCOO^\ominus + H_3O^\oplus$$

Thus, acid strength may be expressed in terms of the equilibrium constant (dissociation constant), K_a, for the above reaction, or more conveniently as the **acidity constant**, pK_a, defined by the expression

$$pK_a = -\lg (K_a/\text{mol dm}^{-3})*$$

As with pH scale, values are normally in the range 0–14**, and a lower value of pK_a indicates a stronger acid. Since it is a logarithmic scale, one unit change in pK_a means a *tenfold* difference in acidity.

Measurement of basicity

In the Brönsted sense, the base strength of a compound is a measure of its ability to accept a proton. For an amine in aqueous solution, we may use the equilibrium constant, K_b, for the reaction

---

*lg = $\log_{10}$, ASE recommendation. pK_a values quoted in this book are based on K_a values for aqueous solutions at 298K.

**Values in the range 0–14 are fairly easily determined by titrimetric and pH measurements in aqueous solutions. For stronger ($pK_a < 0$) and weaker ($pK_a > 14$) acids, measurements may be made in non-aqueous media, and values then equated to the aqueous scale.

$$RNH_2 + H_2\ddot{O} \rightleftharpoons RN\overset{\oplus}{H}_3 + :\overset{\ominus}{O}H$$

or define the **basicity constant, pK_b**, as

$$pK_b = -\lg(K_b/\text{mol dm}^{-3})$$

This again gives a scale from 0 to 14, on which a low value indicates a strong base. However, it is becoming increasingly common to express the strength of a base in terms of the pK_a of its *conjugate acid*. To explain this, we must first of all look at the concept of a 'conjugate acid–base pair'.

CONJUGATE ACIDS AND BASES

In the generalised expression

$$HA + H_2\ddot{O} \rightleftharpoons H_3\overset{\oplus}{\ddot{O}} + \overset{\ominus}{\ddot{A}}$$

the forward reaction involves protonation of a base ($H_2\ddot{O}$) by an acid (HA). In the reverse reaction, the protonated water molecule, $H_3\overset{\oplus}{\ddot{O}}$, acts as an acid and donates a proton to the anion $\overset{\ominus}{\ddot{A}}$ which is therefore functioning as a base. The species $H_3\overset{\oplus}{\ddot{O}}$ is called the **conjugate acid** of the base $H_2\ddot{O}$ and $\overset{\ominus}{\ddot{A}}$ is the **conjugate base** of the acid HA. Thus, HA and $\overset{\ominus}{\ddot{A}}$, and $H_3\overset{\oplus}{\ddot{O}}$ and $H_2\ddot{O}$ each constitute a **conjugate acid–base pair**.

conjugate acid–base pair

$$HA + H_2\ddot{O} \rightleftharpoons H_3\overset{\oplus}{\ddot{O}} + \overset{\ominus}{\ddot{A}}$$

conjugate acid–base pair

The stronger the acid HA, the weaker its conjugate base, $\overset{\ominus}{\ddot{A}}$, and vice versa. This is obvious, because if $\overset{\ominus}{\ddot{A}}$ is a strong base, it will readily be protonated to form HA; equilibrium will be well to the left and HA will be a weak acid.

62

Relationship between pK_a and pK_b

It can readily be shown that for a conjugate acid–base pair

$$pK_a + pK_b = 14$$

Thus there really is no need for a separate pK_b scale, as the base strength of a compound can just as easily be expressed in terms of the pK_a of its conjugate acid. This is now becoming more common practice. Values for methylamine illustrate the point

CH_3NH_2 (base)	pK_b = 3.4
$CH_3\overset{\oplus}{N}H_3$ (conjugate acid)	pK_a = 10.6

Stability of the conjugate anion, $\overset{..}{A}{}^{\ominus}$

Factors such as the size and electronegativity of the atom bearing the negative charge are important, but with multi-atomed organic anions the key factor is *dispersal of charge*. The more the negative charge can be 'shared around' with other atoms, the more stable (less basic) the anion. Depending on the structure, both inductive and mesomeric effects may be influential.

ACIDITY OF ALCOHOLS

An alcohol such as ethanol (pK_a 15.9) is not sufficiently acidic to protonate a water molecule because its conjugate anion, the ethoxide ion, is a very powerful base

conjugate acid–base pair

$$CH_3CH_2\overset{..}{O}H + H_2\overset{..}{O} \;\;\xrightarrow{\;\;\times\;\;}\;\; CH_3CH_2\overset{..}{\underset{..}{O}}{}^{\ominus} + H-\overset{\oplus}{O}H_2$$

unstable anion,   strong
very strong base   acid

No dispersal of charge is possible, and the whole negative charge is localised on the oxygen atom. Consequently, ethoxide ion cannot exist in aqueous solution where it would instantly be protonated by water molecules.

    Alkoxides *can* be prepared in the absence of water. The usual method is to react the alcohol with sodium metal

$$2\ CH_3CH_2\overset{..}{\underset{..}{O}}H + 2\ Na \longrightarrow 2\ CH_3CH_2\overset{..}{\underset{..}{O}}{:}^{\ominus}\ \overset{\oplus}{Na} + H_2$$

This shows that alcohols are able to function as proton acids when treated with a sufficiently strong base.

The amide ion in sodamide ($\overset{\oplus}{Na}\ \overset{..}{\underset{..}{N}H_2}^{\ominus}$) is also a very strong base and reacts with ethanol according to the equation

$$H_2\overset{\ominus}{\underset{..}{N}} \quad H \overset{..}{\underset{..}{O}}CH_2CH_3 \longrightarrow H_2\overset{..}{N}-H + {:}\overset{..}{\underset{..}{O}}CH_2CH_3^{\ominus}$$

Some alkoxide ion may be formed when potassium hydroxide is dissolved in ethanol

$$^{\ominus}H\overset{..}{\underset{..}{O}}{:} \quad H \overset{..}{\underset{..}{O}}CH_2CH_3 \rightleftharpoons H\overset{..}{\underset{..}{O}}-H + {:}\overset{..}{\underset{..}{O}}CH_2CH_3^{\ominus}$$

but since ethoxide ion is rather less stable than hydroxide ion, and furthermore, water is generated in the reaction, equilibrium must lie well to the left.

ACIDITY OF CARBOXYLIC ACIDS

Although still a relatively weak acid, ethanoic acid (pK_a 4.76) is a much stronger acid than ethanol, and it will for example displace the weaker acid, carbonic acid, from its salts

$$CH_3COOH + NaHCO_3 \longrightarrow CH_3COO^{\ominus}\ \overset{\oplus}{Na} + [H_2CO_3 \rightleftharpoons H_2O + CO_2]$$

Carboxylic acids protonate water, but equilibrium lies well to the left

$$R\overset{..}{\underset{..}{CO}}\overset{..}{\underset{..}{O}}H + H_2\overset{*}{\underset{..}{O}} \rightleftharpoons R\overset{..}{\underset{..}{CO}}\overset{..}{\underset{..}{O}}{:}^{\ominus} + H_3\overset{\oplus}{O}$$

In an aqueous solution of ethanoic acid of concentration 1 mol dm^{-3}, only about 1 per cent of the molecules are ionised.

Dissociation of a carboxylic acid requires the separation of a proton from a carboxylate anion, and a large amount of energy is necessary to overcome the Coulombic (electrostatic) attraction between the oppositely charged ions. Consequently, ionisation of ethanoic acid in the vapour state is a highly endothermic process

$$CH_3\ddot{O}\ddot{O}H_g \rightleftharpoons CH_3C\ddot{O}\ddot{O}^{\ominus}_g + H^{\oplus}_g \quad \Delta H_{\text{ionisation}} = +1446 \text{ kJ mol}^{-1}$$

In aqueous solution ionisation occurs much more readily. Water funcions as a base to accept the proton, but it is also a medium of high relative permittivitiy, able to facilitate ionisation and to stabilise the resulting ions by solvation (see page 89).

$$H-\overset{\overset{..}{|}}{\underset{H}{O}} : \quad H-\overset{\overset{..}{|}}{\underset{:O:}{O}}-C-CH_3 \rightleftharpoons H-\overset{\overset{\oplus}{|}}{\underset{H}{O}}-H + :\overset{..}{\underset{:O:}{O}}{}^{\ominus}-C-CH_3$$

undissociated acid   ions are stabilised by
only weakly solvated   strong solvation

Just how important this is, is illustrated by the fact that an aqueous solution of ethanoic acid is about 100,000 times more acidic than an ethanolic solution of the acid at the same concentration.

These considerations about solvation would also apply to ionisation of ethanol, but since this compound is essentially undissociated in aqueous solution (pK_a 15.9), there must be a large difference in the stabilities of the ethoxide and ethanoate anions. Whereas in the ethoxide ion the negative charge is localised on the oxygen atom, in the ethanoate anion delocalisation disperses the charge over two oxygen atoms

$$CH_3CH_2-\overset{..}{\underset{..}{O}}{}^{\ominus} \qquad CH_3-C\overset{\overset{..}{\diagup}O.}{\underset{\diagdown \ddot{O}.}{}}\Big\}^{\ominus}$$

localised negative charge,   negative charge delocalised,
no resonance stabilisation   strong resonance stabilisation

Thus we may attribute the acidity of carboxylic acids to strong resonance stabilisation of the conjugate anion, which is not possible with the corresponding alkoxide ion.

Of course, both the carboxylic acid and its conjugate anion are resonance stabilised, but resonance is much more effective in the anion than in the undissociated acid. Delocalisation in the acid is restricted by charge separation

high energy limiting form makes only a small contribution

In resonance jargon, we say that the charge-separated limiting form makes only a small contribution to the resonance structure.

limiting forms non-equivalent, low resonance energy

limiting forms equivalent, high resonance energy

Look at the energy diagram* in figure 4.1.

It should be apparent to you from the energy profiles that it is the *differential* effect of resonance which is important. Ionisation of a carboxylic acid is accompanied by an increase in resonance energy, and the position of equilibrium is further to the right than is possible with alcohols where there is no resonance stabilisation of the molecule or its conjugate anion.

ACIDITY OF PHENOLS

Phenol (pK_a 10.0) is less acidic than ethanoic acid (pK_a 4.76) but appreciably more acidic than ethanol (pK_a 15.9). Thus it will not react with sodium hydrogen carbonate, but it does dissolve in aqueous sodium hydroxide solution to form a salt, sodium phenoxide (sodium phenate)

*For a discussion of energy profiles, see page 86.

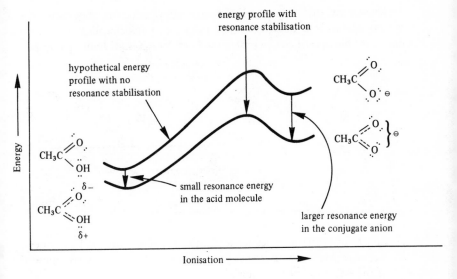

Figure 4.1 *Energy profile for ionisation of ethanoic acid*

$$(Na^{\oplus}) \quad H\overset{..}{O}:^{\ominus} \overset{\frown}{} H—\overset{..}{O}Ph \longrightarrow H\overset{..}{O}—H + :\overset{..}{O}Ph^{\ominus} (Na^{\oplus})$$

The phenoxide ion is more stable than the ethoxide ion, and is therefore a less powerful base. As with the carboxylate anion, stability is linked with the ability to delocalise the negative charge. In addition to the two Kekulé structures, a number of limiting forms can be written with the negative charge on various ring carbon atoms

other limiting forms

Kekulé
structures

Remember that it is the *differential* effect which is important. The phenol molecule is itself resonance stabilised, but delocalisation is more restricted because of charge separation in the non-Kekulé limiting forms

these relatively unstable charge-separated limiting forms make only a small contribution to the mesomer

---

Exercise 4.1
Construct energy profiles for ionisation of phenol, with and without resonance stabilisation. Label your drawings and show the structure of the different species involved.

Because a larger number of limiting forms can be written for the phenoxide ion, it might be expected that phenol would be a stronger acid than ethanoic acid. However, the non-Kekulé structures are not aromatic, and the negative charge is shown on ring carbon atoms, which are less electronegative than oxygen atoms. Although only two limiting forms can be written for the carboxylate anion, they are energetically equivalent and in each structure the negative charge is located on an electronegative oxygen atom. Thus, delocalisation is more effective in the carboxylate anion.

THE EFFECT OF SUBSTITUENTS ON ACIDITY

1. Carboxylic acids

Since chloroethanoic acid (pK_a 2.86) is a stronger acid than ethanoic acid (pK_a 4.76), it is apparent that the presence of a chlorine atom lowers the free energy of the anion relative to that of the undissociated chloroacid. In the unionised acid, the carbon–chlorine dipole has an adverse effect on stability, owing to the close proximity of fractional positive charges

destabilising
electrostatic repulsion

The situation is reversed in the anion, where favourable Coulombic attraction of $C^{\delta+}$ and $COO^{\ominus}$ outweights any small repulsion between the more remote $Cl^{\delta-}$ and $COO^{\ominus}$ groups

weak Coulombic repulsion

strong stabilising
Coulombic attraction

Coulombic interactions across space (or through a solvent) are referred to as **field effects**, but we can just as well consider the influence of the chlorine atom simply in terms of its negative inductive effect, $-I$. This will be destabilising in the chloroacid, but stabilising in the corresponding anion

$-I$ effect of chlorine atom
is destabilising

$-I$ effect of chlorine atom
is stabilising

It is seldom possible to completely disentangle field effects from inductive effects and it is usually simpler to incorporate the former with the latter.

However we choose to describe the influence of the chlorine atom, the net effect is to increase the free energy of the undissociated acid and to decrease the free energy of the corresponding anion. Thus ΔG is smaller for ionisation of chloroethanoic acid than for ionisation of ethanoic acid, figure 4.2.

Figure 4.2 *Energy changes on ionisation of ethanoic and chloroethanoic acids*

We have already quoted increased acidity of halogenocarboxylic acids as evidence for the inductive effect of halogen atoms. This can now be quantified in terms of pK_a values

	CH₃COOH	: ICH₂COOH	: BrCH₂COOH	: ClCH₂COOH	: FCH₂COOH
pK_a	4.76,	3.17	2.90	2.86	2.66

increase in −I effect is paralleled by increase in acidity →

	CH₃COOH	: ClCH₂COOH	: Cl₂CHCOOH	: Cl₃CCOOH
pK_a	4.76	2.86	1.29	0.65

−I effect of chlorine atoms is additive →

The 'damping out' effect of intervening methylene groups is nicely illustrated by the series of chlorobutanoic acids

	CH₃CH₂CHCOOH Cl	CH₃CHCH₂COOH Cl	CH₂CH₂CH₂COOH Cl	CH₃CH₂CH₂COOH
pK_a	2.84	4.06	4.52	4.82

Butanoic acid (pK_a 4.82) is slightly weaker than ethanoic acid (pK_a 4.76).

Replacement of hydrogen by an alkyl group stabilises the undissociated acid in relation to the carboxylate anion

$$CH_3CH_2 \longrightarrow CH_2 \longrightarrow C \underset{OH}{\overset{O}{<}}$$

+I effect of
ethyl group is
stabilising

Benzoic acid (pK_a 4.20) is slightly stronger than ethanoic acid (pK_a 4.76), and this may be attributed to a weak −I effect of the aromatic nucleus. The effect of chloro substituents parallels that in the chlorobutanoic acids

| pK_a | 2.94 | 3.83 | 3.99 | 4.20 |

Decreased acidity, the further the chlorine
atom is from the carboxyl group

pK_a values for the nitrobenzoic acids are

| pK_a | 2.17 | 3.45 | 3.43 | 4.20 |

If the negative inductive effect, relayed through the sigma-bonds of the benzene ring, was solely responsible, we should expect 4-nitrobenzoic to be the least acidic of the three isomers. However, the nitro group is also able to withdraw electrons from the ring by a negative mesomeric effect. This puts positive charge on the ring carbon atom to which the carboxyl group is attached, and so exerts a −I effect in that bond

increased
−I effect

When the nitro group is *meta* to the carboxyl group, positive charge is developed on the *adjacent* ring carbon atom, and this is less effective in stabilising the anion

decreased
−I effect
(operates over a
greater distance)

2. Phenols

The same principles apply here, and strongly electron-withdrawing substituents increase the acidity of the phenols as is illustrated by the pK_a values for the following nitrophenols

| pK_a | 7.21 | 8.35 | 7.15 | 10.00 |

You will notice that when in the 2 or 4 position, the nitro group has a tenfold greater effect on the acidity of phenol than on benzoic acid. The reason is that in the anion, mesomeric shift of electrons places some of the negative charge on the nitro group

72

Similar limiting forms cannot be written in the case of 3-nitrophenol, which is therefore less acidic than the other two isomers.

Exercise 4.2
Draw all the limiting forms for the 3-nitrophenoxide anion, and indicate why delocalisation is less effective in this ion.

The effect of additional nitro groups is additive, and picric acid, 2,4,6-trinitrophenol (pK_a 0.42), is quite strongly acidic.

FACTORS WHICH INFLUENCE THE BASICITY OF ORGANIC COMPOUNDS

Base strength is concerned with the ability of a compound to donate a pair of electrons to a proton. In aqueous conditions this means accepting a proton from a water molecule

$$ B \quad H - OH \; \rightleftharpoons \; \overset{\oplus}{B}H \; + \; \overset{\ominus}{:}OH $$

Negatively charged anions are generally stronger bases than neutral molecules. Thus

$$ \overset{\ominus}{HO}: \quad \text{is stronger than} \quad H_2O $$
$$ \text{and } H_2\overset{\ominus}{N} \quad \text{is stronger than} \quad H_3N $$

We have seen that electronegativity is important. Nitrogen is less electronegative than oxygen and so can tolerate a negative charge less readily than oxygen. Accordingly, the amide ion, $\overset{\ominus}{NH_2}$, is a stronger base than the hydroxide ion, and $R\overset{\ominus}{NH}$ is more basic than $R\overset{\ominus}{O}:$.

Another factor is concentration of charge. An alkoxide ion, $R\overset{\ominus}{O}:$, with

73

localised negative charge, is a much stronger base than the phenoxide ion, $Ph\overset{..}{O}:^{\ominus}$, where the charge is delocalised through resonance. The most important organic bases are the amines, and we shall see that the same factors control the base strength of these compounds.

BASICITY OF AMINES

In the reaction of an amine with water, the position of equilibrium is determined by the relative stabilities of the free base and its conjugate acid cation

$$
\begin{array}{ccc}
\overset{|}{\underset{|}{-N}}: \quad H - \overset{..}{\underset{..}{O}}H & \rightleftharpoons & \overset{|}{\underset{|}{-N}}\overset{\oplus}{} - H \; + \; :\overset{..}{\underset{..}{O}}H^{\ominus} \\
\text{base} & & \begin{array}{c}\text{conjugate}\\\text{acid}\end{array}
\end{array}
$$

| if the groups attached to the nitrogen atom stabilise the free amine relative to its conjugate acid, equilibrium lies to the left and basicity is decreased | if groups attached to the nitrogen atom stabilise the conjugate acid relative to the free amine, then equilibrium moves to the right and basicity is increased |

The real key to basicity, then, is *how well the conjugate cation can accommodate the positive charge.* Stability is linked with the dispersal of charge, and so we should expect inductive and mesomeric (resonance) effects to be important, but as we shall see, other factors operate as well. By analogy with inductive stabilisation of carbocations, where stability increases in the series

$$
CH_3^{\oplus} \; < \; CH_3 \rightarrow \overset{\oplus}{C}H_2 \; < \; \underset{CH_3}{\overset{CH_3}{>}}\overset{\oplus}{C}H \; < \; CH_3 \rightarrow \overset{\overset{CH_3}{\uparrow}}{\underset{\underset{CH_3}{\uparrow}}{C^{\oplus}}}
$$

we should predict that progressive replacement of hydrogen atoms in the ammonium ion by alkyl groups would have a similar effect. And indeed, basicity does increase in the order

$$\overset{..}{N}H_3 \ < \ CH_3\overset{..}{N}H_2 \ < \ \begin{matrix} CH_3 \\ \diagup \\ CH_3 \end{matrix}\hspace{-0.3em}\overset{..}{N}H$$

pK_b 4.75   3.36   3.28

$\xrightarrow{\hspace{3cm}}$

increasing base strength

related to increasing stability of the cations

$$\overset{\oplus}{N}H_4 \ < \ CH_3 \rightarrow \overset{\oplus}{N}H_3 \ < \ \begin{matrix} CH_3 \\ \diagup \\ CH_3 \end{matrix}\hspace{-0.3em}\overset{\oplus}{N}H_2$$

pK_a 9.25   10.64   10.72

$\xrightarrow{\hspace{3cm}}$

decreasing acid strength

However, replacement of the third hydrogen atom by a methyl group slightly decreases base strength

$$CH_3 - \overset{\overset{\displaystyle CH_3}{|}}{\underset{\underset{\displaystyle CH_3}{|}}{N}}: \qquad\qquad CH_3 - \overset{\overset{\displaystyle CH_3}{|}}{\underset{\underset{\displaystyle CH_3}{|}}{\overset{\oplus}{N}H}}$$

pK_b 4.20 pK_a 9.80

The introduction of one and then two methyl groups results in a progressive increase in basicity, so why should a third group have the opposite effect? Clearly this cannot be an electronic effect, so it must be related to the *size* of the methyl group compared with a hydrogen atom. As hydrogen atoms in an ammonia molecule are replaced by much larger methyl groups, it becomes increasingly difficult for the amine and water molecules to get close enough to one another for proton transfer to occur. In other word, proton exchange is subject to *steric hindrance*. There is another, less obvious, factor already mentioned in connection with acidity, and that is *solvation* of the cation. Just as protonation of the amine is made more difficult by the presence of three methyl groups, solvating water molecules are hindered in getting close to the positively charged nitrogen atom in the corresponding cation

steric hindrance to
proton-donating
water molecule

steric hindrance to
solvating water
molecule

Furthermore, as we discussed in the previous chapter, solvation of an anion or cation is most effective the more concentrated the charge. So although charge dispersal stabilises the cation, at the same time it reduces the effectiveness of solvation as a stabilising factor.

Phenylamine (pK_b 9.38) is a much weaker base than ammonia or the alkylamines, and the main factor here is resonance stabilisation of the free base, which is not possible with the conjugate acid cation. The amino group in phenylamine is conjugated with the aromatic nucleus, and so the lone pair of electrons is not localised on the nitrogen atom, but is shared to some extent by ring carbon atoms in the aromatic nucleus. We show this in the usual way by drawing the various limiting forms

charge-separated limiting forms

Kekulé structures

Charge-separated limiting forms will make only a limited contribution, but nevertheless *some* resonance stabilisation occurs which is not possible once the amino group has been protonated

76

resonance-stabilised
free base

resonance stabilisation
no longer possible —
positive charge localised
on the nitrogen atom

So with phenylamine and other aromatic amines, loss of resonance energy is a barrier to the uptake of a proton. Cyclohexylamine, in which resonance is not possible, is a much stronger base than phenylamine

lone pair remains
localised on the
nitrogen atom

Phenylamine
$pK_b = 9.38$

Cyclohexylamine
$pK_b = 3.36$

Incidently, do not be tempted to 'delocalise' the positive charge in the conjugated cation by donation of pi electrons from the ring

this displacement cannot
occur as the nitrogen atom
has no vacant orbital in
which to accommodate the
electron pair

Such displacements are not possible, because although the nitrogen atom carries a positive charge, it already has a complete octet.

The presence of powerfully electron-attracting groups *ortho* or *para* to the amino group will increase the extent of delocalisation. For example, with *para*-nitrophenylamine we can write an additional limiting form in which the lone pair originally associated with the nitrogen atom now appears on an oxygen atom of the nitro group a similar limiting form can be written in the absence of the nitro group

this additional limiting form shows how the nitro group can accommodate the original nitrogen lone pair

In the protonated base, the $-M$ effect of the nitro group is destabilising, thus increasing the 'resonance energy barrier' to the uptake of a proton

relay of the $-M$ effect of the nitro group

destabilising Coulombic repulsion

As the following pK_b values indicate, the effect is additive, and 2,4,6-trinitrophenylamine is an extremely weak base

pK_b	9.38	14.28	11.55	13.02	23.4

Exercise 4.3
Draw all the limiting forms for 3-nitrophenylamine and use these to explain why this compound is a stronger base than the other two nitrophenylamines.

78

5 Nucleophilic Substitution

REACTIONS OF HALOALKANES

Introduction

Haloalkanes, other than methyl compounds, are classified as primary, secondary or tertiary according to the number of alkyl groups linked to the α-carbon atom

methyl	primary	secondary	tertiary
	(1°)	(2°)	(3°)

$(X = \text{halogen})$

Since halogen is more electronegative than carbon, the carbon–halogen bond is polarised

$$-\overset{|}{\underset{|}{C}} \overset{\delta+}{\longrightarrow} \overset{\delta-}{\ddot{X}} :$$

and we might therefore well expect the electron-deficient α-carbon atom to be vulnerable to nucleophilic attack. The characteristic reaction of haloalkanes is indeed **nucleophilic substitution**, but the predominant factor cannot simply be bond polarity, because although bond polarity increases in the series

$$R - \ddot{I} : \; < \; R - \ddot{Br} : \; < \; R - \ddot{Cl} : \; < R - \ddot{F} :$$

haloalkane reactivity actually *decreases* from left to right in the same series.

The general reaction is one in which the halogen atom, X, is replaced by a nucleophilic reagent, Y. This may be a neutral molecule, but is more commonly an anion

$$\ddot{Y}^{\ominus} + R - \ddot{X}: \longrightarrow R - Y + :\ddot{X}:^{\ominus}$$

Some representative nucleophilic substitution reactions are given in table 5.1.

The three factors which largely control the reactivity of the haloalkanes are the strength and polarisability (see page 32) of the carbon–halogen bond, and the leaving ability of the displaced group, X. Polarisability *increases* and bond strength *decreases* from left to right in the series

$$-\overset{|}{\underset{|}{C}} - \ddot{F}: \quad -\overset{|}{\underset{|}{C}} - \ddot{C}l: \quad -\overset{|}{\underset{|}{C}} - \ddot{B}r: \quad -\overset{|}{\underset{|}{C}} - \ddot{I}:$$

In keeping with this, haloalkane reactivity increases from left to right in the same series. Iodine and bromine are particularly **good leaving groups**, chlorine less so, and fluorine is difficult to displace.

Despite their polarity, haloalkanes are virtually insoluble in water, probably because of their inability to hydrogen-bond with water molecules. Consequently, in reaction with aqueous reagents it is usual to add a small amount of solvent such as ethanol or propanone, in which both the nucleophile and the substrate are at least partially soluble.

In a displacement reaction such as

$$^{\ominus}H\ddot{O}: \quad -\overset{|}{\underset{|}{C}} - \ddot{I}: \longrightarrow H\ddot{O} - \overset{|}{\underset{|}{C}} - + :\ddot{I}:^{\ominus}$$

the α-carbon atom is only able to *receive* an electron pair from the attacking hydroxide ion if it previously, or at the same time, *releases* a pair of electrons to the departing iodide ion. Otherwise the α-carbon atom would become pentavalent, with 10 electrons in the valence shell.

Table 5.1 Characteristic nucleophilic substitution reactions of haloalkanes

Nucleophile	Product	Typical reaction conditions
$\overset{..}{\underset{..}{HO}}\!:^{\ominus}$, hydroxide ion	$\overset{..}{\underset{..}{RO}}H$, alcohols	Warm with dilute aqueous Na$\overset{..}{O}$H solution
$\overset{..}{\underset{..}{RO}}\!:^{\ominus}$, alkoxide ion	$R\overset{..}{\underset{..}{O}}R$, ethers	Warm with dilute alcoholic K$\overset{..}{O}$R solution
$RC\overset{..}{\underset{..}{O}}\overset{..}{\underset{..}{O}}\!:^{\ominus}$, carboxylate anion	$RC\overset{..}{\underset{..}{O}}O\overset{..}{\underset{..}{O}}R$, esters	Warm with RCOOAg
$\overset{..}{\underset{..}{C}}N^{\ominus}$, cyanide ion	RCN , nitriles	Boil with a solution of K$\overset{..}{C}$N in propanone
$\overset{..}{N}H_3$, ammonia	$R\overset{..}{N}H_2$, amines ($R_2\overset{..}{N}H$, $R_3\overset{..}{N}$ and $R_4N^{\oplus}:\overset{..}{\underset{..}{X}}\!:^{\ominus}$ also formed)	Heat with alcoholic $\overset{..}{N}H_3$ solution under pressure

So we can envisage two mechanisms for this reaction which differ in the *timing of attack by the hydroxide ion.* Let us now take a detailed look at one example of each of these mechanisms.

Reaction of 2-iodo-2-methylpropane (tert butyl iodide) with dilute aqueous alkali

$$(CH_3)_3C \overset{\frown}{} \ddot{I}: + \ H\ddot{O}:^{\ominus} \longrightarrow (CH_3)_3C - \ddot{O}H + :\ddot{I}:^{\ominus}$$

Kinetic studies show that the rate of this reaction is proportional to the concentration of the haloalkane, but independent of the concentration of the hydroxide ion, that is, the reaction is kinetically **first order**.

$$\text{Rate} = k \ [(CH_3)_3C - \ddot{I}:]$$

where k is the **rate constant**
for the reaction

Although with dilute alkali the main product is the alcohol, appreciable amounts of the alkene 2-methylpropene are formed at the same time

$$(CH_3)_3C_3 - \ddot{I}: \ \xrightarrow{\ H\ddot{O}:^{\ominus}\ } \begin{cases} (CH_3)_3C - \ddot{O}H & \sim 80 \text{ per cent} \\ \underset{CH_3}{\overset{CH_3}{\diagdown}}C = CH_2 & \sim 20 \text{ per cent} \end{cases}$$

We will discuss this competing reaction later on. The interesting observation at this stage is that if we change the substrate from 2-iodo-2-methylpropane to 2-chloro-2-methylpropane, the reaction is much slower, but the *ratio* of alcohol to alkene remains unchanged.

These observations are consistent with a two-step mechanism in which the first step is ionisation of the haloalkane

$$(CH_3)_3C - \ddot{I}: \ \overset{slow}{\rightleftharpoons} \ (CH_3)_3C^{\oplus} + :\ddot{I}:^{\ominus}$$

This step is relatively slow as it involves bond *breaking*, whereas the second step, combination of $(CH_3)_3C^{\oplus}$, with $:\overset{..}{O}H^{\ominus}$, entails bond *making* and occurs relatively quickly

$$(CH_3)_3C^{\oplus} + :\overset{..}{O}H^{\ominus} \xrightarrow{\text{fast}} (CH_3)_3C \longrightarrow \overset{..}{O}H$$

We can now see why the rate of reaction is independent of the hydroxide ion concentration: provided that there are enough hydroxide ions present to react with the carbocations as they are formed, any excess hydroxide ion will simply have to wait around for the production of more carbocation. Thus the overall rate of formation of product depends only on the rate of formation of the carbocation, and the first step is therefore called the slow **rate-determining step.**

The proposed mechanism also accounts for the observation concerning the ratio of alcohol to alkene in the product. The alkene is formed by loss of a proton from the carbocation, and so although 2-chloro-2-methyl-propane and 2-iodo-2-methylpropane react at different rates, the proportion of alkene in the product is independent of the identity of the substrate from which the carbocation is generated

the rate of formation
of the carbocation
differs for the two
substrates

Only one species, the substrate molecule $(CH_3)_3C \longrightarrow \overset{..}{I}:$, is involved in the rate-determining step, and so the reaction is classified as a **unimolecular process**, or **unimolecular reaction**. A convenient shorthand description for the mechanism is the symbol S_N1. The 'S' stands for substitution, 'N' for nucleophilic, and '1' for unimolecular. We have seen that a unimolecular reaction is also kinetically first order, but you should be particularly careful to distinguish the two concepts. The term 'unimolecular' refers to the numbers of species (molecules or ions) thought to be taking part in the rate-determining step, whereas the description 'first order' relates to the observed kinetics of reaction. Molecularity is a theoretical concept: kinetic order is something which is determined experimentally.

Both the carbocation $(CH_3)_3C^{\oplus}$ and the iodide ion $\overset{..}{\underset{..}{I}}{}^{\ominus}$ are products of the ionisation step, but only the iodide ion remains at the end of the reaction. The carbocation is an extremely short-lived species and is referred to as a reaction **intermediate.** We shall have more to say about reaction intermediates later in this chapter (see page 85).

The ionisation process

Even in the groundstate (the 'resting state') of a molecule, the various atoms are in constant vibration. Absorption of energy by the substrate molecule causes these bonded atoms to vibrate more violently. In particular, as electron density is transferred from a bonding position between the α-carbon atom and the iodine atom to a non-bonding orbital on the iodine atom

$$(CH_3)_3C \overset{\displaystyle \frown}{\underset{..}{\overset{..}{I}}} :$$

the two atoms begin to acquire opposite charges — or rather, the magnitude of these charges increases, since the carbon–iodine bond is already slightly polar in the groundstate.

Electrostatic attraction of opposite charges will then oppose further charge separation and more energy is required to enable the atoms to pull further apart. At the point of maximum energy input to the substrate molecule, the two charged atoms will be kept together mainly by electrostatic attraction, with very little electron density remaining in a bonding position between them. On paper, a partial bond (whether in the process of being built up or broken down) is usually represented by drawing an extended broken line between the atoms concerned. Extension of the line indicates that the atoms are further apart than the normal bonding distance.

$$(CH_3)_3C \overset{\delta+}{} \text{---} \overset{\delta-}{\underset{..}{\overset{..}{I}}} :$$

This 'in between' state of maximum energy is called a **transition state** or **activated complex,** and the energy absorbed by the substrate molecule in order to reach this state from the groundstate is called the **activation**

energy for the process*. The transient nature of the activated complex is emphasised by enclosing the species in square brackets

$$\left[\underset{(CH_3)_3 C}{\overset{\delta+}{}} \text{----} \overset{..}{\underset{..}{I}} \overset{\delta-}{:} \right] TS$$

the letters TS are often used to indicate a transition state

Although this representation is adequate for our purposes, you might like to note that since the substrate molecule is tetrahedral, and the intermediate is planar in structure, the transition state must have an 'in between' spacial arrangement, in which the three methyl groups are moving from a tetrahedral configuration towards a planar one

C — C — C bond angle
between 109°
and 120°

Structure of the intermediate

The intermediate carbocation has a planar structure in which the central positively charged carbon atom and the three methyl groups all lie in one plane. The α-carbon atom is in a state of sp^2 hybridisation, and has a vacant $2p$ orbital oriented at right angles to the plane of the three carbon-carbon sigma-bonds

vacant $2p$ orbital

*More specifically, the free energy of activation, $\Delta G^{\#}$. However, since the concept is more correctly applied to a statistical collection of molecules, we shall use the less precise term 'energy' when discussing reactions of individual molecules.

Evidence for a planar carbocation intermediate comes from studies on the hydrolysis of optically active haloalkanes, where it is found that substitution is accompanied by partial racimisation of the resulting alcohol. For example, considerable racimisation occurs during hydrolysis of optically active 3-iodo-3-methylhexane with aqueous sodium hydroxide solution. The formation of two enantiomers from an optically pure substrate is readily explained in terms of a planar cationic intermediate which can be attacked by the hydroxide ion approaching from either side of the plane

$$CH_3CH_2 \overset{CH_3}{\underset{CH_3CH_2CH_2}{-}} C - \ddot{I}: \; \rightleftharpoons \; \overset{CH_3}{\underset{CH_3CH_2 \quad CH_2CH_2CH_3}{\overset{|}{C}}}{\oplus}$$

an optically active
enantiomer of
3-iodo-3-methylhexane

$\overset{..}{H}\overset{\ominus}{O}:$ can attack the
planar carbocation
from either side

$$CH_3CH_2 \overset{CH_3}{\underset{CH_3CH_2CH_2}{-}} C - \overset{..}{O}\overset{..}{H}$$

retention of
configuration

$$\overset{..}{H}\overset{..}{O} - C \overset{CH_3}{\underset{CH_2CH_2CH_3}{-}} CH_2CH_3$$

inversion of
configuration

You might well imagine from this argument that racimisation should be *complete*. In fact, this is seldom the case, and the most likely explanation is that attack by the hydroxide ion occurs before the departing iodide ion has moved very far away from the α-carbon atom. The iodide ion is said to remain within **shielding distance** of the α-carbon atom, and so attack on that side is sterically more difficult.

Energy profiles

Atoms in the transition state may lose energy and attain a more stable state by either moving closer together and re-forming the sigma bond beween them, or by moving further apart as the cation $(CH_3)_3C^{\oplus}$ and the anion $: \overset{..}{\underset{..}{I}}:^{\ominus}$.

These events may be shown graphically in the form of an **energy profile***, figure 5.1.

*Various other terms are used, such as 'reaction profile' and 'reaction coordinate diagram'.

Figure 5.1 *Energy profile for ionisation of 2-iodo-2-methylpropane*

Much use is made of energy profiles in the discussion of reaction mechanisms, and it should be noted that these are intended only as a diagrammatic summary of energy changes occurring during the course of a reaction, or one step of a reaction. Energies of activation may be stated where these have been determined for a particular process, but normally there is no attempt to quantify either the energy or reaction coordinates.

It may not be immediately obvious why the intermediate cation should be at a lower energy level than the transition state leading to its formation. To explain this, we have to take into account the *influence of the solvent*. Most ionic reactions are carried out in the liquid phase, and one function of the solvent is to dissolve the reagent and bring it into close contact with substrate. However, the solvent is involved in the reaction in a far more intimate way.

The role of the solvent

Many substitution reactions require the use of a reagent in aqueous or aqueous–alcoholic solution. Water is a polar solvent of high relative permittivity (dielectric constant), and one effect of such a medium is to reduce the attraction of oppositely charged ions. (The force between the ions is inversely proportional to the relative permittivity.) But of even greater significance is the property of a polar solvent known as its *solvating power*.

Individual water molecules have a polar structure emanating from unequal sharing of electrons in each of the oxygen–hydrogen sigma-bonds

The very fact that water is a liquid at room temperature (remember that hydrogen sulphide, $H_2\ddot{S}$, has a higher relative molecular mass, but is gaseous at room temperature) is attributed to **hydrogen bonding** between water molecules. A very weak electrostatic attraction occurs between a hydrogen atom of one molecule and the oxygen atom of an adjacent molecule, leading to a loose three-dimensional network

hydrogen
bonds

Alcohols behave similarly, and have higher boiling points than isomeric alkoxyalkanes (ethers) of the same relative molecular mass.

A crystal of sodium chloride consists of a lattice of sodium ions ($Na^{\oplus}$) and chloride ions ($\ddot{:}\ddot{Cl}\ddot{:}^{\ominus}$). The energy required to overcome the electrostatic attraction between these oppositely charged ions is over 400 kJ mol^{-1}, and sodium chloride has a very high melting point (1074K). Despite this, the compound readily dissolves in water at room temperature. Since very little temperature change occurs when the solid goes into solution, the energy required to bring about separation of the sodium and chloride ions is not simply taken from the kinetic energy of the solvent water molecules. As the crystal dissolves in water, each sodium ion becomes

88

surrounded by water molecules which orient themselves so that the negative end of the water dipole is nearest the positively charged sodium ion

$$\delta+ H\diagdown \quad\diagup H\,\delta+$$
$$O\quad\delta-$$
$$\delta+ H\diagdown\,\delta-\qquad\qquad\delta-\diagup H\,\delta+$$
$$O \cdots Na^{\oplus}\cdots O$$
$$\delta+ H\diagup\qquad\qquad\diagdown H\,\delta+$$
$$\delta-\;O$$
$$\delta+ H\diagup\qquad\diagdown H\,\delta+$$

As a result, the sodium ions are individually surrounded by a 'cloud' of water molecules, each forming a weak **dipole–ion bond** with the sodium ion.

The chloride ions are similarly surrounded by water molecules, oriented the other way round with the hydrogen atoms (positive ends of the water dipole) closest to the negatively charged chloride ion

$$H\,\delta+$$
$$\delta-\;O\diagup$$
$$H\,\delta+$$
$$\delta+ H\diagdown\qquad\delta+\qquad\qquad\delta+\qquad\delta-$$
$$O\,-\,H\cdots Cl^{\ominus}\cdots H\,-\,O$$
$$\delta-\qquad\qquad\qquad\qquad\diagdown H\,\delta+$$
$$H\,\delta+$$
$$O\;\delta-$$
$$\delta+ H\diagup$$

Water molecules closest to the ions are further polarised by the ions, and so attract adjacent water molecules more strongly. By this means a **solvent shell** or **solvent envelope**, several molecules thick, may be formed around the ions.

Each individual dipole–ion bond is, of course, very weak. But the total energy from all the bonds involved is quite high — big enough to largely offset the electrostatic attraction holding the ions together in the solid crystal. This kind of interaction between solvent and ions is called **solvation**. The ions are said to be **solvated** by the solvent molecules. When the solvent is water, solvation may be referred to as **hydration**.

We can now see why the solvent is so important in the ionisation of substrate molecules such as haloalkanes. Highly polar solvents such as water (or water–alcohol mixtures which are often used in haloalkane reactions) are able to stabilise the transition state for ionisation, and so lower the activation energy for its formation. The importance of this effect is emphasised by the observation that enthalpy of ionisation of 2-iodo-2-methylpropane in aqueous solution is only about one-tenth of that in the vapour phase.

It should also be clear why the intermediate ions are at a lower energy level than the transition state for their formation. The strength of ion-dipole interaction is proportional to the magnitude of the charges involved, so that solvation of individual ions, each with a unit charge, is more effective than solvation of the transition state where only fractional charges are developed.

$$(CH_3)_3C \overset{\delta\delta+}{\underset{}{}} \overset{\delta\delta-}{\ddot{\underset{}{I}}}\!: \quad \rightleftharpoons \quad [(CH_3)_3C \overset{\delta+}{----} \overset{\delta-}{\ddot{I}}\!:] \quad \rightleftharpoons \quad (CH_3)_3C^{\oplus} + :\ddot{I}:^{\ominus}$$

| polar molecule | more polar transition state | ions with unit charges |

solvation increasingly effective →

Thus the increase in **solvation energy** on going from the groundstate to the transition state to the intermediate provides a large part of the 'driving force' for ionisation.

The relative permittivities of some common solvents are given in table 5.2.

Table 5.2 Relative permittivities of some common solvents

Solvent	Relative permittivity, Σ_r
Water	79
Methanoic acid	58
75 per cent aqueous ethanol	65
Ethanol	24
Propanone	21
Ethanoic acid	6

The second step – combination of ions

Combination of $(CH_3)_3\overset{\oplus}{C}$ with $:\overset{\ominus}{\underset{..}{O}}H$ requires a certain amount of activation energy, and the two ions have to pass through another transition state on their way to form the product molecule, $(CH_3)_3C\overset{..}{\underset{}{-}}OH$. In this second transition state, formation of the new sigma-bond is underway, but the carbon and oxygen atoms each still have appreciable charges

$$\left[(CH_3)_3\overset{\delta+}{C}----\overset{\delta-}{\underset{..}{O}}H\right]$$

The $C\!-\!C\!-\!C$ bond angle will again be between $120°$ and $109°$ as the groups move back towards a tetrahedral arrangement. A large amount of energy is released on formation of the new sigma-bond, and an energy profile for the second step will appear as in figure 5.2.

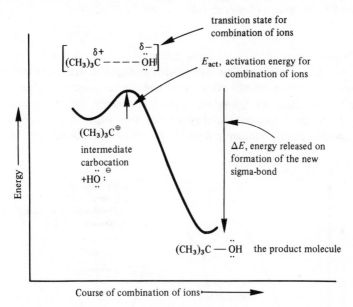

Figure 5.2 *Energy profile for combination of ions*

By combining the energy profiles for the two separate steps, we obtain a composite profile for the whole reaction, figure 5.3.

Figure 5.3 *Energy profile for hydrolysis of 2-iodo-2-methylpropane*

Oppositely charged ions have a strong electrostatic attraction for one another, and it might at first seem a little strange that activation energy is required for their combination. However, since energy is released on solvation of ions, an equivalent amount of energy has to be supplied in order to 'free' the ions from their solvent shells before they can approach one another closely enough to form the transition state. See figure 5.4.

Figure 5.4 *Energy profile illustrating desolvation of ions*

Rearrangement of carbocations

When 2-bromo-3,3-dimethylbutane undergoes unimolecular hydrolysis,
two products are obtained: 3,3-dimethylbutan-2-ol, and another alcohol,
2,3-dimethylbutan-2-ol

2-bromo-3,3-dimethylbutane   3,3-dimethylbutan-2-ol   2,3-dimethylbutan-2-ol

Ionisation of the haloalkane gives the cation

and uptake of hydroxide ion by this cation gives the expected product,
3,3-dimethylbutan-2-ol

However, the first-formed secondary carbocation is appreciably less stable
than a tertiary carbocation, and it readily undergoes a **rearrangement
reaction** involving migration of a methyl group (with the bonding pair of
electrons) from the adjacent carbon atom to the electron-deficient carbon
atom. In this way the positive charge is transferred from one carbon atom
to the other

$$CH_3 - \overset{\overset{\displaystyle CH_3}{|}}{\underset{\underset{\displaystyle CH_3}{|}}{C}} - \overset{\oplus}{CH} - CH_3 \longrightarrow CH_3 - \overset{\overset{\displaystyle CH_3}{|}}{\underset{\underset{\displaystyle CH_3}{|}}{\overset{\oplus}{C}}} - CH - CH_3$$

$$(2°) \qquad\qquad\qquad\qquad (3°)$$

During the migration, the methyl group never actually breaks away as a separate methyl carbanion, but passes through a transition state in which it is partially bonded with *both* carbon atoms

$$\left[\; CH_3 - \overset{\overset{\displaystyle CH_3}{\diagup\overset{\oplus}{}\diagdown}}{\underset{\underset{\displaystyle CH_3}{|}}{C}} - C - CH_3 \;\right]_{TS}$$

We can think of the transition state in molecular orbital terms as one involving partial overlap of an sp^3 hybrid orbital of the methyl group with the original sp^3 hybrid orbital of one carbon atom, and the originally vacant $2p$ orbital of the adjacent carbon atom. The two carbon atoms are in an intermediate state of hybridisation, between sp^2 and sp^3, and dispersal of the positive charge lowers the energy of the transition state

Migration of a methyl group from one carbon atom to the adjacent carbon atom is called a 1,2-**methyl** (or **methide**) **shift**. Other alkyl or aryl groups, or even hydrogen atoms can migrate in a similar way (a 1,2-**hydride shift**).

94

$$CH_3 - \overset{\overset{\displaystyle H}{|}}{\underset{\underset{\displaystyle CH_3}{|}}{C}} - \overset{\oplus}{CH} - CH_3 \longrightarrow CH_3 - \overset{\overset{\displaystyle H}{|}}{\underset{\underset{\displaystyle CH_3}{|}}{\overset{\oplus}{C}}} - \overset{\overset{\displaystyle H}{|}}{CH} - CH_3$$

$$(2°) \qquad\qquad\qquad (3°)$$

In each case, *the driving force is the formation of a lower-energy carbocation*, for example, a tertiary structure from a secondary, and so on. The ease with which a particular atom or group migrates (referred to as **migratory aptitude**) is related to its ability to donate electrons to the adjacent positively charged carbon atom. For common groups, migratory aptitude increases in the series

$$H < Alkyl < Aryl$$

The alternative mechanism for substitution is one in which attack by the nucleophile accompanies displacement of the halogen atom. We will take as an example the reaction of iodoethane with dilute aqueous sodium hydroxide solution.

Reaction of iodoethane with dilute aqueous alkali

$$CH_3CH_2 - \overset{..}{\underset{..}{I}}: + :\overset{..}{\underset{..}{O}}H^{\ominus} \longrightarrow CH_3CH_2 - \overset{..}{\underset{..}{O}}H + :\overset{..}{\underset{..}{I}}:^{\ominus}$$

For many haloalkanes, particularly primary haloalkanes such as iodo-ethane, the activation energy for ionisation is too great for this to occur as a separate step under normal conditions. Instead, there is just one transition state for the reaction in which expulsion of the iodide ion is facilitated by attack of the hydroxide ion. The anion closely approaches the substrate molecule and begins to form a new bond with the α-carbon atom before the bond between carbon and iodine is fully broken. Sometimes the hydroxide ion is described as giving the iodide ion a 'nucleophilic push'

nucleophilic push by
the hydroxide ion

Studies with isotopically labelled substrates confirm that the incoming nucleophile becomes attached to the same carbon atom that originally carried the displaced group. Hydrolysis of iodoethane labelled in the α-position with ^{14}C gives ethanol similarly labelled in the same position

$$\overset{\ominus}{\underset{\cdot\cdot}{HO}}{:} + CH_3\ {}^{14}CH_2 - \overset{\cdot\cdot}{\underset{\cdot\cdot}{I}}{:} \longrightarrow CH_3\ {}^{14}CH_2 - \overset{\cdot\cdot}{\underset{\cdot\cdot}{O}}H + {:}\overset{\cdot\cdot}{\underset{\cdot\cdot}{I}}{:}^{\ominus}$$

isotopic
α-carbon atom

hydroxyl group bonded to
the same carbon atom

Because of the large bulk of the iodine atom, the most favourable direction for approach of the hydroxide ion is on the side opposite to the point of attachment of the iodine atom, known as **rear-side attack**

$\overset{\cdot\cdot}{\underset{\cdot\cdot}{HO}}{:}^{\ominus}$ most easily attacks from the → rear side

attack from the front is sterically **hindered**

This will also minimise any electron pair repulsion which may occur between the iodine and oxygen atoms in a frontal attack. The hydroxide ion must also approach with the **correct orientation**. Oxygen must be at the front in order to donate an electron pair to the α-carbon atom. As the negatively charged ion nears the α-carbon atom, the sigma electron pair in the carbon–iodine bond will be repelled towards the iodine atom, causing the bond to become appreciably more polar. Carbon and iodine have about the same electronegativities, and the bond is not very polar in the groundstate — but it is very readily *polarised*, both by solvent molecules and on close approach of an attacking anion

$\overset{\ominus}{\underset{\cdot\cdot}{HO}}{:}$

induced polarisation on close approach of the hydroxide ion

While the hydroxide ion donates electrons to the α-carbon atom, initiating formation of the new oxygen–carbon bond, the iodine atom simultaneously withdraws sigma electron density from the iodine–carbon bond and begins to retreat from its bonding position with the α-carbon

96

atom. Coincident with this, the methyl group and the two hydrogen atoms begin to move from their tetrahedral positions in the substrate towards one in which they are coplanar with the α-carbon atom. By the time the transition state is reached, at the point of maximum energy on the reaction profile, this process is complete and we may represent the transition state in the following way

Note that the oxygen atom, having donated electron density to the α-carbon atom, now has less than a unit negative charge, and is shown with a fractional charge, δ−. So is the iodine atom, which is beginning to form an anion. On the other hand, the α-carbon atom is both receiving and releasing electrons. The two partial bonds are regarded as equivalent to one ordinary sigma-bond, and therefore the normal octet of valence electrons around the carbon atom is not exceeded.

As before, we stress the fleeting nature of the transition state by drawing the structure within square brackets, and with a negative sign outside to indicate that the fractional charges on the oxygen and iodine atoms together add up to one unit of negative charge.

By synchronising the two processes, much of the energy required for breaking the carbon–iodine bond is supplied by energy released on formation of the new carbon–oxygen bond. Activation energy for such a transition state is considerably less than would be required for simple ionisation of the same substrate molecule.

As the forward reaction continues, formation of the carbon-oxygen bond is completed, and the product molecule separates from the iodide ion. The whole process is summarised by a single mechanistic equation

An energy profile for this reaction is of the relatively simple form shown in figure 5.5.

Figure 5.5 *Energy profile for hydrolysis of iodoethane. The oxygen-carbon bond is stronger than a carbon-iodine bond and the overall process is weakly exothermic*

Two species are involved in the transition state, and so the reaction is classified as a **bimolecular process**, and given the symbol S_N2. (Substitution, Nucleophilic, bimolecular). The S_N1 reaction is a **stepwise process**, whereas an S_N2 reaction is said to be a **synchronous**, or better, a **concerted process**.

98

Under normal conditions, a bimolecular reaction would be kinetically **second order**, the rate of reaction depending on the concentration of both the substrate and the attacking nucleophile.

$$\text{Rate} = k \; [\overset{..}{\underset{..}{HO}} \overset{\ominus}{:}] \; [CH_3CH_2 \overset{..}{\underset{..}{I}} :]$$

where k is the rate constant for the reaction

However, if a large excess of hydroxide ion is employed, then small changes in its concentration will have no observable effect on the rate, which will therefore be proportional only to the concentration of the substrate. To distinguish this from a true first order reaction, the term **pseudo first order** is applied.

$$\text{Rate} = k \; [\overset{\ominus}{\underset{..}{HO}} :] \; [CH_3CH_2 \overset{..}{\underset{..}{I}} :]$$

$$= k' \; [CH_3CH_2 \overset{..}{\underset{..}{I}} :]$$

where k' incorporates the (constant) concentration of $\overset{..}{\underset{..}{HO}} \overset{\ominus}{:}$

The value of the pseudo first order rate constant, k', will vary slightly with the actual concentration of $\overset{..}{\underset{..}{HO}} :^{\ominus}$. Observation of such variation therefore provides a method for the detection of pseudo first order reactions.

Distinction between a transition state and an intermediate

Because in a bimolecular reaction there is only one transition state in going from reactants to products, be careful not to confuse this with a reaction intermediate. For a reaction such as hydrolysis of a haloalkane, it is estimated that the whole displacement process takes only about 10^{-12} second, the duration of a single vibration. So the reactants are in the transition state for an extremely short period. It is a very high energy condition, with but a momentary existence, and certainly cannot be isolated, or even detected during the reaction. Some important differences between a transition state and an intermediate are summarised in table 5.3.

Table 5.3 Comparison of transition state and intermediate

Transition state	Intermediate
1. Occupies a maximum (peak) on an energy profile	Occupies a minimum (trough) on an energy profile
2. Has only a momentary existence	Usually short-lived*, but has a finite lifetime. Regarded as a highly reactive temporary product
3. Cannot be isolated	Cannot normally be isolated, but certain exceptionally stable intermediates have been prepared — see chapter 8
4. Not easily detected	Often detected, for example, by spectroscopic methods
5. Bond making and/or bond breaking is involved	These processes do not occur in an intermediate

*Various techniques have been devised for prolonging the life of short-lived intermediates (for example, by freezing in some sort of matrix at very low temperatures) but these are rather specialised and are beyond the scope of the present discussion.

Reversibility of nucleophilic substitution

Writing an equation with an arrow ($\longrightarrow$) rather than an equilibrium sign ($\rightleftharpoons$) implies that the reaction goes to completion, or at least gives worthwhile yields of the required product. However, in the reactions we have been discussing, both unimolecular and bimolecular, the displaced group ($: \overset{..}{\text{I}} :^{\ominus}$) is also nucleophilic, and in principle the reverse reaction is quite possible

$$HO \overset{..}{:}{}^{\ominus} + R - \overset{..}{I} : \; \rightleftharpoons \; HO - R \quad : \overset{..}{I} :{}^{\ominus}$$

Nevertheless, since good yields of the alcohol are obtained, equilibrium lies well to the right in the above equation. What is it that determines the position of equilibrium and hence yield of the required product?

Clearly this is not simply a difference in nucleophilicity, since in aqueous solution the iodide ion is a rather better nucleophile than the hydroxide ion. The major factor is the *strength of the new bond*, and a carbon–oxygen bond is stronger than a carbon–iodine bond. Allied with this, the hydroxide ion is a **poor leaving group**, and so activation energy for the reverse step is greater than for the forward reaction.

$$\overset{\cdot\cdot}{HO}\overset{\ominus}{}: \;+\; R \xrightarrow{} \overset{\cdot\cdot}{I} : \;\rightleftharpoons\; \overset{\cdot\cdot}{HO} \longrightarrow R \;+\; : \overset{\cdot\cdot}{I}\overset{\ominus}{:}$$

weaker bond,
: $\overset{\cdot\cdot}{I}\overset{\ominus}{:}$ good
leaving group
stronger bond,
$\overset{\cdot\cdot}{HO}\overset{\ominus}{:}$ poor
leaving group

That this is true for both unimolecular and bimolecular reactions is apparent from the energy profiles for the two processes, figure 5.6.

Figure 5.6 *Energy profiles for unimolecular and bimolecular reactions*

101

Stereochemistry of the bimolecular process

Because of the necessity for rear-side approach in a bimolecular reaction, the attacking nucleophile becomes attached to the α-carbon atom on the side opposite to that of the displaced group

This entails the methyl group and the two hydrogen atoms 'flipping over' in a process which is described as **inversion of configuration**. An analogy often quoted is that of an umbrella blowing inside out in a strong wind

Studies with various optically active substrates show that inversion of configuration does indeed occur in reactions believed to be following a bimolecular pathway. The haloalkane 2-bromo-octane can be prepared in two optically active forms

S(+) 2-bromo-octane*   R(−) 2-bromo-octane

When either the **S** or **R** enantiomer is subjected to alkaline hydrolysis by the S_N2 route, the resulting optically active alcohol (octan-2-ol) is of the opposite configuration. For example

---

*The terms **R** (Rectus) and **S** (Sinister) relate to the configuration of the compound; the (+) and (−) signs donate the direction in which the compound rotates plane polarised light. For more detail consult a standard textbook such as Streitwieser, A. and Heathcock, C. H., *Introduction to Organic Chemistry*, 2nd edition, Macmillan, 1981.

S(+) 2-bromo-octane
(R = CH$_2$(CH$_2$)$_4$CH$_3$)

R(−) octan-2-ol

Note that inversion of configuration in the product has to be established by independent methods. The change in sign of rotation is merely fortuitous, and does not itself necessitate a change in configuration, as the product is a different compound. By using a radioactive halogen isotope, observations can be made on the bimolecular displacement of halide ion by the same kind of ion. A classical example involves reaction of optically active 2-iodo-octane with a propanone solution of potassium iodide enriched in the radioactive isotope ^{128}I

S(+) 2-iodo-octane
(R = CH$_2$(CH$_2$)$_4$CH$_3$)

R(−) 2-iodo-octane

The rate of uptake of ^{128}: $\overset{..}{\underset{..}{I}}$:$^{\ominus}$ can be determined by taking small samples at timed intervals, and observing the distribution of the isotope between the 2-iodo-octane and potassium iodide. The rate of loss of optical activity is measured with a polarimeter. It is found that both processes exhibit second order kinetics consistent with bimolecular reaction, and (within the limits of experimental error) the rate of loss of optical activity is just *twice* that of the rate of uptake of iodide ion by the substrate. This is exactly what we should anticipate, because each individual substitution reaction converts a (+) molecule into a (−) molecule and the latter will in turn offset the rotation due to a second (+) molecule.

Exercise 5.2
What observations would you expect to make if in the above reaction displacement occurred (a) with retention of configuration, and (b) with random loss and retention of configuration?

UNIMOLECULAR AND BIMOLECULAR MECHANISMS: AN OVERVIEW

Nucleophilic substitution is of wide applicability. Many different nucleophiles are available, and substrates other than haloalkanes may be used. An extended discussion of these reactions is beyond the scope of this book, but we will end this section with a brief look at some of the factors which influence the reactivity of a particular substrate.

Unimolecular reactions

In the unimolecular process, the rate-determining step is ionisation of the substrate, and the ease with which this can occur depends on two main factors. One is the structure of the substrate, and the other is the ionising power of the solvent used. If we wish a reaction to proceed by the unimolecular mechanism, we must select a substrate with a good leaving group, and which can give rise to a relatively stable carbocation intermediate, and carry out the reaction in a solvent of high ionising power.

The order of increasing stability of carbocations is methyl $< 1°< 2°< 3°$, and the key factor is dispersal of positive charge on the α-carbon atom. The methyl carbocation is least stable because carbon–hydrogen bonds are not easily polarised and most of the positive charge resides solely on the carbon atom. Alkyl groups are better able to release bonding sigma electrons towards the positively charged carbon atom, a process we have described as a positive inductive effect*.

the positive nucleus of the small hydrogen atom is able to 'hold on' to its share of the bonding sigma electrons and the C–H bond is only very slightly polar

+1 effect allows the methyl group to have a small share of the positive charge

the α-carbon atom now has fractionally less than a unit positive charge

---

*An alternative explanation for charge dispersal by methyl groups involves the concept of **HYPERCONJUGATION**. It is postulated that electron density from carbon–hydrogen bonds in a methyl group can be used to partially offset the positive charge on the α-carbon atom. For further details, consult a more advanced textbook such as Streitwieser, A. and Heathcock, C. H., *Introduction to Organic Chemistry*, 2nd edition, Macmillan, 1981.

104

Progressive replacement of hydrogen atoms by methyl groups helps to disperse the positive charge, increasing the stability of carbocations in the series

| methyl | (1°) | (2°) | (3°) |

least stable,
charge **localised** on
the carbon atom

most stable,
charge partly **dispersed**
by the methyl groups

Of course, the amount of energy required for ionisation is greatly reduced under normal reaction conditions because of stabilisation of the ions by solvation. Even so, activation energy for the formation of the methyl carbocation is too great for this to occur, and halomethanes only react by the bimolecular mechanism. Most other primary haloalkanes only rarely, if ever, undergo unimolecular reaction.

The Hammond Postulate
You will have noticed that in the above discussion we have assumed that the more stable a carbocation, the more easily it is formed. Although this may appear self-evident, it is based on a theoretical proposition known as the **Hammond Postulate**. Briefly, this states that when a transition state and intermediate are of comparable energy (that is, close together on an energy profile), they will be of fairly similar structure. Therefore, those factors which stabilise an intermediate will also stabilise the transition state from which it is formed. Alkyl groups which stabilise the positive charge on the carbocation are equally able to stabilise (though to a lesser extent) the developing positive charge in the transition state.

There is another important consequence of this statement. Since a tertiary carbocation requires less activation energy for its formation than a secondary carbocation, it follows that (under comparable conditions) a reaction for which the rate-determining step is formation of a tertiary carbocation will proceed at a *faster rate* than one involving a secondary carbocation intermediate. See figure 5.7.

Figure 5.7 *Energy profiles for ionisation of secondary and tertiary haloalkanes. For easier comparison, the two haloalkanes are shown with the same groundstate energies*

Bimolecular reactions

To encourage unimolecular reaction, we need a substrate with a highly alkylated α-carbon atom, but with bimolecular processes the reverse is true. For a series of haloalkanes

$$CH_3 - \overset{..}{\underset{..}{X}} :, \ CH_3 - CH_2 - \overset{..}{\underset{..}{X}} :, \ CH_3 - \overset{\overset{CH_3}{|}}{CH} - \overset{..}{\underset{..}{X}} :, \ CH_3 - \overset{\overset{CH_3}{|}}{\underset{CH_3}{C}} - \overset{..}{\underset{..}{X}} :$$

replacement of small hydrogen atoms by bulky methyl groups destabilises the transition state by increasing congestion around the α-carbon atom. Compare the bimolecular transition state for hydrolysis of iodomethane with that for hydrolysis of 2-iodo-2-methyl propane

minimal interaction between small hydrogen atoms and the hydroxyl and iodide groups

steric crowding occurs when hydrogen atoms replaced by much larger methyl groups

106

On going from left to right in the above series of haloalkanes, increased steric crowding in the S_N2 transition state is paralleled by decreased rate of reaction.

Whereas in the unimolecular transition state alkyl groups on the α-carbon atom have a stabilising effect by helping to disperse the positive charge, in the bimolecular transition state they have the opposite effect by causing steric crowding. In S_N1 reactions the *electronic* effect of the alkyl groups is dominant: in S_N2 it is their *steric* effect which is more important.

For bimolecular reactions, then, the substrate should be of primary, or possibly secondary structure, with a relatively poor leaving group. Reaction will be helped by the use of a powerful nucleophile, and a solvent of low ionising power. Nucleophilic strength varies with the solvent employed. In aqueous solution the order of decreasing nucleophilicity of some common reagents is

$$\overset{\ominus}{C}N > \overset{\ominus}{I} : \sim H\overset{\ominus}{O} : \sim CH_3\overset{\ominus}{O} : \sim CH_3CH_2\overset{\ominus}{O} : > Ph\overset{\ominus}{O} : > \overset{\ominus}{B}r : > \overset{\ominus}{C}l : > CH_3C\overset{\ominus}{O}O :$$

$$\overset{\ominus}{F} : > H_2\overset{..}{O} \sim CH_3\overset{..}{O}H \sim CH_3CH_2\overset{..}{O}H$$

The various factors which influence the two mechanisms are summarised in table 5.4.

Table 5.4 The main factors which influence unimolecular and bimolecular reactions

Factor	Mechanism favoured	
	S_N1	S_N2
Substrate	3°, few 2°	1°, few 2°
Leaving group	Good ($:\overset{\ominus}{B}r:$, $:\overset{\ominus}{I}:$)	Less good ($:\overset{\ominus}{C}l:$)
Solvent	Highly polar	Less polar
Nucleophile	Weak, and low concentration	Powerful, and in high concentration

Summary of evidence for the unimolecular mechanism

(1) The rate of reaction depends only on the concentration of the substrate

$$\text{Rate} = k \, [\text{substrate}]$$

(2) The rate is independent of the nature or concentration of the nucleophile.
(3) Structural features in the substrate which would help to stabilise an intermediate carbocation increase the rate of reaction. Thus, under comparable reaction conditions, the rate of unimolecular substitution in haloalkanes increases in the series

$$\text{methyl} < 1° < 2° < 3°$$

(4) Optically active haloalkanes are racimised.
(5) Certain carbocation intermediates may undergo rearrangement.
(6) Increasing the polarity of the solvent also increases the rate of reaction.

Summary of evidence for the bimolecular mechanism

(1) The rate of reaction depends on the concentration of both the substrate and the attacking nucleophile

$$\text{Rate} = k[\text{nucleophile}]\,[\text{substrate}]$$

(2) Changing to a more powerful nucleophile increases the rate of reaction.
(3) Structural features generally have smaller effects than in unimolecular reactions, but increased numbers of alkyl groups on the α-carbon atom destabilise the transition state by steric crowding around the α-carbon atom. Consequently, under comparable reaction conditions, the rate of bimolecular substitution of haloalkanes decreases in the series

$$\text{methyl} > 1° > 2° > 3°$$

(4) Studies with optically active compounds confirm that bimolecular substitution is accompanied by inversion of configuration about the α-carbon atom.

A final comment

The main difference between the two mechanisms is that in the unimolecular process the nucleophile attacks after ionisation of the substrate, whereas in bimolecular processes nucleophilic attack *assists* displacement

108

of the leaving group. Obviously it is a matter of timing of the attack by the nucleophile, and there is a spectrum of possible mechanisms with the simplified concepts of S_N1 and S_N2 at the extreme ends.

Some reactions are clearly S_N1 or S_N2, but many exhibit so called 'borderline behaviour'. At its simplest, this is interpreted as reaction of some substrate molecules by the S_N1 mechanism, and others by S_N2. A more sophisticated approach visualises all nucleophilic substitutions occurring via an intermediate **ion pair** in which the two ions remain in close contact with one another. At the S_N1 end of the mechanistic spectrum, the formation of the ion-pair is rate-determining, whereas for S_N2 the slow step is break-up of the ion pair by attack of the nucleophile. According to this theory, when the rates of formation and decomposition of the ion-pair intermediate are of the same order (that is, are competitive), then borderline behaviour is observed.

Relative unreactivity of chloroethene and chlorobenzene

The dominant feature of ethenyl (vinyl) and aryl halides is their resistance to attack by common nucleophiles. They do not react with $\overset{..}{H}\overset{..}{O}:^{\ominus}$, $R\overset{..}{O}:^{\ominus}$ $\overset{..}{C}N^{\ominus}$, or $\overset{..}{N}H_3$ under conditions where haloalkanes would experience substitution or elimination. Chlorobenzene, for example, is unaffected by boiling aqueous sodium hydroxide solution, and has to be heated to about $350°C$ (623K) under pressure before hydrolysis occurs.

Various factors may contribute to this relative inertness, but of great importance is the fact that both chloroethene and chlorobenzene have a resonance structure in which the carbon–chlorine bond is shorter and stronger than that in haloalkanes. For example

$$CH_2 = CH \overset{\frown}{-} \overset{..}{\underset{..}{Cl}}: \quad \longleftrightarrow \quad \overset{\ominus}{C}H_2 - CH = \overset{\oplus}{\underset{..}{Cl}}:$$

The charge-separated limiting form is not very stable (particularly as positive charge is developed on the electronegative chlorine atom) but even a small contribution will lead to a resonance structure represented as

$$\overset{\delta-}{C}H_2 \text{ === } CH \text{ === } \overset{\delta+}{\underset{..}{Cl}}:$$

shorter (169 pm), stronger bond
than in haloalkanes (177 pm)

Enhanced reactivity of 3-chloropropene and chloromethylbenzene

Propenyl (allyl) and phenylmethyl (benzyl) halides are generally more reactive than haloalkanes towards common nucleophiles. These compounds normally react by unimolecular mechanisms and their enhanced reactivity is attributed to the formation of carbocation intermediates which are resonance stabilised. The propenyl cation structure is discussed in chapter 2. A number of limiting forms can be written for the phenylmethyl carbocation

non-benzenoid limiting forms

Kekulé structures

The three non-benzenoid limiting forms make a smaller contribution than the two Kekulé structures, but dispersal of the positive charge is more effective than in even a tertiary alkyl carbocation such as the 2-methylpropyl (*tert*-butyl) carbocation. From the Hammond Postulate we know that the transition state for the formation of a resonance-stabilised carbocation will be similarly stabilised, and so activation energy for ionisation of propenyl and phenylmethyl compounds is that much smaller.

Enhanced reactivity is also observed in S_N2 reactions of these compounds. Here, resonance stabilisation of the bimolecular transition states is the influential factor.

Finally, we may now place the three classes of halide in order of increasing reactivity

ethenyl (vinyl) and aryl	<	alkyl	<	propenyl (allyl) and phenylmethyl (benzyl)
resonance stabilisation of substrate molecule		resonance not involved		resonance stabilisation of intermediate cation (S_N1), or bimolecular transition state (S_N2)

110

REACTIONS OF ALCOHOLS

Alcohols as nucleophiles

Oxygen is better able to accommodate positive charge than halogen, and so unlike haloalkanes, alcohols are weakly nucleophilic and basic. The reaction of alcohols with carboxylic acids (esterification) is considered in chapter 8.

The hydroxyl group is also weakly acidic, and conversion of alcohols into their salts generates the more powerfully nucleophilic (and basic) **alkoxide ion**, for example

$$2R\overset{..}{\underset{..}{O}}H + 2Na^{\cdot} \longrightarrow 2R\overset{\ominus}{\underset{..}{O}} : \overset{\oplus}{Na} + H_2$$

Alkoxides find use as nucleophiles in the synthesis of ethers (Williamson synthesis with methyl and primary haloalkanes), and as bases in the formation of alkenes (chapter 6).

Nucleophilic substitution reactions

Alcohols, like haloalkanes, are polar molecules, but direct displacement of the hydroxyl group is not possible. The carbon–oxygen bond is quite strong, and as a strong base, the hydroxide ion is a poor leaving group. You will recall from earlier discussion that for successful nucleophilic substituion to take place, the displaced group must be a weaker base than the attacking nucleophile. Halide ions (other than fluoride) are weak bases and good leaving groups, but with hydroxide ion, the reverse is true. However, displacement *is* possible under acidic conditions when protonation of the hydroxyl group converts it into a good leaving water molecule. Protonation also has the effect of increasing the positive charge on the α-carbon atom, making it more susceptible to nucleophilic attack.

weakly basic and nucleophilic oxygen atom

poor leaving HO : $^{\ominus}$ group

strong, moderately polar bond

leaving group is now a stable water molecule

more polar, weaker bond

α-carbon atom has a greater positive charge and is more susceptible to nucleophilic attack

Nevertheless, alcohols do not exhibit the same variety of substitution reactions as haloalkanes, because the necessity for a highly acidic medium precludes the use of nucleophiles such as alkoxide ion, cyanide ion, ammonia, etc., which would simply be protonated at low pH. Two important reactions of alcohols are with hydrogen halides and with sulphuric acid, and we will now look at some examples of each of these.

Reaction of alcohols with hydrogen halides

The observed order of increasing reactivity of hydrogen halides with alcohols is the order of increased acidity of the halides, namely

$$HF\colon < HCl\colon < HBr\colon < HI\colon$$

increasing acidity
————————————————————→
increasing reactivity with alcohols

Hydrogen fluoride is a much weaker acid than the other three, and reaction of alcohols with $HF\colon$ is of little practical value. When reacting with a particular hydrogen halide, the alcohols also show a gradation in reactivity, paralleling their basicities

$$CH_3\overset{..}{O}H < RCH_2\overset{..}{O}H < R_2CH\overset{..}{O}H < R_3C\overset{..}{O}H < PhCH_2\overset{..}{O}H$$

methyl   1°   2°   3°   benzyl

increasing reactivity with $HX\colon$
————————————————————————→

All alcohols react with hydrogen bromide and hydrogen iodide to form the corresponding bromoalkanes and iodoalkanes. The more reactive tertiary and phenylmethyl (benzyl) alcohols are also attacked by hydrogen chloride, but methyl, primary and secondary alcohols only give useful yields of chloroalkanes with the aid of a catalyst such as anhydrous zinc chloride ($ZnCl\colon_2$) (see page 115).

Reaction of 2-methylpropan-2-ol with hydrogen chloride: the S_N1 mechanism

The tertiary alcohol 2-methylpropan-2-ol is so reactive that it is converted into 2-chloro-2-methylpropane merely on shaking the alcohol with concentrated hydrochloric acid at room temperature. Apart from the preliminary protonation of the alcohol, the steps are similar to those in unimolecular hydrolysis of a haloalkane

The last step is also reversible, but the use of an arrow ($\longrightarrow$) rather than an equilibrium sign ($\rightleftharpoons$) implies that equilibrium lies well over to the right.

Exercise 5.4
Draw a fully labelled energy profile for the above reaction, showing the structure of the two transition states involved. Do not forget to include the protonation step.

As with haloalkanes, unimolecular substitution in alcohols may lead to rearranged products where the structure of the alcohol is such that the intermediate carbocation can undergo rearrangement (see page 93).

Reaction of ethanol with hydrogen iodide: the S_N2 mechanism

There is generally less tendency for alcohols to undergo bimolecular substitution, as the required acidic conditions prevent the use of most strong nucleophiles. For halide ions in aqueous media, the order of increasing nucleophilic strength is

113

$$: \overset{..}{\underset{..}{Cl}} : ^{\ominus} \quad < \quad : \overset{..}{\underset{..}{Br}} : ^{\ominus} \quad < \quad : \overset{..}{\underset{..}{I}} : ^{\ominus}$$

Bromide and iodide ions will displace a water molecule from most protonated alcohols, but attack by the chloride ion may require the use of a catalyst.

Preliminary protonation is followed by the normal concerted bimolecular reaction

The energy profile is of the familiar form for an S_N2 reaction, with the addition of the protonation step, figure 5.8.

Figure 5.8 *Energy profiles for bimolecular substitution in alcohols*

114

Reaction of ethanol with hydrochloric acid: the role of the catalyst

At the beginning of this section it was noted that in order to give appreciable yields of chloroalkanes, methyl, primary and secondary alcohols all require the aid of a catalyst such as anhydrous zinc chloride, $ZnCl_2$. Since reaction is bimolecular, a subsidiary role of $ZnCl_2$ is to increase the concentration of attacking chloride ion. Its main function, however, is as a **Lewis acid catalyst**, when it complexes with the oxygen atom of the alcohol

$$CH_3CH_2 - \overset{..}{O}: \quad ZnCl_2 \qquad \overset{\delta+}{CH_3CH_2} \rightarrow \overset{\oplus}{O} - \overset{\ominus}{ZnCl_2}$$

zinc atom has unfilled orbitals and can accept an electron pair from the oxygen atom

positive charge weakens the carbon–oxygen bond and increases the positive charge on the α-carbon atom

Substitution then takes place by attack of the chloride ion on the alcohol-catalyst complex

$$\overset{\ominus}{:Cl:} \quad \overset{CH_3}{\underset{H}{CH_2}} - \overset{\oplus}{O} - \overset{\ominus}{ZnCl_2} \longrightarrow :Cl - \overset{CH_3}{CH_2} + \left[\overset{..}{\underset{H}{O}} - \overset{\ominus}{ZnCl_2} \right] \longrightarrow HO - ZnCl: + :Cl:^{\ominus}$$

Alternatively, the hydrogen halide may be replaced with a solution of the corresponding sodium halide in sulphuric acid. For example, good yields of 1-bromopropane can be obtained by heating propan-1-ol under reflux with sodium bromide in sulphuric acid. The technique is less useful with secondary alcohols which tend to give alkenes as the main product. A further limitation is the tendency of secondary alcohols to give rearranged products.

Finally, it should be noted that alcohols will not react with concentrated aqueous solutions of sodium halides, showing that protonation *is* a necessary prerequisite for either the unimolecular or bimolecular process.

115

Reaction of alcohols with sulphuric acid

Alcohols can undergo a number of different reactions with sulphuric acid. Which one predominates in a particular situation depends on the structure of the alcohol, the concentration of the acid, and the temperature. As you would expect, the preliminary step in all the reactions is protonation of the alcohol.

Formation of hydrogen sulphate and sulphate esters
When treated with concentrated sulphuric acid at room temperature or just above, ethanol forms ethyl hydrogen sulphate and diethyl sulphate esters. This is an S_N2 reaction involving attack on the protonated alcohol by the weakly nucleophilic hydrogen sulphate anion

$$HO - S - O : \quad CH_2 - OH_2 \quad HO - S - O - CH_2 \; + \; OH_2$$

Note the structure of sulphuric acid and its conjugated base. In subsequent equations a more abbreviated form is used.

The hydrogen sulphate ester is itself a strong acid, which can ionise at the —OH group, and repetition of the above steps lead to the diethyl sulphate ester

$$CH_3CH_2OSO_2 - O : \quad CH_3 - OH_2 \quad CH_3CH_2OSO_2OCH_2CH_3 \; + \; OH_2$$

diethyl sulphate

Secondary and tertiary alcohols react in the same way at relatively low temperatures. Isolation of the esters is difficult as they rapidly decompose into alkenes on raising the temperature.

Formation of ethers
If ethanol is treated with a *small* amount of concentrated sulphuric acid and heated to about 140°C (413K), the main reaction is formation of ethoxyethane. This is another bimolecular substitution reaction, in which the attacking nucleophile is an unprotonated alcohol molecule

116

$$CH_3CH_2 \overset{\cdot\cdot}{\underset{\mid}{O}} : \quad \overset{CH_3}{\underset{\mid}{C}}H_2 \overset{\oplus}{\underset{\cdot\cdot}{O}}H_2 \longrightarrow CH_3CH_2 \overset{\oplus}{\underset{\mid}{O}} \overset{\cdot\cdot}{\underset{\mid}{}}CH_2CH_3 + \overset{\cdot\cdot}{O}H_2$$

The first-formed product is the protonated ether, but this will rapidly lose a proton to a base such as another alcohol molecule or a hydrogen sulphate ion.

Reaction will, of course, proceed via a bimolecular transition state

$$\left[CH_3CH_2 \overset{\delta+}{\overset{\cdot\cdot}{\underset{\underset{H}{\mid}}{O}}} - - - \overset{CH_3}{\underset{\underset{H\;\;H}{\diagup\diagdown}}{C}} - - - \overset{\delta+}{\underset{\cdot\cdot}{O}}H_2 \right]^{\oplus}$$

Look carefully at the structure and remind yourself of the various processes underway in the transition state.

Using a limited amount of acid ensures that at equilibrium a relatively large number of alcohol molecules remain unprotonated. The neutral alcohol molecule is a weaker nucleophile than the hydrogen sulphate anion, but it can successfully compete as it is present in much greater concentration. When an excess of acid is employed, the position is reversed and at higher temperatures the predominant product is the alkene, ethene. This reaction is discussed in the next chapter (page 138).

REACTIONS OF PHENOLS

Phenols as nucleophiles

Although they readily react with acid chlorides and acid anhydrides, phenols do not undergo direct (acid-catalysed) esterification with carboxylic acids nor yet do they readily react with haloalkanes. The phenoxide ion, on the other hand, is a much stronger base and nucleophile (though weaker than the alkoxide ion) and can be used in the Williamson etherification reaction with haloalkanes. The formation of 'phenol-formaldehyde' resins, and the synthesis of *ortho*-hydroxybenzoic acid (salicylic acid) are further examples of nucleophilic processes involving the phenoxide ion.

Nucleophilic displacement of the hydroxyl group

The hydroxyl group in phenols is difficult to displace. Unlike alcohols, phenols do not react with hydrogen halides, sulphur oxide dichloride or phosphorus trichloride. Some reaction does occur with phosphorus penta-chloride, but the main product is the ester, triphenyl phosphate, $(PhO)_3PO$. Phenylamine is formed when phenol is heated under pressure with ammonia, but a catalyst $(ZnCl_2)$ is required to obtain good yields.

There are various reasons for this lack of reactivity towards nucleo-philes. The carbon–oxygen bond is stronger than in alcohols, phenols are not readily protonated, and as we have seen, the hydroxyl group is itself a poor leaving group. Furthermore, the phenyl carbocation is highly unstable (the positive charge cannot be delocalised), making S_N1 unlikely, and normal S_N2 is sterically impossible (compare the lack of reactivity in chlorobenzene).

REACTIONS OF ETHERS (ALKOXYALKANES)

Ethers have a polar structure, but since the negative inductive effect of the oxygen atom operates over two oxygen–carbon bonds, neither α-carbon atom is particularly positively charged

resultant electric dipole moment
$\mu = 4.34 \times 10^{-30}$ C m (1.30 D)

Although they form coordination complexes with Lewis acids, for example, with boron trifluoride

ethers are not sufficiently nucleophilic to displace halogen from halo-alkanes, etc.

Furthermore, the alkoxide ion is a very poor leaving group, and so ethers are not themselves susceptible to nucleophilic displacement, for example by aqueous sodium hydroxide solution. They are equally inert to

118

moderate concentrations of acids such as sulphuric acid, or hydrochloric acid. However, ethers are rapidly cleaved by treatment with concentrated hydriodic acid, even at room temperature.

Reaction of methoxymethane (dimethyl ether) with hydriodic acid

As with alcohols, reaction is initiated by protonation of the oxygen atom

$$H_2\overset{..}{\overset{\frown}{O}} \quad H \overset{\frown}{-} \overset{..}{\underset{..}{I}}: \quad \rightleftharpoons \quad H_3\overset{\oplus}{\overset{..}{O}} + :\overset{..}{\underset{..}{I}}:^{\ominus}$$

$$\begin{array}{c} CH_3 \\ \diagdown \\ CH_3 \diagup \end{array} \overset{..}{\overset{\frown}{O}} \quad H \overset{\frown}{-} \overset{\oplus}{O}H_2 \quad \rightleftharpoons \quad \begin{array}{c} CH_3 \\ \diagdown \\ CH_3 \diagup \end{array} \overset{\oplus}{\overset{..}{O}} - H + \overset{..}{O}H_2$$

This has the effect of increasing the positive charge on the two α-carbon atoms, and converting the poor leaving methoxy group into the good leaving methanol molecule

weaker, more polar bond

$$\overset{\delta+}{CH_3} \longrightarrow \overset{..\oplus}{O}CH_3$$
$$\underset{H}{|}$$

the α-carbon atom has a larger positive charge than in the neutral ether molecule

methanol is a better leaving group than the methoxide ion

Bimolecular substitution follows, in which the attacking species is the strongly nucleophilic iodide ion

$$^{\ominus}:\overset{..}{\underset{..}{I}}: \quad \begin{array}{c} H \\ \diagdown \\ C \\ H \diagup \quad | \\ H \end{array} \overset{\frown}{-} \overset{\oplus}{O}CH_3 \quad \rightleftharpoons \quad \left[:\overset{\delta-}{\underset{..}{I}} ---- \overset{H}{\underset{H}{\overset{|}{C}}} ---- \overset{\delta+}{\underset{|}{\overset{..}{O}}CH_3} \right] \quad \rightleftharpoons \quad :\overset{..}{\underset{..}{I}} - CH_3 + :\overset{..}{O}CH_3 \\ \underset{H}{|}$$

Exercise 5.6

Can you suggest why similar reactions are not observed with sulphuric acid or hydrochloric acid?

119

The necessity for preliminary protonation of the ether molecule rules out the use of nucleophiles such as hydroxide ion and alkoxide ion which obviously cannot exist in acid conditions.

An interesting problem arises with an asymmetrical ether such as methoxyethane. The protonated substrate has two possible positions for attack by the iodide ion

but the main products are iodomethane and ethanol. The iodine atom is quite large, and preferential reaction at the α'-carbon atom is readily explained in terms of the increased steric crowding present in the transition state for attack on the α''-carbon atom

transition state for
attack on α'-carbon atom

transition state for
attack on α''-carbon atom

Incidentally, raising the temperature increases the reaction rate, but at higher temperatures nucleophilic attack by iodide ion on the ethanol molecule converts it into iodoethane.

REACTIONS OF AMINES

Amines are regarded as derivatives of ammonia and are classified as **primary, secondary** or **tertiary** according to the number of alkyl or aryl groups attached to the nitrogen atom

$$\overset{..}{N}H_3 \qquad R\overset{..}{N}H_2 \qquad R_2\overset{..}{N}H \qquad R_3\overset{..}{N}$$

ammonia   (1°)   (2°)   (3°)

Be careful not to confuse this terminology with that applied to the halo-alkanes and alcohols. With those compounds, primary, secondary and tertiary relate to the structure of the hydrocarbon skeleton to which the halogen or hydroxyl group is attached. There are some parallels in structure and reactivity of amines and alcohols, but also some important differences.

Amines as nucleophiles and bases

Amines are stronger nucleophiles and bases than alcohols, and can participate in both nucleophilic substitution and elimination reactions.

Synthesis of amines by reaction of ammonia with haloalkanes (an S_N2 process) is complicated by further reaction of the first-formed primary amine

followed by

Further reaction leads eventually to the quaternary ammonium salt, tetra-ethylammonium iodide, $(CH_3CH_2)_4 \overset{\oplus}{N} : \overset{..}{\underset{..}{I}} :^{\ominus}$.

Nucleophilic reaction of amines with carbonyl compounds, acyl halides and acid anhydrides is discussed in chapters 7 and 8. Amines are sufficiently basic to bring about bimolecular elimination in haloalkanes. Bulky structures such as N-methyl-2,6-dimethylpiperidine

are sometimes used for this purpose because of little competition from bimolecular substitution.

Nucleophilic substitution

The carbon-nitrogen bond in amines is only weakly polar. For example, ethylamine has an electric dipole moment of $\mu = 4.07 \times 10^{-30}$ C m (1.22 D), compared with ethanol, $\mu = 5.67 \times 10^{-30}$ C m (1.71 D). The amide ion, $\overset{..}{N}H_2^{\ominus}$, is a very powerful base, stronger than $H\overset{..}{O}:^{\ominus}$, and cannot be directly displaced by nucleophilic attack. In parallel with the alcohols, protonation of the nitrogen atom converts the non-leaving amino group into a better leaving ammonia molecule.

$$-\overset{|}{\underset{|}{C}}-\overset{..}{N}H_2 \qquad \text{not displaced as } \overset{..}{N}H_2^{\ominus}$$

$$-\overset{|}{\underset{|}{C}}-\overset{\oplus}{N}H_3 \qquad \begin{array}{l}\text{displacement as the more stable} \\ \overset{..}{N}H_3 \text{ molecule now possible}\end{array}$$

However, the ammonia molecule is a stronger base than a water molecule, and it is still not a good leaving group. When ethylammonium bromide is heated, some bromoethane and ammonia are formed in an S_N2 reaction (the reverse of the preparative reaction above)

$$\overset{\ominus}{:}\overset{..}{Br}: \quad \overset{CH_3}{\underset{|}{C}}H_2-\overset{\oplus}{N}H_3 \quad \longrightarrow \quad :\overset{..}{Br}-CH_2 + \overset{..}{N}H_3 \quad (S_N2)$$

Although this is the main reaction, various side reactions occur, and it is not a process of general applicability.

Trimethylamine is a better leaving group, and when tetramethylammonium bromide is heated, the products, bromomethane and trimethylamine, are formed in good yield

$$\overset{\ominus}{:}\overset{..}{Br}: \quad CH_3-\overset{\oplus}{N}(CH_3)_3 \quad \longrightarrow \quad :\overset{..}{Br}-CH_3 + \overset{..}{N}(CH_3)_3 \quad (E2)$$

6 Elimination

REACTIONS OF HALOALKANES

Introduction

When haloalkanes (other than halomethanes) undergo nucleophilic substitution, there is invariably a side reaction involving the formation of an alkene (or alkenes). For example, alkaline hydrolysis of 2-iodopropane is accompanied by formation of some propene

$$HO^{\ominus} + (CH_3)_2 CH\ddot{I} \nearrow (CH_3)_2CH - \ddot{O}H + :\ddot{I}:^{\ominus}$$

$$\searrow CH_3CH = CH_2 + :\ddot{I}:^{\ominus} + H_2\ddot{O}$$

To explain this alternative **elimination reaction**, we need first of all to look again at the structure of the substrate molecule. We have already seen that polarity of the carbon–halogen bond leaves the α-carbon atom electron deficient. This means that it is more electronegative than the adjacent β-carbon atom, and so the C_α–C_β sigma-bond is also polarised. (We speak of 'relay of the negative inductive effect of the halogen atom'.)

$$-\overset{|}{\underset{|}{C}}_\beta \overset{\delta\delta+}{\longrightarrow} \overset{|}{\underset{|}{C}}_\alpha \overset{\delta+}{\longrightarrow} \ddot{X}:^{\delta-}$$

relay of −I effect

As a consequence of the fractional positive charge developed on the β-carbon atom, hydrogen atoms attached to this carbon atom (that is, β-hydrogen atoms) are very slightly electron deficient. They are therefore weakly acidic and are referred to as **activated β-hydrogen atoms**

activated
β-hydrogen atom

When the haloalkane is able to ionise, β-hydrogen atoms in the resulting carbocation will be even more acidic

$$\overset{\delta\delta+}{H} \rightarrow \overset{|\delta+}{\underset{|}{C_\beta}} \rightarrow \overset{|\oplus}{\underset{|}{C_\alpha}}$$

α-carbon with unit positive
charge exerts a much stronger
−I effect than a halogen atom

β-hydrogen is
more acidic than in
a neutral haloalkane
molecule

Since by definition, nucleophiles can also function as bases, it is not surprising that when a halide is treated with a nucleophile which is also strongly basic, there is an alternative to substitution, involving removal of a β-hydrogen atom by the base

$$\overset{\delta\delta\delta+}{H} \rightarrow \overset{|\delta\delta+}{\underset{|}{C_\beta}} \rightarrow \overset{|\delta+}{\underset{|}{C_\alpha}} \rightarrow \overset{\cdot\cdot\ \delta-}{\underset{\cdot\cdot}{X}} :$$

$$\overset{\ominus}{HO} :$$

attack (as a base)
on the β-hydrogen
atom leads to
elimination

attack (as a nucleophile)
on the α-carbon atom
leads to **substitution**

β-elimination involves the loss of both the halogen atom (as $: \overset{\cdot\cdot}{\underset{\cdot\cdot}{X}} :^{\ominus}$) and the β-hydrogen atom (as $H^{\oplus}$), and in parallel with nucleophilic substitution reactions, there are two extreme mechanisms for the reaction: a unimolecular process called **unimolecular elimination**, shorthand symbol E1, and a bimolecular process called **bimolecular elimination**, symbol E2. We will now consider each of these mechanisms in detail.

Formation of 2-methylpropene from 2-iodo-2-methylpropane: the unimolecular mechanism, E1

When 2-iodo-2-methylpropane is warmed with moderately concentrated aqueous alkali, very little substitution occurs. Instead, the main product is the alkene, 2-methylpropene

$$(CH_3)_3 C \overset{..}{\underset{..}{-}} \overset{\ominus}{\ddot{I}} : \; + \; H\ddot{O} : \quad \nearrow \quad \underset{\text{very little}}{(CH_3)_3 C \overset{..}{-} \overset{..}{O}H} \; + \; : \overset{..}{\underset{..}{I}} : ^{\ominus}$$

$$\searrow \quad \underset{CH_3}{\overset{CH_3}{\diagdown}} C = CH_2 \; + \; : \overset{..}{\underset{..}{I}} : ^{\ominus} \; + \; H_2\overset{..}{\underset{..}{O}}$$

main product

The rate of formation of the alkene is found to depend only on the concentration of the haloalkane. From this and other evidence, it is concluded that the first step in unimolecular elimination is the same as that in unimolecular substitution, that is, slow ionisation of the haloalkane

In substitution reactions, the intermediate carbocation gets rid of the positive charge by accepting an electron pair from the attacking nucleophile. When elimination occurs, the charge is lost by expulsion of a proton.

Now if on paper we simply remove a proton from a β-carbon atom in the carbocation, the resulting structure would look like this

The α-carbon atom is positively charged and has only six electrons in the valence shell. And although the β-carbon atom has a complete octet, it also has a negative charge. Clearly, a more stable arrangement would be for the β-carbon atom to share its new electron pair with the α-carbon atom. The charges cancel one another, and a new electron pair bond — a pi bond — is formed between the two atoms

125

In reality, removal of the proton and formation of the pi-bond occur as one continuous process. Think of the electron pair not as two 'particles', but as two units of electron density. Then as the sigma electron density in the C_β — H bond decreases, so the (new) pi electron density builds up in the C_β — C_α position. The various processes underway in the transition state may be shown as

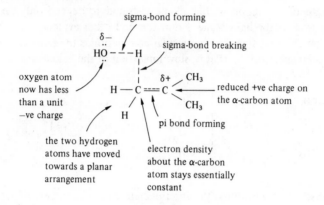

In going from the carbocation to the alkene product, the C_β atom changes from sp^3 to sp^2 hybridisation, so that in the transition state it is in an intermediate state of hybridisation between sp^3 and sp^2. When the changeover is complete, the electron pair on the β-carbon atom will be in a $2p$ orbital, and it is overlap of this orbital with the vacant $2p$ orbital on the α-carbon atom that leads to the formation of the new pi-bond. It is clear from this that at the time of attack by the hydroxide ion, the carbocation must be in a conformation with the β-hydrogen atom sticking up at right angles to the plane of the groups about the α-carbon atom

On removal of the proton, the remaining two β-hydrogen atoms move into a position coplanar with the rest of the molecule which leaves the two $2p$ orbitals in a suitable orientation for sideways overlap to occur

2p orbital on β-carbon atom with electron pair

vacant 2p orbital on the positively charged α-carbon atom

new pi-bonding molecular orbital of the alkene

Activation energy for the removal of the β-hydrogen atom is much less than that required for ionisation of the substrate, so it is formation of the intermediate carbocation which is the slow rate-determining step. The two-step reaction may be summarised in equation form as

Note that although removal of the β-proton proceeds via a bimolecular transition state, the first step (ionisation of the haloalkane) is rate-determining and the reaction is therefore classified as unimolecular elimination, E1.

The energy profile for this type of reaction is similar in outline to that for unimolecular substitution. However, the overall process is **endothermic**, because on going from reactants to products, two sigma-bonds are replaced by one new higher energy pi-bond. See figure 6.1.

Formation of more than one alkene
Whereas only one alkene is possible with 2-iodo-2-methylpropane (1), unimolecular elimination from 2-iodo-2-methylbutane (2) gives a mixture of two alkenes

127

Figure 6.1 *Energy profile for unimolecular elimination of HI from 2-iodo-2-methyl-propane*

$$CH_3 - \overset{\overset{\displaystyle CH_3}{|}}{\underset{\underset{\displaystyle CH_3}{|}}{C}} - \ddot{\underset{\cdot\cdot}{I}}: \quad \overset{-H\ddot{I}:}{\longrightarrow} \quad \overset{\displaystyle CH_3}{\underset{\displaystyle CH_3}{>}} C = CH_2$$

(1)   2-methylpropene

$$CH_3 - CH_2 - \overset{\overset{\displaystyle CH_3}{|}}{\underset{\underset{\displaystyle CH_3}{|}}{C}} - \ddot{\underset{\cdot\cdot}{I}}: \quad \overset{\displaystyle -H\ddot{I}:}{<}$$

(2)

$$\overset{\displaystyle CH_3}{\underset{\displaystyle CH_3CH_2}{>}} C = CH_2$$

2-methylbut-1-ene

+

$$CH_3CH = C \overset{\displaystyle CH_3}{\underset{\displaystyle CH_3}{<}}$$

2-methylbut-2-ene

This difference in behaviour is readily explained in terms of the two carbocation intermediates involved. Ionisation of 2-iodo-2-methylpropane (1) gives a symmetrical carbocation in which there are three similar β-carbon atoms

$$CH_3 \overset{\underset{\beta}{}}{-} \overset{\oplus}{C} \overset{\overset{CH_3 \; \beta}{}}{\underset{CH_3 \; \beta}{\diagdown}}$$

Elimination of a proton from any one of these gives the identical alkene, 2-methylpropene. In the carbocation resulting from ionisation of 2-iodo-2-methylbutane (2) there are two methyl groups and one ethyl group joined to the positively charged carbon atom

$$CH_3CH_2 \overset{\underset{\beta''}{}}{-} \overset{\oplus}{\underset{\alpha}{C}} \overset{\overset{CH_3 \; \beta'}{}}{\underset{CH_3 \; \beta'}{\diagdown}}$$

Loss of a proton from either methyl group (labelled β', above) will give 2-methylbut-2-ene. But a different alkene, 2-methylbut-2-ene, is formed when the proton is lost from the first carbon atom of the ethyl group (labelled β'').

The question then arises: are the two alkenes produced in equal quantities, or does one of them predominate? There is an empirical* rule, known as the **Saytzeff rule**, which states: 'In elimination reactions where more than one alkene is possible, the predominant alkene will be the one with the largest number of alkyl groups attached to the doubly bonded carbon atoms' (known as the *most alkylated* alkene). We shall see in the next chapter that the stability of alkenes increases with alkylation; for example

$CH_2 = CH_2$	$CH_2CH = CH_2$	$CH_3CH = CHCH_3$	$(CH_3)_2C = CHCH_3$	$(CH_3)_2C = C(CH_3)_2$
non-alkylated	monoalkylated	dialkylated	trialkylated	tetraalkylated

increased alkylation is paralleled by increased stability

$\longrightarrow$

So the Saytzeff Rule predicts that the *predominant product will be the most stable of the possible alkenes*. In the above example, then, 2-methylbut-2-ene, which is trialkylated, is formed in greater amount than 2-methylbut-1-ene, which is only dialkylated.

*'Empirical' means based on observation rather than theory. The Markovnikov Rule is another example. An empirical rule tells us what to expect in certain situations, but does not attempt to *explain* what happens.

129

To gain an understanding of why the more stable alkene is formed more readily, we must look in detail at the structures of the transition states leading to the two alkenes. Each contains an incipient (forming) double bond, and the factor which determines the stability of the alkene (extent of alkylation) will also influence the stability of the transition state from which it is formed. This is a consequence of the Hammond Postulate (page 105).

transition state for the formation of 2-methylbut-1-ene

(2.1)

transition state for the formation of 2-methylbut-2-ene

(2.2)

So the *more stable alkene is formed via a lower-energy transition state*. There are two different reaction paths, requiring different energies of activation. If the difference is small, mixed alkenes result; when the difference is large, the more stable alkene will predominate and may even be the *only* product. See figure 6.2.

TS_1 = transition state for ionisation
$TS_{2.1}$ = transition state for 2-methylbut-1-ene (alkene 1)
$TS_{2.2}$ = transition state for 2-methylbut-2-ene (alkene 2)

Figure 6.2 *Energy profile for the formation of mixed alkene products*

130

Explain the observation that unimolecular elimination from 2-iodo-3, 3-dimethylbutane gives very little 3,3-dimethylbut-2-ene; instead, a mixture of 2,3-dimethylbut-1-ene and 2,3-dimethylbut-2-ene is formed in which the latter alkene predominates. (*Hint*: can the first formed carbocation undergo rearrangement? − see page 93.)

Formation of cis and trans isomers

When unimolecular elimination gives a mixture of *cis* and *trans* isomers, the more stable *trans* alkene is usually the major product. Steric crowding, not present in the transition state for the *trans* alkene, destabilises the transition state for the *cis* isomer.

Formation of propene from 2-bromopropane: the bimolecular mechanism, E2

When 2-bromopropane is warmed with an alcoholic solution of potassium hydroxide, the main reaction is formation of propene

$$CH_3CH(\overset{..}{\underset{..}{Br}} :)CH_3 + \overset{\ominus}{HO} : \quad \longrightarrow \quad CH_3CH = CH_2 + H_2\overset{..}{O} + : \overset{..}{\underset{..}{Br}} : ^{\ominus}$$

As we should expect in an E2 reaction, the rate of formation of the alkene is found to be proportional to the concentrations of both the haloalkane substrate and the attacking nucleophile (base).

$$\text{Rate} = k \,[CH_3CH(\overset{..}{\underset{..}{Br}} :)CH_3] \,[\overset{\ominus}{HO} :]$$

By analogy with the S_N2 process, bimolecular elimination is thought to occur in one step, via a transition state in which removal of the β-proton is concerted with expulsion of the halide ion

131

It is interesting to examine this transition state in a little more detail. In contrast with E1, the E2 transition state carries a unit negative charge, distributed mainly over the oxygen and halogen atoms. The total electron density around the β-carbon atom remains essentially unchanged. As electrons are withdrawn from the carbon–hydrogen bond, they are immediately shared with the α-carbon atom. Likewise, as the α-carbon atom receives these electrons, it releases the sigma electrons towards the bromine atom. We have seen that in bimolecular substitution, part of the 'driving force' for displacement of the halide ion comes from energy released on formation of the new bond with the attacking nucleophile. In other words, the departing halide ion is helped on its way by a *'nucleophilic push'* of the attacking reagent

The analogous situation in bimolecular elimination is that much of the energy required to break the carbon–halogen bond is provided by energy released on formation of the new pi-bond. The 'driving force' is now a nucleophilic push, not directly from the attacking nucleophile, but by transfer of sigma electron density from the carbon–hydrogen bond

In passing through the transition state from haloalkane to alkene, the α-carbon atom has to undergo a change in hybridisation from sp^3 to sp^2.

132

As sp^3-p overlap is reduced in the carbon–bromine bond, so a p orbital has to be generated on the α-carbon atom in order to form the new pi-bond. The most favourable conformation for this to occur is for the β-hydrogen atom and the bromine atom to be *anti* (*trans*) to one another

the β-hydrogen atom attacked is *anti* to the leaving group (bromine atom)

Since the negative charge supplied by the hydroxide ion is dispersed in the transition state, solvation is relatively ineffective as a stabilising factor. For a given haloalkane, the transition state for bimolecular elimination is generally less stable than that for bimolecular substitution. This is important when selecting the best conditions for favouring either substitution or elimination.

Exercise 6.2
For bimolecular reaction of a given haloalkane, would you expect an increase in temperature to increase, decrease, or have no effect on the ratio of substitution to elimination?

Exercise 6.3
Draw a fully labelled energy profile for the E2 reaction discussed above – elimination of HBr : from 2-bromopropane.

Before continuing, let us briefly summarise the evidence for the unimolecular and bimolecular mechanisms.

Evidence for the E1 mechanism

1. In common with unimolecular substitution, the slow step is ionisation of the substrate molecule, and so the rate of unimolecular elimination depends only on the concentration of the substrate

$$\text{Rate} = k \, [\text{haloalkane}]$$

2. Changing from a weaker to a stronger base has no effect. A more powerful base may remove the β-proton more easily, but the slow step remains the formation of the intermediate carbocation.

3. The rate of unimolecular elimination is influenced by the nature of the solvent, since a change from a less polar to a more polar solvent will facilitate ionisation.

4. With certain haloalkane substrates, more than one alkene may be formed as a result of rearrangement in the first-formed carbocation intermediate.

Evidence for the E2 mechanism

1. As expected, the rate of reaction is found to be proportional to the concentration of both the substrate and the attacking base

$$\text{Rate} \; k \; [\overset{\ominus}{\underset{..}{\text{HO}}} :] \; [\text{haloalkane}] \qquad .$$

2. Since the base is involved in the rate-determining step, a change from a less powerful to a more powerful base causes an increase in rate.

3. Bimolecular elimination reactions exhibit a **kinetic isotope effect**. Independent measurements show that a carbon–deuterium bond is stronger than a carbon–hydrogen bond by about $5 \, \text{kJ mol}^{-1}$. Thus, slightly more activation energy is required for removal of $D^{\oplus}$ than for $H^{\oplus}$ in the E2 transition state, and β-deuterated haloalkanes react more slowly than 'normal' haloalkanes. For example, deuterated 2-bromopropane, $CD_3CH(\overset{..}{\underset{..}{Br}} :)CD_3$, undergoes bimolecular elimination in alcoholic potassium hydroxide solution at only 15 per cent of the rate of 'normal' 2-bromopropane. The kinetic isotope effect is shown diagrammatically in figure 6.3.

4. As no carbocation intermediate is involved, rearrangements are not observed in E2 reactions.

Let us now review the various factors which influence substitution and elimination, and see to what extent a chemist can exercise control over the two processes.

Figure 6.3 *Energy profile for bimolecular elimination of HB̈r ∶ from 2-bromopro-pane and hexadeutero-2-bromopropane. (Small differences in groundstate energies are not shown)*

Substitution versus elimination

From the foregoing discussion, it is obvious that S_N1, S_N2, E1 and E2 are *competing* reactions. Substitution is invariably accompanied by some elimination, and vice-versa. Frequently there is little a chemist can do to prevent the unwanted reaction, but by careful choice of reaction conditions he may be able to optimise the yield of the required product. Factors which influence the course of substitution and elimination are

(1) Structure of the haloalkane.
(2) Nature and concentration of the nucleophile.
(3) Solvent employed.
(4) Temperature at which the reaction is carried out.

Unimolecular processes
Those factors which favour S_N1 (use of a tertiary haloalkane and a highly ionising solvent) also favour E1, since the first step (ionisation) is common to both. Whether the intermediate carbocation picks up the nucleophile or eliminates a β-proton will depend largely on the relatively nucleophilicity and basicity of the attacking reagent. Thus for a given reagent, the ratio of substitution to elimination remains fairly constant.

Bimolecular processes
The question now is whether the reagent is more successful in attacking the α-carbon atom or the β-hydrogen atom. The main factors involved are

135

(1) Nucleophilicity versus basicity of the reagent.

(2) The size of the reagent. A large attacking reagent might find it more difficult to get close to the α-carbon atom than a β-hydrogen atom, and would also form a sterically crowded, less stable transition state.

(3) Structure of the haloalkane. A highly branched substrate is more likely to undergo elimination because of increased steric hindrance to the α-carbon atom (with consequent destabilisation of the transition state for substitution), and the larger number of β-hydrogen atoms available for attack.

Control over substitution

Given the right conditions, primary and secondary haloalkanes will usually provide substitution products in reasonable yield. For tertiary haloalkanes this may be more difficult. Reaction with nucleophiles which are also strong bases (such as $H\ddot{O}:^{\ominus}$ and $R\ddot{O}:^{\ominus}$) may give only alkenes, and even some secondary haloalkanes may give alkenes as the main product. Tertiary haloalkanes can sometimes be hydrolysed simply by refluxing with water. In other cases, an aqueous suspension of lead(II) oxide (PbO) or silver oxide (Ag_2O) may be used, or dilute aqueous sodium carbonate solution. All these reagents provide a polar medium with a very low concentration of hydroxide ion, and so discourage $S_N2/E2$.

Control over elimination

Since little can be done about the ratio of substitution to elimination for a particular haloalkane by unimolecular processes, conditions are selected which favour bimolecular reaction. If a choice of substrate is possible, then a secondary or tertiary structure is preferable to a primary one. For example, when treated with sodium ethoxide in ethanol at about 60°C, 1-bromopropane and 2-bromopropane both form propene. However, the primary compound gives only about 10 per cent yield, while the secondary haloalkane gives about 80 per cent alkene.

The usual reagent for elimination reactions is a concentrated alcoholic solution of either sodium or potassium hydroxide (the latter is the more soluble). Alcohol is appreciably less polar than water, thus discouraging ionisation. Since the reaction is bimolecular, a high concentration of the base will increase the rate. Furthermore, some powerfully basic ethoxide ion may be generated in an equilibrium

$$\overset{\ominus}{\text{HO}}\overset{..}{:}\ \text{H}\ \overset{..}{\underset{..}{\text{O}}}\ \text{CH}_2\text{CH}_3 \ \rightleftharpoons\ \overset{..}{\text{HOH}} + \ \overset{..}{:}\overset{\ominus}{\underset{}{\text{OCH}_2\text{CH}_3}}$$

Support for this comes from the observation that the main *substitution* product is the ether, not the alcohol

$$\text{CH}_3\text{CH}_2\overset{\ominus}{\underset{..}{\text{O}}}\overset{..}{:} + \text{CH}_3\text{CH}_2\text{CH}_2\overset{..}{\underset{..}{\text{I}}}: \ \xrightarrow{\text{S}_\text{N}1}\ \text{CH}_3\text{CH}_2\overset{..}{\text{O}}\text{CH}_2\text{CH}_2\text{CH}_3 + \overset{..}{:}\overset{\ominus}{\underset{..}{\text{I}}}:$$

Higher concentrations of alkoxide are obtained by 'dissolving' sodium or potassium metal in anhydrous alcohol, but such a reagent is much more expensive, of course. For difficult cases, better yields may result from the use of the more bulky 'iso-propoxide' or 'tert-butoxide' ions

increase in size of base

For a given haloalkane, the bimolecular transition state for elimination is of higher energy than that for substitution. Therefore, elimination is also favoured by a relatively high temperature.

The various points we have considered are summarised in table 6.1.

Table 6.1 Summary of factors and conditions which favour the individual processes of substitution and elimination

Factor	S_N1	S_N2	E1	E2
Structure of haloalkane	$3° \gg 2° > 1°$	$1° > 2° > 3°$	$3°$	$3°$ or $2°$
Nature of reagent	weak nucleophile	strong nucleophile	strong base	strong base
Concentration of reagent	low	high	low	high
Nature of solvent	highly polar	lower polarity	polar	low polarity
Temperature	moderate	moderate	high	high

DEHYDRATION OF ALCOHOLS

Nucleophilic substitution reactions of alcohols with sulphuric acid were discussed in the previous chapter (see page 116). The oxygen atom of a protonated hydroxyl group is powerfully electron attracting. This not only increases the positive charge on the α-carbon atom, but by inductive relay along the sigma-bonds, the β-hydrogen atoms are also affected

$$\overset{\delta\delta\delta+}{H} \rightarrow \overset{|\delta\delta+}{\underset{|\beta}{C}} \rightarrow \overset{|\delta+}{\underset{|\alpha}{C}} \rightarrow \overset{\oplus}{\underset{\cdot\cdot}{OH_2}}$$

β-hydrogen atom becomes appreciably acidic

powerful −I effect in the oxygen–carbon bond

It is not surprising, then, that when alcohols are treated with concentrated sulphuric acid, a competing reaction is dehydration (elimination of $H_2\overset{\cdot\cdot}{\underset{\cdot\cdot}{O}}$) to the corresponding alkene.

Dehydration of ethanol: bimolecular elimination, E2

To proceed at a reasonable rate, this reaction has to be carried out with an excess of concentrated sulphuric acid at about 170°C (443K)

$$CH_3CH_2\overset{\cdot\cdot}{\underset{\cdot\cdot}{O}}H \xrightarrow{\text{conc. } H_2SO_4} CH_2 = CH_2 + H_2\overset{\cdot\cdot}{\underset{\cdot\cdot}{O}}$$

The use of excess sulphuric acid ensures that a high proportion of alcohol molecules will be protonated. Consequently, there are relatively few unprotonated alcohol molecules available to compete as nucleophiles, and the principal attacking reagent is now the conjugate base of the acid, the hydrogen sulphate anion. This species is weakly nucleophilic, but it is also basic enough to remove a β-hydrogen atom. Because of the comparative instability of primary carbocations, it is unlikely that the protonated alcohol will ionise to any extent, and reaction proceeds in one step via a bimolecular transition state

note *anti* arrangement
of β-H and $H_2O^{\oplus}$ groups

these four H atoms
have moved towards
the planar arrangement
of the alkene

Because the hydrogen sulphate anion is a relatively weak base, activation energy for formation of the bimolecular transition state is quite high. Consequently, acid-catalysed dehydration of primary alcohols is often rather slow, even at elevated temperatures.

Alternative procedures include the use of phosphoric(V) acid, or passing the alcohol vapour over heated aluminium(III) oxide (alumina, Al_2O_3). The latter compound functions as a Lewis acid catalyst.

Dehydration of 2-methylpropan-2-ol: unimolecular elimination, E1

Secondary and tertiary alcohols give rise to more stable carbocation intermediates, and elimination from these compounds is unimolecular. Some tertiary alcohols dehydrate so readily that care has to be taken to remove all traces of acid before they can even be distilled without decomposition. 2-Methylpropan-2-ol gives good yields of 2-methylpropene simply on warming the alcohol with 20 per cent sulphuric acid. Following protonation of the alcohol, the mechanistic steps are ionisation

followed by expulsion of the β-proton

139

Loss of the β-proton, which in a carbocation is much more acidic, occurs very rapidly, and it is ionisation of the protonated substrate which is the slow rate-determining step.

Formation of mixed products

As with unimolecular dehydrohalogenation of haloalkanes, where the structure of the substrate permits formation of more than one alkene, the predominant product will be the more stable alkene (Saytzeff Rule, page 129). Since secondary and tertiary alcohols dehydrate via an intermediate carbocation, elimination may also be accompanied by rearrangement. For this reason, it is often advantageous to convert the alcohol into a haloalkane, as primary and secondary haloalkanes both dehydrohalogenate by an E2 mechanism where rearrangement is not possible.

REACTIONS OF AMINES

In the previous chapter, we saw that amines do not normally undergo nucleophilic substitution, but that certain quaternary ammonium salts decompose on heating by an S_N2-type reaction (see page 122). When the structure of the quaternary ammonium ion has one or more β-hydrogen atoms, the use of a strongly basic anion will bring about elimination. For example, tetraethylammonium hydroxide decomposes on heating to ethane, water and triethylamine

$$\overset{\ominus}{HO} : \quad H\!-\!CH_2\!-\!CH_2\!-\!\overset{\oplus}{N}(CH_2CH_3)_3 \quad \longrightarrow \quad HO\!-\!H \;+\; CH_2\!=\!CH_2 \;+\; \overset{..}{N}(CH_2CH_3)_3$$

Exercise 6.4
Draw the structure of the bimolecular transition state for the above reaction.

This reaction, known as **Hofmann elimination**, gives an alkene free from substitution products, but where the structure of the substrate is such that more than one alkene can form, the predominant product is the least alkylated alkene (contrast this with the Saytzeff Rule for unimolecular elimination in haloalkanes and alcohols, page 129).

The controlling factor is the *size* of the groups on the β-carbon atom. Reaction proceeds preferentially via the most stable, that is, the *least sterically crowded, transition state.*

2-Butyltrimethylammonium hydroxide decomposes on heating to give but-1-ene, but-2-ene, water and trimethylamine

$$
\begin{array}{c}
\underset{\beta'}{CH_3}\diagdown \\
\qquad \underset{\diagup}{\overset{\oplus}{CHN(CH_3)_3}} \;\; \overset{\ominus}{:\ddot{O}H} \\
\underset{\beta''}{CH_3CH_2}
\end{array}
\begin{array}{c}
\overset{-\beta'\,H}{\nearrow} \quad CH_2 = CHCH_2CH_3 \\
\\
\overset{-\beta''\,H}{\searrow} \quad CH_3CH = CHCH_3
\end{array}
\quad + \; \ddot{N}(CH_3)_3 \; + \; \ddot{O}H_2
$$

Which is the major product? Draw structures to illustrate steric crowding in the bimolecular transition state leading to the minor alkene product.

7 Nucleophilic Reactions of Carbonyl Compounds

INTRODUCTION

Aldehydes and ketones have a polar structure (chapter 1) and as a result the electron-deficient carbonyl carbon atom is susceptible to nucleophilic attack

Remember, however, that if a carbon atom is to receive a pair of electrons from a nucleophile, it must give up a share of another pair of electrons. In bimolecular substitution of haloalkanes, a pair of sigma electrons is removed by the departing halogen atom

electron pair
on halide ion

With aldehydes and ketones there is no suitable leaving group, but instead the carbonyl carbon atom is able to release its share of the pair of pi electrons to the bonded oxygen atom

electron pair
on oxygen atom

Reactants passing through the bimolecular transition state in S_N2 processes go on to form the final product. In nucleophilic attack on a carbonyl group, however, a transition state is formed which leads not to the final product, but to an **intermediate anion**. The anion can attain stability by reaction with a positively charged species (that is, an electrophile), and in most carbonyl reactions this is a proton

$$Y-\overset{\diagdown}{\underset{\diagup}{C}}-\overset{\ominus}{\underset{\cdot\cdot}{O}}: \quad H-Y \;\rightleftharpoons\; \left[Y-\overset{\diagdown}{\underset{\diagup}{C}}-\overset{\delta-}{\underset{\cdot\cdot}{O}}---H---Y \right]^{\ominus} \;\longrightarrow\; Y-\overset{\diagdown}{\underset{\diagup}{C}}-\overset{\cdot\cdot}{O}H + \overset{\cdot\cdot}{Y}^{\ominus}$$

transition state

The proton may come from the reagent H–Y, or from some other supplier such as a molecule of water. The net result is a product in which the reagent H–Y has added across the original carbonyl double bond

$$\overset{\diagdown}{\underset{\diagup}{C}}=\overset{\cdot\cdot}{\underset{\cdot\cdot}{O}} + H-Y \;\longrightarrow\; -\overset{|}{\underset{|}{C}}-\overset{\cdot\cdot}{\underset{|}{O}}:$$
        Y H

This is classified as a **nucleophilic addition reaction**. Formation of the intermediate is the slow rate-determining step, protonation of the anion occurring relatively quickly. The energy profile for this type of reaction is thus similar in outline to that for an S_N1 process, figure 7.1.

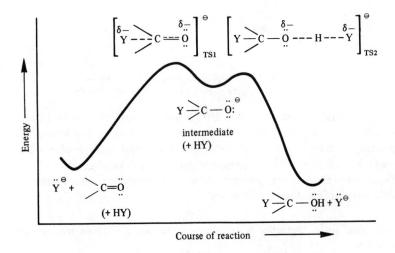

Figure 7.1 *Energy profile for a generalised nucleophilic addition reaction*

143

The oxygen atom of a carbonyl group is weakly basic, and in some reactions protonation may occur *before* attack by the nucleophile

$$\text{>C=}\ddot{\text{O}}\ \ H\text{—A} \ \rightleftharpoons\ \text{>C=}\overset{\oplus}{\underset{..}{\text{O}}}\text{=H} + \text{A}^{\ominus}$$

Resonance stabilisation of the resulting cation increases the positive charge on the carbon atom

$$\text{>C=}\overset{\oplus}{\underset{..}{\text{OH}}} \ \leftrightarrow\ \text{>}\overset{\oplus}{\text{C}}\text{—}\ddot{\text{OH}}$$

and this lowers the activation energy necessary for uptake of the nucleophile.

STRUCTURE AND STABILITY OF THE TRANSITION STATE

In the rate-determining transition state, groups attached to the carbonyl carbon atom will have moved from planar positions in the substrate molecule (carbonyl carbon atom sp^2-hybridised) towards the tetrahedral arrangement of the intermediate anion (carbonyl carbon atom sp^3-hybridised)

| planar | groups closer together in the transition state | tetrahedral intermediate |

So formation of the transition state is accompanied by increased *steric crowding* (see page 106) about the carbonyl carbon atom. This is minimal in methanal, where R and R' are both hydrogen atoms, larger in aldehydes, where R is alkyl and R' hydrogen, and most acute in ketones where R and R' are both alkyl or aryl groups*. As a result, reactivity towards nucleophilic reagents decreases in the series

---

*With alkyl groups, inductive destabilisation of the transition state may also be significant.

144

Aromatic aldehydes and ketones are usually less reactive than their aliphatic counterparts and this difference is not solely due to the steric effect of large aryl groups. Benzaldehyde is stabilised by conjugation of the carbonyl group with the aromatic nucleus

and this stabilisation (resonance) energy is largely lost on going from the groundstate to the transition state. Consequently, activation energy is greater than for the formation of the corresponding transition state from ethanal, where resonance is not involved.

Reactivity may be affected in other ways. For example, many reagents are used in aqueous solution and a water-insoluble carbonyl compound will obviously react more slowly than one which is partially or completely miscible.

We will now look in detail at some characteristic nucleophilic addition reactions. For simplicity, tetrahedral intermediates will be drawn in the planar form

and transition states will normally be omitted. However, remember that transition states will be involved both in the formation and further reaction of all such intermediates.

REACTION OF ETHANAL WITH HYDROGEN CYANIDE, HCN

Hydrogen cyanide adds to the carbonyl double bond of an aldehyde or ketone to give a product containing both a cyano (nitrile) group and a hydroxyl group, called a **cyanohydrin**.

$$
\begin{array}{c}
CH_3 \\
\diagdown \\
C = \ddot{O} + H\ddot{C}N \longrightarrow \\
\diagup \\
H
\end{array}
\qquad
\begin{array}{c}
:\!OH \\
| \\
CH_3 - C - CN \\
| \\
H
\end{array}
$$

ethanal cyanohydrin
(2-hydroxypropanonitrile)

Ionisation of HC̈N in aqueous solution gives rise to cyanide ion $CN^{\ominus}$, which is the attacking nucleophile

$$
H_2\ddot{O} \quad H - \ddot{C}N \;\rightleftharpoons\; H_2\overset{\oplus}{O}H + CN^{\ominus}
$$

Cyanide ion has the structure $\overset{\ominus}{C} \equiv N$, and it is the negatively charged *carbon* atom which donates electrons. Consequently, it is more convenient to write the formula the other way round, as $N \equiv \overset{\ominus}{C}$.

Addition takes place in two steps. Slow uptake of cyanide ion

$$
N \equiv \ddot{C}^{\ominus} \quad
\begin{array}{c}
CH_3 \\
\diagdown \\
C = \ddot{O}: \\
\diagup \\
H
\end{array}
\quad \overset{slow}{\rightleftharpoons} \quad
\begin{array}{c}
CH_3 \\
| \\
N \equiv C - C - \ddot{O}:^{\ominus} \\
| \\
H
\end{array}
$$

is followed by rapid protonation of the intermediate anion

$$
\begin{array}{c}
CH_3 \\
| \\
N \equiv C - C - \ddot{O}:^{\ominus} \quad H - \overset{\oplus}{O}H_2 \\
| \\
H
\end{array}
\quad \overset{fast}{\rightleftharpoons} \quad
\begin{array}{c}
CH_3 \\
| \\
N \equiv C - C - \ddot{O}H + \ddot{O}H_2 \\
| \\
H
\end{array}
$$

The protonating agent here is the hydroxonium ion, generated by reaction of HCN with water. We might equally well have shown a water molecule, or even an undissociated molecule of hydrogen cyanide.

The bimolecular transition state for the first, slow, rate-determining step, involves both the cyanide ion and the carbonyl substrate

$$
\left[\begin{array}{c}
\quad\quad\quad CH_3 \\
\quad\quad\quad \backslash \\
N \equiv C - - - C = = O : \\
\quad\quad\quad / \\
\quad\quad\quad H
\end{array} \right]^{\ominus}
$$

and so the rate of reaction depends on the concentration of both of these reagents

$$\text{Rate} = k\,[\overset{\ominus}{C}N]\,[CH_3C\overset{..}{H}\overset{..}{O}]$$

An interesting observation about this reaction is that the rate also varies with the pH. Hydrogen cyanide is only weakly acidic ($pK_a = 9.3$), and is therefore only partially ionised in aqueous solution. At low pH this ionisation is suppressed still further, and so the concentration of cyanide ion is minimised, and reaction slows down. On the other hand, the addition of a few drops of aqueous sodium hydroxide solution to the reaction mixture increases the concentration of cyanide ion

$$\overset{\ominus}{HO} : \quad H - C \equiv N \quad \rightleftharpoons \quad HO - H + \overset{\ominus}{C} \equiv N$$

and reaction speeds up.

Strongly alkaline conditions must be avoided, however, because of competition from the more powerfully nucleophilic hydroxide ion. Reaction is most rapid at about pH 5, and this is readily achieved by treating the carbonyl compound with sodium cyanide solution and then adding a small amount of strong acid.

You will have noticed that both steps in this reaction are reversible. Equilibrium between reactants and the intermediate must be in favour of the reactants, and it is rapid protonation of the intermediate anion which drives reaction to the right. Examination of energy profiles for the two steps emphasises this point, figures 7.2 and 7.3.

147

Figure 7.2 *Energy profile for attack by cyanide ion on a carbonyl compound*

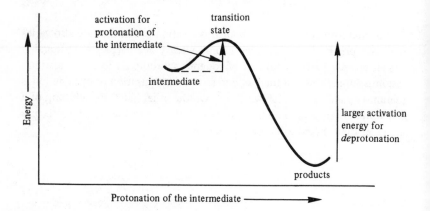

Figure 7.3 *Energy profile for protonation of the anionic intermediate*

Most aldehydes and simple ketones will form cyanohydrins, but the reaction is of little practical value with alkyl-aryl or aryl-aryl ketones, where steric crowding results in a very unstable transition state. Alkaline hydrolysis of cyanohydrins regenerates the carbonyl compound, but on warming with dilute acid the corresponding hydroxycarboxylic acid is formed by hydrolysis of the nitrile group

148

$$-\overset{|}{\underset{|}{C}} - C \equiv \overset{..}{N} \quad \xrightarrow{H_2\overset{..}{O}, H^\oplus} \quad -\overset{|}{\underset{|}{C}} - \overset{....}{C} \overset{....}{OOH}$$

with $:\overset{..}{O}H$ on the left carbon and $:\overset{..}{O}H$ on the right carbon.

REACTION WITH SODIUM HYDROGEN SULPHATE(IV), SODIUM HYDROGEN SULPHITE, NaHSO₃

Sodium hydrogen sulphite in aqueous solution adds to most aldehydes and simple ketones to form addition compounds. Since the reagent was formerly called sodium bisulphite, the products are known as **bisulphite addition compounds.** For example, if ethanal is shaken at room temperature with a saturated aqueous solution of NaHSO₃, 'ethanal bisulphite' separates out as a white solid

$$\overset{CH_3}{\underset{H}{>}}C = \overset{..}{O} + NaHSO_3 \longrightarrow CH_3 - \overset{H}{\underset{:\overset{..}{O}H}{\overset{|}{C}}} - \overset{..}{SO_2} - \overset{..}{O} \overset{\ominus}{:} Na^\oplus$$

The structure of these compounds was for some time in doubt, but it has now been established that the bond is from the sulphur atom to the carbon atom. In more detail, the structure is

$$CH_3 - \overset{H}{\underset{:\overset{..}{O}H}{\overset{|}{C}}} - \overset{:\overset{..}{O}:}{\underset{:O:}{\overset{||}{S}}} - \overset{..}{O} \overset{\ominus}{:} Na^\oplus$$

Compounds of the form $R - \overset{:O:}{\underset{:O:}{\overset{||}{\underset{||}{S}}}} - \overset{..}{O}H$ are alkyl **sulphonic acids**, so

a bisulphite compound is in fact the sodium salt of an α-hydroxy sulphonic acid. Ethanal bisulphite is sodium 1-hydroxyethane sulphonate.

The attacking nucleophile is often shown as the hydrogen sulphite ion, $HSO_3^\ominus$, but kinetic studies indicate that the more likely nucleophile is the sulphate(IV) (sulphite) ion, $SO_3^{2\ominus}$. This is produced in an equilibrium which lies well to the left

$$\underset{\ddot{\cdot\,}}{H_2\ddot{O}} \quad H\!-\!\underset{\ddot{\cdot\,}}{O}\!-\!\overset{\overset{\displaystyle :\ddot{O}:^{\ominus}}{|}}{\underset{\underset{\displaystyle :O:}{\|}}{S}} \quad \rightleftharpoons \quad H_2\overset{\oplus}{O}H \;+\; \overset{\ominus}{:}\ddot{O}\!-\!\overset{\overset{\displaystyle :\ddot{O}:^{\ominus}}{|}}{\underset{\underset{\displaystyle :O:}{\|}}{S}}$$

but $SO_3^{2\ominus}$ is a much stronger nucleophile than $HSO_3{}^{\ominus}$.

It may initially seem surprising that reaction occurs via the sulphur atom rather than the negatively charged oxygen atom. However, we have to remember that sulphur is more nucleophilic than oxygen, and the sulphur atom does have the ability to utilise a pair of electrons from the next inner shell. We can formulate the mechanism in two steps

$$\overset{\ominus}{:}\ddot{O}\!-\!\overset{\overset{\displaystyle :\ddot{O}:^{\ominus}}{|}}{\underset{\underset{\displaystyle :O:}{\|}}{S}}: \quad \underset{H}{\overset{CH_3}{>}}C\!=\!\ddot{O}: \quad \overset{slow}{\rightleftharpoons} \quad O\!=\!\overset{\overset{\displaystyle :\ddot{O}:^{\ominus}}{|}}{\underset{\underset{\displaystyle :O:}{\|}}{S}}\!-\!\overset{\overset{\displaystyle CH_3}{|}}{\underset{\underset{\displaystyle H}{|}}{C}}\!-\!\ddot{O}:^{\ominus}$$

followed by

$$O\!=\!\overset{\overset{\displaystyle :\ddot{O}:^{\ominus}}{|}}{\underset{\underset{\displaystyle :O:}{\|}}{S}}\!-\!\overset{\overset{\displaystyle CH_3}{|}}{\underset{\underset{\displaystyle H}{|}}{C}}\!-\!\ddot{O}:\quad H\!-\!\overset{\oplus}{\ddot{O}}H_2 \quad \longrightarrow \quad O\!=\!\overset{\overset{\displaystyle :\ddot{O}:^{\ominus}}{|}}{\underset{\underset{\displaystyle :O:}{\|}}{S}}\!-\!\overset{\overset{\displaystyle CH_3}{|}}{\underset{\underset{\displaystyle H}{|}}{C}}\!-\!\ddot{O}H_2$$

The $SO_3{}^{2\ominus}$ anion is quite large, and so steric factors are important. Ketones with bulky alkyl or aryl groups do not usually form bisulphite compounds.

Many bisulphite derivatives have sharp melting points which can be used for identification of the aldehyde or ketone. Bisulphite formation has also been used for the isolation and purification of carbonyl compounds, by virtue of the fact that the original compound is easily regenerated on warming the adduct with dilute alkali. Conversely, non-carbonyl products can be freed from small amounts of carbonyl compounds by shaking with cold saturated bisulphite solution.

REACTION WITH WATER, H₂Ö

In an aqueous solution of methanal, the ultraviolet absorption characteristic of the carbonyl group is almost completely suppressed. This is thought to be due to conversion of the aldehyde into the corresponding α-diol

carbonyl
chromophore
λ_{max} = 277 nm

methanediol

We can formulate a mechanism for this process based on the general pattern, but differing in detail. The attacking water molecule is a neutral nucleophile, so in donating an electron pair to the carbonyl carbon atom, the oxygen atom of the water molecule will itself acquire a unit positive charge

Thus the first-formed intermediate is not an anion, but a dipolar neutral species. It will be highly solvated by water molecules and this will lower the activation energy for its formation (via the usual transition state, of course!). Reaction is completed by rapid transfer of a proton from the positively charged to the negatively charged oxygen atom, the proton carrier being a water molecule.

Exercise 7.1
Write mechanistic equations for the protonation and deprotonation steps, which may occur in either order.

The intensity of absorption is proportional to concentration, so it is possible to use ultraviolet spectroscopy to determine the position of equilibrium. Ethanal in aqueous solution gives rise to about 50 per cent diol, but with propanone equilibrium is well to the left. This is in keeping with our earlier observations concerning steric crowding in the transition state.

Simple α-diols exist only in solution, but further evidence for their formation comes from a study of the behaviour of aldehydes and ketones with $H_2^{18}O$. Reversible formation of the diol will result in ^{18}O isotope being transferred to the aldehyde or ketone

$$\underset{/}{\overset{\diagdown}{C}} = \ddot{O} + H_2^{18}\ddot{O}: \quad \rightleftharpoons \quad \underset{/}{\overset{\diagdown}{C}} \underset{\ddot{O}H}{\overset{^{18}\ddot{O}H}{<}} \quad \rightleftharpoons \quad \underset{/}{\overset{\diagdown}{C}} = {^{18}}\ddot{O} + H_2O$$

It is found that with propanone very little $^{18}O*$ is incorporated in neutral solution, but uptake is rapid on the addition of a trace of acid or alkali. So reaction with water is both acid and base catalysed.

One diol which is stable enough to be isolated and characterised is that formed from 1,1,1-trichloroethanal, known as 'chloral hydrate'

$$: Cl_3C \overset{\overset{\textstyle H}{|}}{\underset{\underset{\textstyle :OH}{|}}{C}} \ddot{O}H$$

Replacing the three hydrogen atoms on the methyl group of ethanal by bulky chlorine atoms will clearly increase steric crowding in the transition state, but once the diol is formed, the chlorine atoms have a stabilising effect. To account for this, we must first of all look at the mechanism for the reverse reaction. This involves loss of $H\ddot{O}:^{\ominus}$ and removal of a proton to re-form the carbonyl group

---

$*^{18}O$ is readily estimated by mass spectrometry.

Hydroxide ion is a poor leaving group and probably has to be converted into the better leaving water molecule, but loss of either $HO:^{\ominus}$ or H_2O will be opposed by the powerful $-I$ effect of the chloromethyl group

There is another factor which may be even more influential. From a study of the infrared spectrum of this compound, it appears that two of the chlorine atoms are able to form intramolecular hydrogen bonds with the hydroxyl groups

Hydrogen bonding lowers the internal energy of the molecule, and the formation of five-membered rings is particularly favourable.

REACTION WITH ALCOHOLS, $R\ddot{O}H$

Alcohols react with aldehydes and ketones in the same way as water, giving rise to **hemiacetals** or **hemiketals**. Ethanal reacts with ethanol, for example, to form 1-ethoxyethanol

153

$$
\begin{array}{c}
CH_3 \\
\diagdown \\
C \\
\diagup \quad \diagdown \\
H \qquad \overset{..}{O}H
\end{array}
\quad
\begin{array}{c}
\overset{..}{O}CH_2CH_3
\end{array}
$$

Reaction is slow unless acid catalysed, and these compounds, like the α-diols, can only be isolated from solution if stabilised by strongly electron-withdrawing substituents. Under conditions for acid catalysis, hemiacetals may further react to form much more stable **acetals**. For example

1-ethoxyethanol,
a hemiacetal

1,1-diethoxyethane,
an acetal

Formation of the corresponding **ketals** is often slow and incomplete. These reactions are of particular importance in carbohydrate chemistry.

REACTION WITH AQUEOUS HYDROGEN BROMIDE, HBr :

There is evidence that water-soluble aldehydes and ketones such as ethanal and propanone will also react with hydrogen halides such as hydrogen bromide. In general, the steps may be summarised as

However, the α-bromoalcohol is unstable and cannot be isolated from solution.

The statement sometimes seen in A-level textbooks to the effect that carbonyl compounds do not undergo the same acid-catalysed addition reactions as alkenes is obviously not accurate. The fact is, carbonyl compounds very readily undergo such additions, but as we have seen, the main difference is that the products usually are only stable in solution.

Exercise 7.2
Write mechanistic equations to compare the addition of hydrogen bromide to propene and propanone. Suggest why propanone reacts at a faster rate than propene.

REACTION WITH AMMONIA, $\overset{..}{N}H_3$, and its derivatives, $\overset{..}{N}H_2 \text{---} G$

Aldehydes and ketones react with a number of compounds of the form $\overset{..}{N}H_2 \text{---} G$, where G is hydrogen or some group replacing hydrogen in the ammonia molecule. The initial addition reaction is usually followed by the elimination of a molecule of water, the whole process being described as **nucleophilic addition** with **elimination**, or as a **condensation reaction**.

$$\underset{}{\Large >}C = \overset{..}{\underset{..}{O}} + \overset{..}{N}H_2 \text{---} G \ \ = \ \ \underset{}{\Large >}C \overset{\overset{..}{O}H}{\underset{\overset{..}{N}H \text{---} G}{<}} \ \ \xrightarrow{\ -H_2\overset{..}{O}\ } \ \ \underset{}{\Large >}C = \overset{..}{N} \text{---} G$$

unstable addition product   elimination product

Condensation products of aldehydes and ketones with ammonia are called **IMINES**. Aliphatic imines are generally unstable and further react to form polymers of various relative molecular masses. Products from reaction of an aromatic aldehyde or ketone with an arylamine are more stable and are known as **SCHIFF BASES**.

Of more value, are reactions with derivatives of ammonia. Some of the more common reagents, together with the names of the condensation products are given in table 7.1.

Table 7.1 Condensation products of aldehydes and ketones with various derivatives of ammonia

Reagent, $\overset{..}{N}H_2 \text{---} G$		Product, $\underset{}{\Large >}C = \overset{..}{N} \text{---} G$	
Structure	*Name*	*Structure*	*Name*
$\overset{..}{N}H_2 \text{---} \overset{..}{N}H_2$	Hydrazine	$\underset{}{\Large >}C = \overset{..}{N} \text{---} \overset{..}{N}H_2$	Hydrazone
$\overset{..}{N}H_2 \text{---} \overset{..}{N}HPh$	Phenylhydrazine	$\underset{}{\Large >}C = \overset{..}{N} \text{---} \overset{..}{N}HPh$	Phenylhydrazone
$\overset{..}{N}H_2 \text{---} \overset{..}{N}HCONH_2$	Semicarbazide	$\underset{}{\Large >}C = \overset{..}{N} \text{---} NHCONH_2$	Semicarbazone
$\overset{..}{N}H_2 \text{---} \overset{..}{O}H$	Hydroxylamine	$\underset{}{\Large >}C = \overset{..}{N} \text{---} \overset{..}{O}H$	Oxime

155

These compounds can usually be isolated in crystalline form with characteristic melting points, which is useful in the identification of 'unknown' aldehydes and ketones.

The mechanistic steps are essentially the same for all of these reactions, so we will consider just one example in detail.

REACTION WITH HYDROXYLAMINE, $\overset{..}{N}H_2 — \overset{..}{\underset{..}{O}}H$

Progress of this reaction can be conveniently monitored by ultraviolet spectroscopy, as the absorption peak for the $\overset{\diagup}{\underset{}{}}C = \overset{..}{N} —$ chromophore

(λ_{max} = 269 nm) is different from that of the carbonyl group (λ_{max} = 277 nm). As reaction proceeds, the peak due to the carbonyl group gradually disappears, but it is only slowly replaced by the peak associated

with the $\overset{\diagup}{\underset{}{}}C = \overset{..}{N} —$ group. It would therefore seem unlikely that the

carbonyl compound is directly converted into the oxime, otherwise the new peak would appear while the old one was fading. This observation is consistent with the formation of an addition compound which has a short, but measurable existence before undergoing elimination to form the oxime. This idea is further supported by the fact that with certain carbonyl compounds such as hexafluoropropanone, the first-formed addition compound is stable enough to be isolated.

We may formulate mechanisms for the two stages as follows.

The addition stage

This follows the normal pattern of slow uptake of the nucleophile, succeeded by rapid proton exchange

$$\overset{..}{\underset{..}{H}O} — \overset{..}{N}H_2 \quad \diagup C = \overset{..}{\underset{..}{O}} \quad \overset{slow}{\rightleftharpoons} \quad \overset{..}{\underset{..}{H}O} — \overset{\oplus}{N}H_2 — \overset{|}{\underset{|}{C}} — \overset{..}{\underset{..}{O}}\colon^{\ominus}$$

$$\overset{..}{\underset{..}{H}O} — \overset{\oplus}{N}H_2 — \overset{|}{\underset{|}{C}} — \overset{..}{\underset{..}{O}}\colon^{\ominus} \quad \xrightarrow[fast]{-H^{\oplus},\, +H^{\oplus}} \quad \overset{..}{\underset{..}{H}O} — \overset{..}{N}H — \overset{|}{\underset{|}{C}} — \overset{..}{\underset{..}{O}}H$$

Incidentally, the direction of addition of hydroxylamine illustrates the greater nucleophilicity of nitrogen compared with oxygen.

156

The elimination stage

The mechanism here parallels that discussed in chapter 4 for bimolecular elimination in haloalkanes. Concerted removal of a proton provides the nucleophilic push necessary for expulsion of the hydroxide ion

(note the *trans* (*anti*) arrangement of attacking and leaving groups)

Exercise 7.3
Draw the structure of the bimolecular transition state for this step

---

The hydroxide ion is a poor leaving group, and reaction is much faster in moderately acid solution where protonation converts the hydroxyl group into a better leaving water molecule. The solution must not be too acidic, however, otherwise protonation of the hydroxylamine may slow down or even inhibit reaction.

no longer
nucleophilic

REACTION WITH OTHER DERIVATIVES OF AMMONIA

Hydrazine, phenylhydrazine and semicarbazide are all rather weak nucleophiles, and condensation proceeds most readily at about pH 4 to 5. The solution is then sufficiently acidic for catalysis of the addition and elimination stages, but without appreciable deactivation of the nucleophile by protonation of the amino group.

157

REACTION WITH LITHIUM TETRAHYDRIDOALUMINATE(III), LiAlH₄

This reagent is more commonly known as lithium aluminium hydride

$$Li^{\oplus} \quad H - \underset{\underset{H}{|}}{\overset{\overset{H}{|}}{Al}}^{\ominus} - H$$

Like other complex metal hydrides, it is able to bring about the addition of a molecule of hydrogen across the carbonyl double bond

$$\begin{array}{c} \diagdown \\ \diagup \end{array} C = \overset{..}{\underset{..}{O}} \quad \xrightarrow{\text{LiAlH}_4} \quad -\overset{|}{\underset{|}{C}} - \overset{..}{\underset{..}{O}}H$$

Aldehydes are reduced to primary alcohols and ketones to secondary alcohols. For example

$$CH_3C\overset{..}{H}O \quad \longrightarrow \quad CH_3CH_2\overset{..}{\underset{..}{O}}H$$
$$\text{ethanal} \qquad\qquad\qquad \text{ethanol}$$

and

$$\begin{array}{c} CH_3 \\ \diagdown \\ CH_3 \diagup \end{array} C = \overset{..}{\underset{..}{O}} \quad \longrightarrow \quad \begin{array}{c} CH_3 \\ \diagdown \\ CH_3 \diagup \end{array} CH - \overset{..}{\underset{..}{O}}H$$

propanone   propan-2-ol

The effective nucleophile is the **hydride ion**, $\overset{..}{H}{}^{\ominus}$, donated by the metal hydride anion, $AlH_4{}^{\ominus}$. Uptake of the nucleophile is accompanied by complexing of the residual AlH_3 with the negatively charged oxygen atom

$$\begin{array}{c} \diagdown \\ \diagup \end{array} C = \overset{..}{\underset{..}{O}} \quad \longrightarrow \quad -\overset{|}{\underset{\underset{H}{|}}{C}} - \overset{..}{\underset{..}{O}} - \overset{\ominus}{Al}H_3 \ (Li^{\oplus})$$
$$H - \underset{\ominus}{Al}H_3 \ (Li^{\oplus})$$

In successive reactions, the remaining three hydrogen atoms are also transferred to carbonyl molecules, forming the structure

$$\left[\begin{array}{c} | \\ -C - \overset{..}{O} - \\ | \\ H \end{array} \right]_4 Al^{\ominus} \quad (Li^{\oplus})$$

When a protic solvent such as ethanol is (cautiously!) added to the reaction mixture, decomposition occurs with protonation of the oxygen atom

$$\left[\begin{array}{c} | \\ -C - \overset{..}{O} - \\ | \\ H \end{array} \right]_4 Al^{\ominus} \longrightarrow 4 \begin{array}{c} | \\ -C - \overset{..}{O}H \\ | \\ H \end{array}$$

Hence the overall reaction involves addition of $\overset{..}{H}{}^{\ominus}$ (from the reagent) to the carbon atom, and $H^{\oplus}$ (from the solvent) to the oxygen atom.

REACTION WITH SODIUM TETRAHYDRIDOBORATE(III), NaBH₄

Better known as sodium borohydride, this reagent is a similar but less vigorous reducing agent than lithium tetrahydridoaluminate(III)

$$Na^{\oplus} \quad H \overset{H}{\underset{H}{\overset{|}{-}B^{\ominus}-}} H$$

It can be used in aqueous or alcoholic solution to reduce aldehydes and ketones, but unlike lithium tetrahydridoaluminate(III), does not attack carboxylic acids, nitriles or nitrocompounds. Reaction again involves donation of hydride ion by the reagent to the carbonyl carbon atom, followed by protonation of the oxygen atom

159

$$4 \diagup C = \ddot{O} + BH_4^{\ominus}(Na^{\oplus}) \longrightarrow \left[\begin{array}{c} | \\ -C - \ddot{O} - \\ | \\ H \end{array} \right]_4 \overset{\ominus}{B}(Na^{\oplus}) \longrightarrow 4 \begin{array}{c} | \\ -C - \ddot{O}H \\ | \\ H \end{array}$$

REACTION WITH GRIGNARD REAGENTS, RMgẌ :

Haloalkanes and aromatic halides react in ethoxyethane solution with magnesium metal to form an alkyl (or aryl) magnesium halide known as a **Grignard reagent**. For example

$$CH_3CH_2\ddot{B}r : + Mg \xrightarrow[\text{solution}]{\text{etherial}} CH_3CH_2MgBr :$$

ethyl magnesium
bromide

In this process, two electrons are transferred from the magnesium to the alkyl (or aryl) group. The reagent forms a complex mixture of highly solvated species in solution, but behaves as though it simply dissociated into $\ddot{R}^{\ominus}$ and $MgẌ :^{\oplus}$. The carbanion $\ddot{R}^{\ominus}$ is a powerful nucleophile and base, and therefore Grignard reagents can only be prepared and used under anhydrous conditions. With water, for example, rapid proton abstraction occurs

$$(MgẌ :^{\oplus}) \quad {}^{\ominus}\ddot{R} \quad H - \ddot{O}H \longrightarrow R - H + : \ddot{O}H^{\ominus} (MgẌ :^{\oplus})$$

From the volume of hydrocarbon liberated this way, it is possible to estimate the concentration of the Grignard reagent in solution.

With aldehydes and ketones, attack by the carbanion on the carbonyl group is accompanied by complexing of the $MgẌ :^{\oplus}$ cation with the negatively charged oxygen atom

$$MgẌ :^{\oplus} \quad {}^{\ominus}\ddot{R} \quad \diagup C = \ddot{O} \longrightarrow \diagdown C \diagup \overset{\ominus}{\underset{R}{\overset{\oplus}{O} : MgẌ :}}$$

On treatment with water or dilute acid, the complex is decomposed to yield the corresponding alcohol

The net result, then, is to add $\overset{..}{R}{}^{\ominus}$ and $H^{\oplus}$ across the original carbonyl double bond.

Exercise 7.4
Draw the structure of the alcohol formed by reaction of ethyl magnesium bromide with (a) ethanal, and (b) propanone. What general conclusions can be made about the classes of alcohols so formed?

Exercise 7.5
When treated with solid carbon dioxide, followed by the usual workup, phenyl magnesium iodide is converted into benzene carboxylic acid (benzoic acid). Write mechanistic equations for the reactions involved.

ACIDIC HYDROGEN IN CARBONYL COMPOUNDS

In discussing the reactivity of the haloalkanes, we considered the effect that electron withdrawal by the halogen atom has on the β-hydrogen atoms, causing them to be weakly acidic. A comparison of the relevant partial structures shows that in carbonyl compounds hydrogen atoms adjacent (α) to the carbonyl group will be similarly activated

$$\text{Haloalkanes} \qquad \overset{\displaystyle |\delta\delta+}{\underset{\displaystyle \overset{\textstyle\uparrow}{\delta\delta\delta+\;H}}{-C_\beta}} \longrightarrow \overset{\displaystyle |\delta+}{\underset{\displaystyle |}{C_\alpha}} \longrightarrow \overset{\delta-}{\ddot{X}}: \qquad -\text{I effect}$$

$$\delta\delta\delta+\;H \longleftarrow \text{activated } \beta\text{-hydrogen}$$

$$\text{Carbonyl} \atop \text{compounds} \qquad \overset{\displaystyle |\delta\delta+}{\underset{\displaystyle \overset{\textstyle\uparrow}{\delta\delta\delta+\;H}}{-C_\alpha}} \longrightarrow \overset{\displaystyle |\delta+}{\underset{\displaystyle |}{C}} \overset{\delta-}{=\ddot{O}}: \qquad \begin{array}{l} -\text{M effect} \\[4pt] -\text{I effect, relayed to the} \\ \alpha\text{-carbon atom} \end{array}$$

activated α-hydrogen

Thus, ethanal and propanone contain activated α-hydrogen atoms, but benzene carbaldehyde (benzaldehyde) does not

CH$_3$ — C = Ö   CH$_3$〉C = Ö   〈benzene ring〉 — C = Ö

H   CH$_3$ H

α-hydrogen α-hydrogen   no α-hydrogen present

In reaction of haloalkanes, removal of β-hydrogen by a base leads to the formation of an alkene

HO:⁻ H   HÖ — H

—C — C —   →   〉C = C〈 +

:X: + :Ẍ:⁻ charge on halide ion

Attack by the base may occur after expulsion of the halide ion (E1), or simultaneously (E2). See chapter 6.

There is no similar leaving group in carbonyl compounds, but removal of an α-hydrogen atom by a base is accompanied by displacement of the carbonyl pi electron pair on to the oxygen atom

charge now
on oxygen
atom

The anionic intermediate so formed, called an **enolate anion**, has an alkene double bond in its structure, but instead of the negative charge being taken away by a displaced halide ion, here it is accommodated on the oxygen atom. Actually this is only partly true. If we examine the structure of the anion more closely, we can see that the negatively charged oxygen atom is *conjugated* with the alkene double bond. Two limiting forms can be written, showing that the negative charge is in fact *shared* by both the oxygen and α-carbon atoms

In other words, the anion is *resonance stabilised*. We saw in chapter 3 that the acidity of an acid HA is largely determined by the relative stability of its conjugate anion, $\overset{..}{A}{}^{\ominus}$. With carbonyl compounds, then, the formation of a resonance-stabilised anion increases the acidity of the α-hydrogen atoms.

Another consequence of delocalisation is that we have an anion which can donate the negative charge (electron pair) to another species either through the oxygen atom, or through the α-carbon atom

resonance-stabilised
anion

negative charge shared
by oxygen and carbon atoms

Depending on the nature of the reaction, the anion may function as a powerful base or as an equally powerful nucleophile.

REACTION OF THE ANION AS A BASE

As a strong base, the anion will readily remove a proton from a donor molecule such as water, or even another molecule of the carbonyl compound. Uptake of a proton by the α-carbon atom would, of course, simply re-form the carbonyl compound. But protonation of the oxygen atom gives a new compound

$$\text{>C=C—O}^{\ominus} \quad H\text{—OH} \quad \rightleftharpoons \quad \text{>C=C—OH} + \text{:OH}^{\ominus}$$

— an unsaturated alcohol. This contains both an alkENE double bond and a hydroxyl (-OL) group, and is therefore called an **enol**. Both steps in its formation are reversible, so the enol will exist in equilibrium with the carbonyl or **keto** form

$$H\text{—C—C=O} \quad \xrightarrow{-H^{\oplus}, +H^{\oplus}} \quad \text{>C=C—OH}$$

carbonyl or
keto form   enol form

The phenomenon of structural isomers existing in dynamic equilibrium with one another is called **tautomerism**, and the isomers are referred to as **tautomers**. Interconversion of these particular tautomers involves a change in position of a proton, and is therefore called **prototropy**, or a **prototropic change**.

Of the various forms of tautomerism, prototropy is the most common. With simple aldehydes and ketones, the enol form is not very stable, and equilibrium lies well in favour of the carbonyl (keto) form. (The term 'keto' is used for both aldehydes and ketones.) The amount of each tautomer in an equilibrium mixture can be determined by spectroscopic methods, and in propanone, for example, the enol content is less than 0.01 per cent.

$$CH_3\text{—C—}CH_3 \quad \rightleftharpoons \quad CH_2\text{=C—}CH_3$$

:O: :OH

keto form   enol form
99.99 per cent   0.01 per cent

164

Attempts to prepare ethenol (vinyl alcohol) by catalytic addition of water to ethyne result only in the formation of ethanal

$$H \equiv CH + H - \overset{..}{O}H \longrightarrow \left[\begin{array}{c} HC = CH \\ | \quad | \\ H \quad :\underset{..}{O}H \end{array} \right] \rightleftharpoons CH_3 - C \overset{\displaystyle H}{\underset{\displaystyle \overset{\diagdown}{O}:}{\diagup}}$$

ethenol cannot   ethanal is the only
be isolated   product obtained

Equilibrium again lies very much in favour of the more stable keto tautomer. However, there are some carbonyl compounds which exist mainly in the enol form. One such compound is the diketone, pentan-2,4-dione (acetylacetone), which is 80 per cent enol.

$$CH_3 - \underset{\underset{\displaystyle :O:}{\|}}{C} - CH_2 - \underset{\underset{\displaystyle :O:}{\|}}{C} - CH_3 \rightleftharpoons CH_3 - \underset{\underset{\displaystyle :OH}{|}}{C} = CH - \underset{\underset{\displaystyle :O:}{\|}}{C} - CH_3$$

keto form   enol form
20 per cent   80 per cent

The condensed structure shown here is deceptive. It has been demonstrated that the actual structure is a six-membered ring, formed by **intramolecular hydrogen bonding**. (*Intra*molecular, you will recall, means within one molecule, as opposed to *inter*molecular, meaning between adjacent molecules.)

intramolecular
hydrogen bond

Of possible ring sizes, a six-membered ring is particularly favourable. But the most important factor is conjugation which arises between the carbon–carbon double bond of the enol, and the carbon–oxygen double bond of the remaining carbonyl group

enone conjugation

The enol has a resonance-stabilised structure, represented by the two principal limiting forms

$$\text{>C} = \text{C} - \text{C} = \overset{..}{\text{O}} : \quad \longleftrightarrow \quad \text{>}\overset{\oplus}{\text{C}} - \text{C} = \text{C} - \overset{..}{\underset{..}{\text{O}}} : {}^{\ominus}$$

A further form may be written which involves the oxygen atom of the hydroxyl group

$$\overset{..}{\text{HO}} \overset{\oplus}{\underset{..}{\text{C}}} - \text{C} = \text{C} - \overset{..}{\text{O}} : \quad \longleftrightarrow \quad \overset{..}{\text{HO}} = \overset{\oplus}{\text{C}} - \text{C} = \text{C} - \overset{..}{\underset{..}{\text{O}}} : {}^{\ominus}$$

Not only is the molecule stabilised by resonance, but because this leads to larger partial charges on the carbonyl oxygen and hydroxyl hydrogen atoms, the strength of hydrogen bonding between these two atoms is also increased, bringing about further stabilisation. In cyclic form, the resonance structure can be shown as

Another tautomeric compound with a relatively stable enol form is the keto ester, ethyl 3-oxobutanoate. ('Keto' here does mean that the ester contains a ketone group in its structure. 'Oxo', you will recall, is the systematic term for a carbonyl group when it appears as a substituent rather than as the principal functional group.) The common name for this compound is ethyl acetoacetate (that is, the ethyl ester of acetoacetic acid, $CH_3\overset{..}{\underset{..}{C}}OCH_2\overset{..}{\underset{..}{C}}O\overset{..}{\underset{..}{O}}H$).

166

Conjugation in the ester group

helps to stabilise the keto form, and the ester group is less effective in stabilising the enol by conjugation with the alkene double bond. Consequently, the enol content is only about 7 per cent at room temperature.

Incidentally, the position of equilibrium in tautomeric compounds is markedly influenced by the solvent, when one is present. In non-polar solvents such as hexane, the enol content is increased. Conversely, in a highly polar solvent such as water, the enol form is suppressed. Some examples are given in table 7.2.

Table 7.2 Percentage enol content of two tautomeric compounds

Compound	No solvent	Hexane solution	Aqueous solution
Pentan-2,4-dione	80	92	15
Ethyl 3-oxobutanoate	7	50	1

This behaviour is attributed to the ability of a polar solvent to stabilise the keto more than the enol form − probably by intermolecular hydrogen bonding with the carbonyl group of the keto tautomer.

Even when equilibrium lies well in favour of the keto form, the compound may still show reactions associated with the enol tautomer. This is because reaction of the enol lowers its concentration and so more keto changes to enol in order to restore equilibrium. In this way, a compound may behave as though it were all in the enol or keto form.

Convincing proof of the reality of tautomerism comes from the fact that in suitable cases the two tautomers can actually be separated. For example, if ethyl 3-oxobutanoate is slowly distilled in quartz apparatus, the more volatile enol form comes off first. This disturbs the equilibrium in the residual liquid, and some keto changes over to enol. This process continues until all the ester has distilled over in the enol form. Quartz apparatus is necessary to exclude traces of alkali, always present in ordinary glassware, which catalyse the interchange of the two tautomers.

REACTION OF THE ANION AS A NUCLEOPHILE

At the beginning of this section, we described the anion as a resonance hybrid for which there are two limiting forms

resonance structure

The more electronegative oxygen atom can accommodate negative charge better than a carbon atom, so we might expect a larger 'contribution' from the right-hand structure. However, negative charge is available through the carbon atom, and as a nucleophile the anion usually behaves as though the negative charge was in fact localised on the carbon atom.

If a small amount of dilute aqueous sodium hydroxide solution is added to an aldehyde or ketone containing α-hydrogen, an equilibrium is set up in which a proportion of the carbonyl molecules is converted into the corresponding anions. For example, with ethanal

The remaining molecules will, of course, be susceptible to nucleophilic attack by these anions

Notice that the new anionic intermediate formed in this way is an *alkoxide* ion. The negative charge cannot be delocalised and the inter-

168

mediate is a very strong base. Consequently, it is readily protonated, even by a water molecule. The final product is a hydroxy aldehyde, 3-hydroxy-butanal

Since it is both an aldehyde and an alcohol, it is known as an **aldol** (*ALD*e-hyde-alcoh*OL*), and the reaction is the **aldol reaction**.

We have seen that the whole sequence is initiated by removal of an acidic α-hydrogen atom from the substrate aldehyde or ketone. If you examine the structure of the aldol product, you will observe that it too has acidic hydrogen atoms on the α-carbon atom. In fact, because of the negative inductive effect of the adjacent hydroxyl group, the α-hydrogens will be even more acidic than those in the original carbonyl compound

So it is not surprising, then, that aldols readily undergo base catalysed dehydration

If we redraw the structures involved, you will see that this follows the general pattern of β-elimination* from haloalkanes and alcohols

*Hydrogen atoms α to the carbonyl group are β to the displaced hydroxyl group.

The overall reaction is one in which two molecules of a carbonyl compound combine to form a new compound with the elimination of a molecule of water. This is called a **condensation reaction**, and the product (in the above example, but-2-enal), is the **condensation product**.

Despite the fact that $HO:^{\ominus}$ is a poor leaving group, the majority of aldols readily (some even spontaneously) dehydrate to give the condensation product. Now this cannot be explained simply by the increased acidity of the α-hydrogen atoms. Instead, we have to look more closely at the structure of the condensation product where the newly formed alkene double bond is conjugated with the remaining carbonyl group

resonance-stabilised
conjugated enone system

From the Hammond Postulate (page 105) we know that if a product and the transition state from which it is formed resemble one another in structure, then any factor stabilising the product will also tend to stabilise the transition state. The enone product is stabilised by conjugation of the carbonyl group with the alkene double bond. Similar stabilisation of the incipient (forming) double bond in the transition state lowers the activation energy for its formation, and so provides the 'driving force' for dehydration.

transition state
for elimination
of water

the carbonyl
group is conjugated
with the incipient
double bond

With a mixture of two carbonyl compounds such as ethanal and propanone, the enolate anion of one compound may attack a molecule of the other compound acting as substrate, and vice versa, giving rise to a mixture of four possible products. Such a reaction is called **crossed condensation.**

Exercise 7.6
Draw the structure of the four products resulting from crossed condensation of ethanal with propanone.

The proportions in which these products are formed depend on a number of factors, including the ratio of the two carbonyl compounds, the relative stabilities of the two enolate anions, and the relative reactivities of the two carbonyl substrates. Carbonyl compounds such as methanal (HCHO) and benzene carbaldehyde (benzaldehyde, PhCHO) have no α-hydrogen and so cannot undergo the aldol condensation*. The manner in which they react with aqueous sodium hydroxide solution is the subject of the next section.

REACTION OF BENZENE CARBALDEHYDE WITH AQUEOUS SODIUM HYDROXIDE SOLUTION: THE CANNIZZARO REACTION

If benzene carbaldehyde is warmed with concentrated aqueous sodium hydroxide solution, or even allowed to stand for some time at room temperature with alcoholic (ethanolic) potassium hydroxide solution, a process of self-oxidation and reduction occurs, with the formation of an equi-

*They can, of course, take part in crossed condensation with other aldehydes or ketones.

molecular mixture of phenylmethanol (benzyl alcohol) and the sodium or potassium salt of benzene carboxylic acid

Now although this process is quite different from the aldol reaction, it does involve nucleophilic attack on the carbonyl carbon atom. Experiment shows the reaction to be second order, the rate depending on the concentration of both the aldehyde and the hydroxide ion

$$\text{Rate} = k\ [\text{PhCHO}]\ [\overset{\ominus}{\text{HO}}:]$$

Reaction is thought to be initiated by slow, reversible addition of hydroxide ion to the carbonyl carbon atom

Protonation of $-\overset{..}{\underset{..}{\text{O}}}:^{\ominus}$ is unlikely in strongly alkaline solution, and in any case, the resulting structure (with two hydroxyl groups attached to the same carbon atom) would not be stable. However, there is another way in which the anion can get rid of the negative charge, namely by expulsion of a **hydride ion**, $\overset{..}{\text{H}}{}^{\ominus}$. There must, of course, be an acceptor for this highly unstable species, and this is another molecule of the aldehyde

Expulsion of the very poor leaving hydride ion is made possible by a 'nucleophilic push' from the negatively charged oxygen atom, and the formation of the stable benzene carboxylic acid molecule

172

'nucleophilic push'

The other product of this step is the strongly basic alkoxide ion, $PhCH_2\overset{..}{\underset{..}{O}}:^{\ominus}$, and reaction is completed by proton transfer from the acid to the base

| strong base, negative charge localised on the oxygen atom | weak acid | very weak acid | weak base, negative charge delocalised |

Although compounds with no α-hydrogen cannot undergo aldol self-condensation, they can, of course, take part in crossed condensation with other compounds. Benzene carbaldehyde, for example, cannot form an enolate anion, but it can be attacked by enolate anions of other compounds such as ethanal, etc.

THE HALOFORM REACTION

Ethanal and methyl ketones with the structural unit $CH_3\overset{..}{C}O$ — readily react with halogen (chlorine, bromine and iodine) in alkaline solution to give the corresponding trihaloalkane, known as a **haloform**, together with the salt of a carboxylic acid. For example, when propanone is warmed with an aqueous solution of sodium chlorate(I) (sodium hypochlorite), the products are trichloromethane (chloroform) and sodium ethanoate

$$CH_3\overset{..}{C}OCH_3 \xrightarrow[\text{warm}]{: Cl_2, \ HO:^{\ominus}} \ :\overset{..}{Cl}_3CH + CH_3\overset{..}{C}OO:^{\ominus}$$

Reaction is found to be second order

$$\text{Rate} = k \ [\text{ketone}] \ [H\overset{..}{O}:^{\ominus}]$$

173

but for given concentrations of ketone and alkali, chlorination, bromination and iodination all take place at the *same rate*. As with the aldol reaction, the slow rate-determining step is conversion of the ketone into the corresponding anion

$$
\overset{\ominus}{HO}: \quad H-CH_2-\underset{\underset{:O:}{\|}}{C}-CH_3 \xrightarrow{\text{slow}} \; HO-H + \overset{\ominus}{CH_2}-\underset{\underset{:O:}{\|}}{C}-CH_3
$$

Relatively rapid reaction between the carbanion and halogen occurs in what is essentially a bimolecular nucleophilic substitution (S_N2) process

$$
CH_3-\underset{\underset{:O:}{\|}}{C}-\overset{\ominus}{CH_2} \quad :Cl-Cl: \longrightarrow \; CH_3-\underset{\underset{:O:}{\|}}{C}-CH_2-Cl: + :Cl:^{\ominus}
$$

Because of the negative inductive effect of the halogen atom, the two remaining α-hydrogen atoms are even more acidic than the first, and so are rapidly replaced by repetition of the above steps. The next step also occurs relatively quickly, as the trichlorinated ketone is activated towards nucleophilic attack by hydroxide ion

relay of −I effect increases positive charge on carbonyl carbon atom

−I effect helps to stabilise the negatively charged transition state

Having reached this stage, the anionic intermediate can get rid of the negative charge by expulsion of the trichloromethyl carbanion

This is a better leaving group than hydroxide ion, because although the negative charge is on carbon rather than oxygen, it is dispersed to some extent by the negative inductive effect of the three chlorine atoms

$$: Cl \longleftarrow C \begin{matrix} Cl: \\ \\ Cl: \end{matrix} \qquad \begin{matrix} \text{inductive stabilisation} \\ \text{of the} \\ \text{trichloromethylcarbanion} \end{matrix}$$

Another factor may well be the relief of steric compression which will accompany loss of the expelled anion.

Reaction is completed by the (probably indirect) transfer of a proton from the acid to the base

$$CH_3COOH + \overset{\ominus}{C}Cl_3 \longrightarrow CH_3COO^{\ominus} + CHCl_3$$

Treatment with iodine in alkaline solution is used as a diagnostic test for ethanal and methyl ketones. The product, triiodomethane (**iodoform**), precipitates as fine yellow needles with a very characteristic odour. Note that a positive result is also obtained with ethanol and other alcohols with a $CH_3CH(OH)$ — grouping (for example, propan-2-ol, butan-2-ol, etc.). This is because an alkaline solution of iodine contains the oxoiodate(I) ion (hypoiodate ion, $\overset{..\,..}{IO}{}^{\ominus}$) which can oxidise the alcohol group to a carbonyl group

$$CH_3 - CH(OH) - \xrightarrow{\;\;IO^{\ominus}\;\;} CH_3 - \underset{\underset{O:}{\|}}{C} -$$

8 Nucleophilic Reactions of Carboxylic Acids and their Derivatives

INTRODUCTION

In this chapter we shall look at the nucleophilic reactions of carboxylic acids and their common derivatives, the acid chlorides, anhydrides, esters and amides. The formal resemblance in structure of these compounds and the aldehydes and ketones might lead us to expect them to exhibit the same kind of chemical reactivity. In fact, although they are often attacked by the same nucleophiles which react with aldehydes and ketones, the presence of another reactive group such as chloro (acid chlorides) or amino (acid amides) considerably modifies the behaviour of these compounds.

We have seen that in typical nucleophilic addition reactions of aldehydes and ketones, attack by a nucleophile $\overset{..}{Y}{}^{\ominus}$ on the carbonyl carbon atom is followed by protonation of the carbonyl oxygen atom. (The order of the two steps is reversed in acid-catalysed processes.)

$$\overset{\ominus ..}{Y} \overset{R}{\underset{R(H)}{\diagdown}} C = \overset{..}{O}: \; \rightleftharpoons \; Y - \overset{\overset{R}{|}}{\underset{\underset{R(H)}{|}}{C}} - \overset{..}{\underset{..}{O}}:^{\ominus} \; \overset{H^{\oplus}}{\rightleftharpoons} \; Y - \overset{\overset{R}{|}}{\underset{\underset{R(H)}{|}}{C}} - \overset{..}{O}H$$

Another way for negatively charged intermediates to attain stability is by expulsion of an anion (see, for example, the haloform reaction, page 173), but with aldehydes and ketones the only suitable leaving group is the original nucleophile, $\overset{..}{Y}{}^{\ominus}$. The species $\overset{..}{R}{}^{\ominus}$ and $\overset{..}{H}{}^{\ominus}$ are both extremely poor leaving groups, and reaction is normally completed by uptake of a proton.

Where carboxylic acids and their derivatives differ from aldehydes and ketones is in the possession of a second functional group which can be displaced from an anionic intermediate. Some examples are given in table 8.1.

176

Table 8.1 Some possible leaving groups in carboxylic acids and their derivatives

Generalised structure	Class of compound	Possible leaving group, G
	carboxylic acid	$— \overset{..}{\underset{..}{O}}H$
	acid chloride	$— \overset{..}{\underset{..}{C}l} :$
	acid anhydride	$— \overset{..}{\underset{..}{O}}\overset{..}{\underset{..}{C}}OR$
	ester	$— \overset{..}{\underset{..}{O}}R$
	acid amide	$— \overset{..}{N}H_2$

By analogy with the reaction of aldehydes and ketones, we can now formulate a mechanism for nucleophilic attack on an acid derivative in which uptake of the nucleophile to give a tetrahedral anionic (or dipolar) intermediate is followed by expulsion of the group G as an anion

again, a
'nucleophilic push'
assists expulsion
of group G

An energy profile for such a process will be of the familiar general form, figure 8.1.

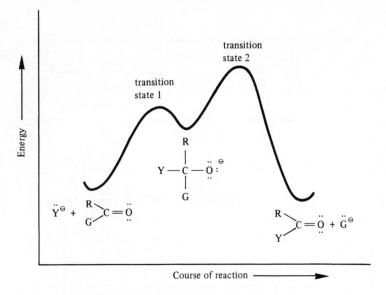

Figure 8.1 *Energy profile for a generalised nucleophilic addition with elimination reaction of carboxylic acid derivatives*

Note the structure of the two transition states

$$
\begin{bmatrix}
& R & \\
\delta- \ Y ---- C === O: & \\
& G & \\
\end{bmatrix}^{\ominus} \text{TS1}
\qquad
\begin{bmatrix}
& R & \\
\delta- \ :O === C ---- G \ \delta- & \\
& Y & \\
\end{bmatrix}^{\ominus} \text{TS2}
$$

new sigma-bond   pi-bond   pi-bond   sigma-bond
forming   breaking down   re-forming   breaking down

As we have seen many times before, in each of these transition states, energy released on formation of a new bond is available to assist in breaking the old bond.

The characteristic reaction of carboxylic acid derivatives, then, is a two-step **addition** with **elimination** process. Which of the two steps — formation of the intermediate or expulsion of the group G — is slowest (that is, rate-determining) will depend on the nature of the attacking nucleophile, the structure of the substrate and in particular, the leaving ability of the group G.

We will discuss the evidence for the two-step mechanism later in this chapter, but let us first look at some of the factors which influence the reactivity of carboxylic acid derivatives.

178

Structure of the substrate

Carboxylic acids and their derivatives have a resonance structure, and loss of resonance energy on going from substrate to intermediate increases the activation energy for uptake of the nucleophile.

resonance stabilisation in the substrate	similar stabilisation not possible in the intermediate

This 'resonance energy barrier' to be overcome is greatest in the acid amides $(G = \ddot{N}H_2)$ and lowest in the acid chlorides $(G = \ddot{C}l \cdot)$

nitrogen atom readily shares the lone pair of electrons — larger resonance energy	chlorine atom less readily shares its lone pair of electrons — resonance energy minimised

Viewed in orbital terms, interaction of a $2p$ orbital on the carbonyl carbon atom with the larger $3p$ orbital on the chlorine atom is less effective than $2p$–$2p$ overlap which occurs with oxygen and nitrogen atoms.

Leaving ability of the group G

As we discussed in chapter 5, the more stable (less basic) the group G as an anion, the more easily will it be displaced. Thus, leaving ability increases in the series

$$-\ddot{N}H_2 \; < \; -\ddot{O}R, \, -\ddot{O}H \; < \; -\ddot{O}-\ddot{O}CR \; < \; -\ddot{C}l \cdot$$

The two factors — loss of resonance energy and group leaving ability — operate in the same direction, so that reactivity increases in the series

179

amides $<$ esters, acids $<$ anhydrides $<$ acid chlorides

| poor leaving group, greatest loss of resonance energy on forming the $\longrightarrow$ intermediate | good leaving group, least loss of resonance energy on forming the intermediate |

At one end of the reactivity scale, acid chlorides are readily attacked by weak nucleophiles such as water, alcohol and ammonia. At the other end, acid amides are not attacked by water and alcohols (unless acid catalysed), from which solvents they may be crystallised. In the middle, esters only very slowly react with water, but are more rapidly hydrolysed in acid or alkaline solution. We will now examine a selection of these reactions in more detail.

REACTIONS OF CARBOXYLIC ACIDS

Carboxylic acids are themselves rather limited in their reactions with nucleophiles. The hydroxide ion is a poor leaving group, and the resonance energy barrier is too high for attack by weak nucleophiles such as ammonia and its derivatives. Furthermore, reaction with such compounds cannot be acid catalysed because of protonation of the nucleophile. For example

$$\underset{\text{nucleophilic}}{\ddot{H}\ddot{O} - \ddot{N}H_2} + HA \rightleftharpoons \underset{\text{non-nucleophilic}}{\ddot{H}\ddot{O} - \overset{\oplus}{N}H_3} + \ddot{A}^{\ominus}$$

On the other hand, more powerful nucleophiles such as alkoxide ion, $R\ddot{O}:^{\ominus}$, cannot be used because they too become protonated in an acid-base reaction with the carboxylic acid

$$\underset{\substack{\text{strong} \\ \text{base}}}{R\ddot{O}:^{\ominus}} + \underset{\substack{\text{weak} \\ \text{acid}}}{HOOCR} \rightleftharpoons \underset{\substack{\text{very weak} \\ \text{acid}}}{R\ddot{O}H} + \underset{\substack{\text{weak} \\ \text{base}}}{:\ddot{O}OCR^{\ominus}}$$

Two characteristic reactions are esterification and conversion into the acid chloride. In the former reaction, protonation of the carbonyl oxygen atom enables the carbon atom to react with a weakly nucleophilic alcohol molecule. The mechanistic steps are exactly the reverse of those for acid-catalysed hydrolysis of an ester, and will be discussed later in this chapter.

In the other reaction, the hydroxyl group is first of all converted into a better leaving group.

Formation of acid chlorides

This is normally carried out by treating the carboxylic acid with a phosphorus chloride (PCl₅ or PCl₃) or with sulphur dichloride oxide (thionyl chloride, SOCl₂). In reaction with SOCl₂ the steps are

followed by the usual two-step displacement reaction in which the attacking nucleophile is a chloride ion

---

Exercise 8.1

Draw curved arrows to show decomposition of the $\overset{..}{\underset{..}{S}}O_2\overset{..}{\underset{..}{Cl}}:^{\ominus}$ ion.

REACTIONS OF ACID CHLORIDES

As we have seen, acid chlorides are the most reactive of the acid derivatives, and are readily attacked by even a very weak nucleophile such as water. The principal reactions are summarised in table 8.2.

181

Table 8.2 Nucleophilic reactions of acid chlorides

Reagent		Product	
water	H_2O	acids	$RCOOH$
alcohols	$R'OH$	esters	$RCOOR'$
phenols	$PhOH$	esters	$RCOOPh$
ammonia	NH_3	amides	$RCONH_2$
amines	RNH_2	substituted amides	$RCONHR$
carboxylate anions	$R'COO:^{\ominus}$	anhydrides	$\begin{matrix} RCO \\ \\ R'CO \end{matrix}\!\!>\!\!O$
Grignard reagents	$R'MgX$	tertiary alcohols	$RC(OH)R'_2$
metal hydrides	$LiAlH_4$	primary alcohols	RCH_2OH

All of these mechanistically similar reactions involve the uptake of a nucleophile to form a dipolar (or anionic) tetrahedral intermediate, followed by expulsion of the chloride ion. For example, the reaction between ethanoyl chloride and ammonia can be formulated as

followed by

The hydrogen chloride by-product must be removed (why?), and with cheap reagents like ammonia this is achieved by having an excess of the reagent. With more expensive primary and secondary amines, a tertiary amine such as pyridine may be used. This cannot form an amide (there being no hydrogen on the nitrogen atom to carry off the positive charge — verify this by drawing the structure of the intermediate formed by attack of a generalised tertiary amine, $R_3\ddot{N}$ on ethanoyl chloride), but is basic enough to remove the hydrogen chloride.

Exercise 8.2
Write mechanistic equations to show the reaction of ethanoyl chloride with sodium ethanoate to form ethanoic anhydride.

Acid chlorides are also attacked by Grignard reagents. Uptake of the carbanion is followed by expulsion of the chloride ion to form a ketone. This then further reacts to give the corresponding tertiary alcohol (see page 160).

Reaction of acid chlorides with aromatic hydrocarbons (the Friedel-Crafts acylation reaction) is discussed in chapter 10.

REACTIONS OF ACID ANHYDRIDES

The carboxylate anion is a good leaving group, and reactions of anhydrides parallel those of the acid chlorides. However, the large carboxylate group increases steric crowding in the transition state, and anhydrides are generally rather less reactive than the acid chlorides.

AROMATIC COMPOUNDS

Aromatic acid chlorides and anhydrides are less reactive than their aliphatic counterparts, and this may be attributed both to greater resonance stabilisation of the substrate molecules, and to increased steric crowding in the transition state.

REACTIONS OF ACID AMIDES

Although amides are the least reactive of the acid derivatives, they are rapidly hydrolysed on warming in acid or alkaline solution.

Base-catalysed hydrolysis

Hydrolysis of ethanamide with aqueous sodium hydroxide solution proceeds via the normal two-step mechanism

$$^{\ominus}HO\!: \quad \underset{NH_2}{\overset{CH_3}{>}}C=\overset{..}{\underset{..}{O}}: \quad \rightleftharpoons \quad HO-\underset{:NH_2}{\overset{CH_3}{\underset{|}{\overset{|}{C}}}}-\overset{..}{O}:^{\ominus}$$

$$:\overset{\ominus}{\underset{..}{O}}-\underset{:OH}{\overset{CH_3}{\underset{|}{\overset{|}{C}}}}-\overset{..}{NH_2} \quad \underset{slow}{\rightleftharpoons} \quad O=C\!\!\underset{:OH}{\overset{CH_3}{<}} \;\; + \;\; \overset{..}{\underset{..}{NH_2}}{}^{\ominus}$$

Despite the fact that the amide ion is a poor leaving group, hydrolysis rapidly goes to completion because protonation of the strongly basic anion removes it from the equilibrium

$$\overset{\ominus}{\underset{..}{NH_2}} \quad H-\overset{..}{\underset{..}{O}}H \quad \longrightarrow \quad NH_3\!\uparrow \; + \; :\overset{..}{\underset{..}{O}}H^{\ominus}$$

(The carboxylic acid will, of course, form a salt in alkaline solution.) Studies with ^{18}O-labelled amides show that exchange occurs, and that this is rapid compared with hydrolysis; clearly loss of the amide ion is the slow rate-determining step.

Acid-catalysed hydrolysis

Protonation of the carbonyl group* will facilitate attack by a water molecule, but more importantly, proton exchange in the intermediate will convert the poor leaving amide group into the better leaving ammonia molecule

$$H_2\overset{..}{\underset{..}{O}} \quad \underset{:NH_2}{\overset{CH_3}{>}}C=\overset{\oplus}{O}H \quad \underset{slow}{\rightleftharpoons} \quad H_2\overset{\oplus}{O}-\underset{:NH_2}{\overset{CH_3}{\underset{|}{\overset{|}{C}}}}-\overset{..}{O}H \quad \underset{fast}{\overset{-H^{\oplus},\,+H^{\oplus}}{\rightleftharpoons}} \quad HO-\underset{\oplus NH_3}{\overset{CH_3}{\underset{|}{\overset{|}{C}}}}-\overset{..}{O}H$$

*The amino group is only weakly basic; see next section.

184

$$HO \overset{\frown}{\underset{\underset{:\, OH}{\overset{|}{C}}}{\overset{CH_3}{|}}} \overset{\frown}{NH_3^{\oplus}} \quad \overset{fast}{\rightleftharpoons} \quad HO^{\oplus}=C\overset{CH_3}{\underset{:\, OH}{\diagdown}} + NH_3 \quad \overset{-H^{\oplus}, +H^{\oplus}}{\underset{fast}{\rightleftharpoons}} \quad O=C\overset{CH_3}{\underset{:\, OH}{\diagdown}} + NH_4^{\oplus}$$

No exchange is observed in acid-catalysed hydrolysis of ^{18}O-labelled amides, indicating that the slow step is uptake of the water molecule. Once formed, the intermediate rapidly dissociates to products.

RESONANCE AND THE REACTIVITY OF ETHANAMIDE

In the introduction to chapter 2, it was pointed out that the general properties of ethanamide are somewhat different from what we would expect of a compound containing both an amino and a carbonyl group. We can now see why this is so.

Conjugation of the amino and carbonyl groups means that the nitrogen atom is able to share to some extent its non-bonded electron pair with the carbonyl carbon atom

$$\overset{..}{NH_2} \overset{\frown}{-} \overset{\frown}{\underset{\underset{CH_3}{|}}{C}}=\overset{..}{O}: \quad \longleftrightarrow \quad \overset{\oplus}{NH_2}=\underset{\underset{CH_3}{|}}{C}-\overset{..}{\underset{..}{O}}:\overset{\ominus}{}$$

The result is a polar structure in which the nitrogen and oxygen atoms have fractional positive and negative charges. The carbonyl carbon atom carries less positive charge than in aldehydes and ketones, and is correspondingly less readily attacked by weak nucleophiles. And with a fractional positive charge, the nitrogen atom is going to be more difficult to protonate.

Furthermore, since we are dealing with a resonance-stabilised molecule, loss of resonance energy which would occur on uptake of a nucleophile, or protonation of the nitrogen atom, acts as an 'energy barrier' to both of these processes

185

substrate is
resonance stabilised

formation of either product
is accompanied by loss of
resonance stabilisation

If you recall our discussion of basicity in chapter 4, you will recognise yet another factor. Not only is the formation of the conjugate acid accompanied by loss of resonance energy, but the ion is destabilised by unfavourable interaction of the protonated nitrogen atom with the positive end of the carbonyl dipole

destabilising
electrostatic
repulsion

REACTIONS OF ESTERS

Esters are relatively unreactive and are, for example, only very slowly hydrolysed by boiling water. However, since the α-hydrogens are but weakly acidic, it is therefore possible to use powerful anionic nucleophiles such as hydroxide or alkoxide ion. The usual method of hydrolysis is to heat the ester under reflux with aqueous sodium hydroxide or alcoholic potassium hydroxide solution — a process known as **saponification**.

Reaction is second order

$$\text{Rate} = k \, [\text{ester}] \, [\overset{\ominus}{\cdot\cdot}\!\text{OH}]$$

and so *formation* of the intermediate is the slow rate-determining step. For saponification of methyl ethanoate we may write

186

$$\overset{\ominus}{HO} : \overset{\curvearrowright}{\underset{CH_3O}{\overset{CH_3}{\diagdown}}} C = \overset{\curvearrowright}{\overset{..}{O}} : \quad \underset{\text{slow}}{\rightleftharpoons} \quad HO - \overset{CH_3}{\underset{\underset{\ddot{O}CH_3}{|}}{\overset{|}{C}}} - \overset{..}{O} :^{\ominus}$$

followed by

$$:\overset{\ominus}{\overset{..}{O}} \overset{\curvearrowright}{-} \overset{CH_3}{\underset{\underset{: OH}{|}}{\overset{|}{C}}} \overset{\curvearrowright}{-} \overset{..}{O}CH_3 \quad \underset{\text{fast}}{\rightleftharpoons} \quad \overset{..}{O} = C \overset{CH_3}{\underset{\overset{..}{O}H}{\diagup}} \quad + \quad :\overset{\ominus}{O}CH_3$$

The methoxide ion, $CH_3\overset{..}{\underset{..}{O}}:^{\ominus}$, has about the same leaving ability as hydroxide ion, but once displaced it is rapidly protonated and so effectively removed from the equilibrium. Consequently, saponification goes to completion

$$CH_3\overset{\ominus}{\overset{..}{O}} :\overset{\curvearrowright}{} H \overset{\curvearrowright}{-} \overset{..}{O}H \quad \longrightarrow \quad CH_3OH + :\overset{..}{\underset{..}{O}}H^{\ominus} \qquad \begin{matrix}\text{(base catalyst}\\ \text{regenerated)}\end{matrix}$$

also

$$HO\overset{\ominus}{:}\overset{\curvearrowright}{} H \overset{\curvearrowright}{-} \overset{..}{\underset{..}{O}}OCCH_3 \quad \longrightarrow \quad HO - H + :\overset{\ominus}{\underset{..}{O}}OCCH_3$$

Ester hydrolysis must be one of the most studied reactions in organic chemistry. For many years chemists were intrigued by the question of the *position* of bond breaking – between the acyl and alkoxy groups, or between the alkyl group and the oxygen atom?

$$R - \overset{\underset{|}{\overset{\ddots}{O}}:}{C} \overset{|}{\underset{\nearrow}{}} \overset{..}{O} - R \qquad \text{or} \qquad R - \overset{\underset{|}{\overset{\ddots}{O}}:}{C} - \overset{..}{O} \overset{\S}{\underset{\nearrow}{}} R$$

cleavage between the   cleavage between the
acyl and alkoxy groups   alkyl and carboxylate groups

The former is known as **acyl-oxygen fission**, and the alternative as **alkyl-oxygen fission**.

Numerous experiments with isotopically labelled esters have shown that in the majority of cases only *acyl–oxygen* fission is involved — an observation consistent with the two-step mechanism we have been proposing. For example, on saponification of methyl ethanoate labelled in the alkoxy position with ^{18}O, the oxygen isotope is found only in the methanol

$$CH_3 - \overset{\displaystyle \parallel}{\underset{:O:}{C}} - {}^{18}OCH_3 \quad \xrightarrow{\ HO: \ } \quad CH_3 - \overset{\displaystyle \parallel}{\underset{:O:}{C}} - O:{}^{\ominus} + CH_3 - {}^{18}OH$$

Acid-catalysed hydrolysis

Unlike saponification, this reaction is completely reversible, and so the extent of hydrolysis is limited by the position of equilibrium:

$$\text{ester + water} \quad \underset{\text{catalysis}}{\overset{\text{acid}}{\rightleftharpoons}} \quad \underset{\text{acid}}{\text{carboxylic}} + \text{alcohol}$$

Forward reaction will be favoured by an excess of water, and protonation of a small proportion of the alcohol will move the equilibrium from left to right, but with most esters hydrolysis is nothing like complete. For this reason, the base-catalysed process is usually preferred.

We will illustrate the mechanism by examining the hydrolysis of methyl ethanoate. Protonation of the ester carbonyl group will facilitate attack by a water molecule

$$H - \overset{CH_3}{\underset{H}{\overset{\mid}{O:}}} \quad C = \overset{\oplus}{OH} \quad \rightleftharpoons \quad H - \overset{CH_3}{\underset{\mid}{\overset{\oplus}{O}}} - \overset{\mid}{\underset{:OCH_3}{C}} - OH$$

Rapid proton exchange in the intermediate leads to preferential protonation of the more basic alkoxide oxygen atom

$$
\underset{\text{H}}{\overset{\text{CH}_3}{\underset{|}{\text{H}-\overset{\oplus}{\ddot{\text{O}}}-\overset{|}{\underset{|}{\text{C}}}-\ddot{\text{O}}\text{H}}}}\quad \rightleftharpoons \quad \underset{\underset{\oplus}{\text{H}-\ddot{\text{O}}\leftarrow\overset{\delta+}{\text{CH}_3}}}{\overset{\text{CH}_3}{\text{H}\ddot{\text{O}}-\overset{|}{\underset{|}{\text{C}}}-\ddot{\text{O}}\text{H}}}
$$

inductive
dispersal of
charge is
stabilising

This, of course, converts the poor leaving methoxide ion into a good leaving methanol molecule, and acyl–oxygen cleavage then follows

$$
\text{H}\ddot{\text{O}}\overset{\text{CH}_3}{\underset{:\ddot{\text{O}}\text{H} \quad \text{H}}{-\text{C}-\overset{\oplus}{\ddot{\text{O}}}-\text{CH}_3}} \quad \rightleftharpoons \quad \overset{\oplus}{\text{H}\ddot{\text{O}}}=\text{C}\overset{\text{CH}_3}{\underset{\ddot{\text{O}}\text{H}}{\diagdown}} \;+\; \underset{\text{H}}{:\ddot{\text{O}}-\text{CH}_3}
$$

The sequence is completed by deprotonation of the carboxylic acid, probably by reaction with a water molecule

$$
\underset{\text{H}}{\text{H}-\ddot{\text{O}}:} \quad \text{H}-\overset{\oplus}{\ddot{\text{O}}}=\text{C}\overset{\text{CH}_3}{\underset{\ddot{\text{O}}\text{H}}{\diagdown}} \quad \rightleftharpoons \quad \underset{\text{H}}{\text{H}-\overset{\oplus}{\text{O}}-\text{H}} \;+\; \ddot{\text{O}}=\text{C}\overset{\text{CH}_3}{\underset{\ddot{\text{O}}\text{H}}{\diagdown}}
$$

Because each step is completely reversible, this last step is also the first step in the mechanism for acid-catalysed esterification of a carboxylic acid. When a catalytic amount of a strong acid such as sulphuric acid is added to a mixture of ethanoic acid and methanol, various equilibria are set up involving protonation of the hydroxyl group of the acid and the alcohol, but some acid molecules will be protonated on the carbonyl oxygen atom and this will trigger off the whole of the above sequence in reverse.

Exercise 8.3
Try writing the mechanistic sequence for acid-catalysed esterification of ethanoic acid with methanol.

Unlike the hydrolysis procedure, esterification can often be taken to near completion by arranging to distil off the water produced during the reaction.

Supporting evidence for the mechanism again comes from studies with isotopically labelled esters. Acid-catalysed hydrolysis of methyl ethanoate labelled with ^{18}O in the alkoxide position gives products where the oxygen isotope is found *only* in the methanol. Conversely, in acid-catalysed esterification of ethanoic acid with ^{18}O-labelled methanol, no ^{18}O appears in water molecules, thus ruling out any mechanism involving alkyl–oxygen fission in the alcohol.

ADDITIONAL EVIDENCE FOR THE ADDITION-ELIMINATION MECHANISM

The use of an isotopic label can help to distinguish between the addition-elimination mechanism and the possible alternative of direct substitution by an S_N2-type reaction. Consider, for example, saponification of methyl ethanoate which has been labelled with ^{18}O in the carbonyl position. If reaction involved direct displacement of methoxide by hydroxide ion

then all of the isotope would be retained in the carboxylic acid product, or any unreacted ester.

In the accepted two-step mechanism, however, formation of a tetrahedral intermediate anion could lead to different results

Proton exchange between an —OH group and an —O:⁻ group is very rapid and could therefore occur in the intermediate *before* expulsion of methoxide ion to give the product

190

$$\text{HO} - \underset{\underset{:\text{OCH}_3}{|}}{\overset{\overset{\text{CH}_3}{|}}{\text{C}}} - {}^{18}\overset{..}{\text{O}}: {}^{\ominus} \quad \underset{-\text{H}^{\oplus}, +\text{H}^{\oplus}}{\rightleftharpoons} \quad {}^{\ominus}:\overset{..}{\text{O}} - \underset{\underset{:\text{OCH}_3}{|}}{\overset{\overset{\text{CH}_3}{|}}{\text{C}}} - {}^{18}\overset{..}{\text{OH}}$$

Remembering that uptake of the original hydroxide ion is a readily reversible process, it would now be possible for the intermediate to expel the labelled hydroxide ion to re-form the ester

$$^{\ominus}:\overset{..}{\text{O}} - \underset{\underset{:\text{OCH}_3}{|}}{\overset{\overset{\text{CH}_3}{|}}{\text{C}}} - {}^{18}\overset{..}{\text{OH}} \quad \rightleftharpoons \quad \overset{..}{\text{O}} = \text{C} \overset{\text{CH}_3}{\underset{:\text{OCH}_3}{<}} \; + \; {}^{18}:\overset{..}{\text{OH}}{}^{\ominus}$$

Strong evidence for the involvement of such an intermediate comes from the observation that if reaction is stopped well before hydrolysis is complete, part of the recovered ester has indeed lost the ^{18}O label.

Further evidence is provided from a different source. The tetrahedral intermediate is too unstable to be isolated, and normally has too short a lifetime to be detected by spectroscopic methods. We have seen before that the inclusion of a powerfully electron-withdrawing substituent can stabilise an anion in solution (page 175). Of particular interest is the anion formed by reaction of sodium methanoate with ethyl trifluoroethanoate

$$\text{CH}_3\overset{\ominus}{\text{O}}: \quad \overset{:\text{F}_3\text{C}}{\underset{\text{OCH}_2\text{CH}_3}{>}} \text{C} = \overset{..}{\text{O}}: \quad \rightleftharpoons \quad \text{CH}_3\overset{..}{\text{O}} - \underset{\underset{:\text{OCH}_2\text{CH}_3}{|}}{\overset{\overset{\text{CF}:_3}{|}}{\text{C}}} - \overset{..}{\text{O}}:{}^{\ominus}$$

powerful $-I$ effect of three F atoms helps to stabilise the anion

On mixing the two reagents, the ultraviolet or infrared absorption peak characteristic of the carbonyl group disappears, and only reappears on regenerating the ester, for example, by passing dry hydrogen chloride into the solution.

OTHER REACTIONS OF ESTERS

Esters can be made to react with ammonia (giving amides), with primary and secondary amines (giving N-substituted amides), with Grignard

191

reagents (giving tertiary alcohols via ketones), and with organometal reducing agents such as LiAlH$_4$ (giving alcohols). All of these reactions proceed by mechanisms analogous to those we have considered above.

9 Electrophilic Addition Reactions of Alkenes and Alkynes

REACTIONS OF ALKENES

INTRODUCTION

Alkenes have a planar structure and, as you will remember, the so called 'double bond' in fact consists of a **sigma-bond** (end-on overlap of sp^2 hybrid atomic orbitals) and a **pi-bond** (sideways overlap of $2p$ atomic orbitals).

Although a double bond is shorter and stronger than a single bond, the pi component is weaker than a sigma-bond. Pi electrons are of higher energy than sigma electrons, and are held less firmly by the nuclei of the two bonded carbon atoms. They are sometimes said to be 'more mobile' than sigma electrons.

Mechanistically, alkenes have electrons available for donation and are **nucleophilic** species, vulnerable to attack by electron-seeking **electrophilic reagents**. In the groundstate, the pi-bond is essentially non-polar*, but on close approach of an attacking electrophile, $E^{\oplus}$, the pi electrons are readily **polarised**

close approach of
an electrophile

induced polarisation
of the pi-bond

Donation of the pi electron pair to the electrophile leads to the formation of a new sigma-bond from one of the doubly bonded carbon atoms

*Propene has a small electric dipole moment ($\mu = 1.17 \times 10^{-30}$ C m (0.35 D)). This slight polarity may result from a drift of sigma electrons from the sp^3 to the more electronegative sp^2 carbon atom

$$CH_3 \rightarrowtail CH = CH_2$$
$$sp^3 \qquad sp^2$$

to the electrophile, leaving the other carbon atom with a unit positive charge

new sigma-bond

adjacent carbon atom has only
six valence electrons and a
unit positive charge

The carbocation formed in this way could attain stability by re-expelling the electrophile, or by accepting an electron pair from another nucleophile, for example $\overset{..}{Y}{}^{\ominus}$

Such a reaction, in which the original pi-bond is replaced by two new sigma-bonds (C — E and C — Y) is classified as an **electrophilic addition reaction**, the species $E^{\oplus}$ and $\overset{..}{Y}{}^{\ominus}$ having been added across the carbon-carbon double bond

You will notice, however, that as in all the reactions we have been discussing, each of the two steps in alkene addition involve a nucleophile donating an electron pair to an electrophile. The first step, uptake of the electrophile, is the slow rate-determining step; reaction of the intermediate carbocation with an anion takes place relatively quickly. An energy profile for alkene addition is of the general form shown in figure 9.1.

Frequently, the electrophile is a proton, and addition of hydrogen halides is one of the most common alkene reactions. We will now consider representative examples of this and other addition processes.

194

Figure 9.1 *Energy profile for generalised alkene electrophilic addition reaction*

Addition of hydrogen halides to alkenes

Reactions are normally carried out either in the gas phase or in non-aqueous solution. Reasonable yields may sometimes be obtained by using hydrogen bromide or hydrogen iodide in concentrated aqueous solution. Ethene, the least reactive of the common alkenes, reacts with hydrogen bromide very slowly at temperatures below 100°C (373K), and even higher temperatures are required for the addition of hydrogen chloride. High temperature and pressure must be used for addition of hydrogen fluoride, but on the other hand, but-1-ene readily forms 2-bromobutane when bubbled into a mixture of concentrated sulphuric acid and sodium bromide at room temperature.

Generally speaking, the reactivity of alkenes is related to the stability of the intermediate carbocation; ethene is not very reactive because the ethyl carbocation is relatively unstable. The order of reactivity of the hydrogen halides

$$HF\!: \ < \ HCl\!: \ < \ HBr\!: \ < \ HI\!:$$

parallels the order of increasing acid strength. This is just what we should expect if the rate-controlling step is protonation of the alkene.

Addition of hydrogen bromide to ethene

On close approach of the reagent to the ethene molecule, two things will happen:

195

(1) Repulsion between the pi electrons and the sigma electrons in the hydrogen–bromine bond will increase the normal polarisation of that bond.

(2) The pi-bond will itself be polarised by the positive end ($H^{\delta+}$) of the hydrogen bromide molecule

$$: \overset{..}{Br} :^{\delta-}$$
$$\uparrow$$
$$H^{\delta+}$$
$$\underset{H_2C = CH_2}{\overset{\delta+ \quad \delta-}{\frown}}$$

mutual induced polarisation
on close approach of the HBr $:$
molecule

Notice that for this to occur, the HBr $:$ molecule must approach the alkene with the **correct orientation**. Attack with the bromine atom end-on would be fruitless: repulsion between the fractionally negatively charged bromine atom and the pi electron cloud would simply result in the two species 'bouncing apart' again

$$\overset{\delta+}{H}$$
$$| \, \delta-$$
$$: Br :$$
$$\updownarrow$$
$$H_2C = CH_2$$

mutual repulsion

Assuming, then, that the hydrogen bromide molecule has the right orientation and is moving fast enough, collision between the two reactants will result in the transfer of a proton from hydrogen bromide to the alkene. This process will require

(1) donation of the pair of pi electrons from the alkene to the hydrogen atom (proton), accompanied by

(2) release of sigma electrons in the hydrogen–bromine bond to the bromine atom

$$H_2C \overset{\frown}{=} CH_2 \quad H \overset{..}{\underset{..}{\frown} Br} :$$

Compare this with the hydrolysis of bromomethane, discussed in the previous chapter

196

It is apparent that protonation involves displacement of bromide ion from a hydrogen bromide molecule by a nucleophilic alkene molecule.

Bond-making and bond-breaking occur more or less synchronously, so the reactants will pass through a bimolecular transition state which we can formulate in the usual way

Remember that such a drawing is an attempt to summarise the processes we believe to be taking place in the transition state. There is no implication as to the stereochemistry of the participants, and we show the atoms in a linear arrangement merely for convenience and simplicity.

The transition state leads to the planar carbocation intermediate

and addition is completed in the second step by reaction of the carbocation with a bromide ion

This step, like the first, involves donation of an electron pair from a nucleophile, the bromide anion, to an electrophile, the carbocation; and since the species are oppositely charged, the second step is relatively fast. There will be a transition state for this step, of course, in which the two ions are held together mainly be electrostatic attraction. Bond formation is underway, however, and the two unit charges will have been reduced to fractional charges

197

$$\overset{\delta-}{\underset{\cdot\cdot}{:\ddot{B}r}} ----\overset{\delta+}{CH_2}-CH_3$$

Exercise 9.1
Draw an energy profile for the addition of hydrogen bromide to ethene, showing the position of the two transition states and the carbocation intermediate.

Addition of hydrogen bromide to propene

With an unsymmetrical alkene like propene, addition of $H\ddot{B}r:$ might be expected to yield a mixture of two products

$$CH_3CH=CH_2 + H\ddot{B}r: \begin{cases} CH_3CH_2CH_2\ddot{B}r: & \text{(1-bromopropane)} \\ \\ CH_3CH(\ddot{B}r:)CH_3 & \text{(2-bromopropane)} \end{cases}$$

In practice, it is found that one compound usually predominates, and may even be the sole product. Addition of $H\ddot{B}r:$ to propene gives over 90 per cent 2-bromopropane.

The direction of addition of a hydrogen halide, $H\ddot{X}:$, to an unsymmetrical alkene can be predicted by a now somewhat superfluous rule, **Markovnikov's rule**, which states 'addition of a non-symmetrical reagent such as $H\ddot{B}r:$ to an unsymmetrical alkene occurs in such a way that the H atom goes to the carbon atom which already has the greater number of H atoms joined to it'. We should emphasise that this is purely an *empirical* rule, based on experimental observation. It is in no way an *explanation* of what happens, and should not be quoted as such. There are, in fact, a number of exceptions to the rule, but both the 'normal' mode of addition and the exceptions are readily accounted for in terms of the mechanism involved.

Protonation of propene can in principle generate two different carbocations

$$CH_3CH=CH_2 \xrightarrow{H^\oplus} \begin{cases} CH_3CH_2\overset{\oplus}{CH_2} & \text{...a } 1° \text{ carbocation} \\ \\ CH_3\overset{\oplus}{CH}CH_3 & \text{...a } 2° \text{ carbocation} \end{cases}$$

198

By application of the Hammond Postulate (see page 105) we should expect the more stable 2° carbocation to require less activation energy for its formation than the relatively unstable 1° carbocation. This is shown diagrammatically in figure 9.2.

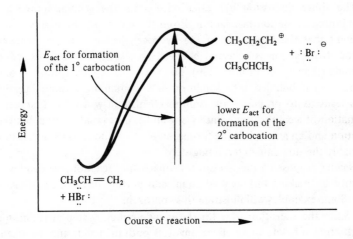

Figure 9.2 *Energy profile for protonation of propene*

In the reaction of HBr $\overset{..}{\underset{..}{:}}$ with propene, many fruitless collisions will occur at both carbon atoms 1 and 2. But because of the lower activation energy for protonation of carbon 1, a much higher proportion of collisions at that position will be successful, leading to 2-bromopropane as the predominant product. Similar reasoning accounts for the observed order of reactivity of simple alkenes with hydrogen halides

$$CH_2 = CH_2 \ < \ CH_3CH = CH_2 \ < \ \underset{CH_3}{\overset{CH_3}{>}}C = CH_2$$

which parallels the order of increasing stability of the corresponding carbocations

$$CH_3 - \overset{\oplus}{CH_2} \ < \ CH_3 - \overset{\oplus}{CH} - CH_3 \ < \ \underset{CH_3}{\overset{CH_3}{>}}\overset{\oplus}{C} - CH_3$$

$$(1°) \qquad\qquad (2°) \qquad\qquad (3°)$$

Under similar conditions, propene reacts *faster* than ethene with a given hyrogen halide such as HBr $\overset{\cdot\cdot}{}$, because of the lower activation energy required for the formation of the secondary propyl carbocation (CH$_3$$\overset{\oplus}{C}HCH_3$), compared with the primary ethyl carbocation (CH$_3$$\overset{\oplus}{C}H_2$).

The above discussion illustrates once again the general approach to establishing a reaction mechanism. From the nature of the two reactants, it seems that the likely role of the hydrogen halide is to protonate the alkene. No reaction is observed between an alkene and aqueous sodium bromide (that is, the bromide ion), but but-1-ene rapidly forms 2-bromobutane when bubbled into sulphuric acid containing sodium bromide. This leads us to propose a two-step mechanism in which the first step is formation of a carbocation. Since we would expect rapid reaction between a cation and an anion, it is the formation of the carbocation which is most probably the slow rate-determining step.

Having proposed a mechanism for a particular reaction, we can test its validity by making various predictions and putting these to experimental test. Some examples will illustrate this approach.

(1) Since the transition state for the rate-determining step in addition of hydrogen halide to an alkene involves both the halide and the alkene, then the reaction should exhibit second order kinetics. For various reasons, kinetic studies with alkenes are often quite difficult, but the rate of hydration of alkenes with aqueous acid, HA, has been shown to depend on the concentration of both the acid and the alkene

$$\text{Rate} = k \text{ [HA] [alkene]}$$

(2) Of two alkenes reacting under similar conditions with the same hydrogen halide, we should predict that the one forming the most stable carbocation intermediate would react the faster — and this is indeed just what is observed.

Exercise 9.2
Which alkene would you expect to react most readily with hydrogen iodide: but-2-ene, or 2-methylbut-2-ene?

---

(3) The proposed second step is attack on the carbocation by the halide anion. This being the case, the presence of other halide ions in the reaction mixture should lead to alternative products. Again, this prediction is verified by experimental observation. If but-1-ene is bubbled

into sulphuric acid containing both sodium bromide and sodium chloride, the product consists of a mixture of 2-bromobutane and 2-chlorobutane.

$$CH_3CH_2CH = CH_2 \longrightarrow CH_3CH_2\overset{\oplus}{C}HCH_3 \begin{array}{c} :\overset{..}{\underset{..}{Br}}:^{\ominus} \\ :\overset{..}{\underset{..}{Cl}}:^{\ominus} \end{array} \begin{array}{c} CH_3CH_2CHCH_3 \\ | \\ :\overset{..}{\underset{..}{Br}}: \\ \\ CH_3CH_2CHCH_3 \\ | \\ :\overset{..}{\underset{..}{Cl}}: \end{array}$$

As further experimental evidence becomes available, so the proposed mechanism must be modified, if necessary, to take account of the new observations. Failing this, some alternative explanation must be found for the 'anomalous' data. Only when a mechanism has been shown to be consistent with *all* the known facts can it be described as the 'accepted mechanism' for a reaction.

Reaction with sulphuric acid

Alkenes are rapidly absorbed by cold concentrated sulphuric acid. Heat is evolved, and the product is the corresponding alkyl hydrogen sulphate. The concentration of acid required depends on the reactivity of the alkene. Propene is absorbed by 75 per cent acid, but for the less reactive ethene, 98 per cent acid is required, under pressure. Not surprisingly in strongly acid conditions, the first step in the reaction is (slow) protonation of the alkene. This is followed by relatively fast uptake of the hydrogen sulphate anion by the intermediate carbocation

With some alkenes, further reaction may occur to give the dialkyl sulphate ester

$$H - \overset{\displaystyle |}{\underset{\displaystyle |}{C}} - \overset{\displaystyle |}{\underset{\displaystyle |}{C}} - \overset{..}{\underset{..}{O}} - \overset{\displaystyle \overset{:O:}{\|}}{\underset{\displaystyle \underset{:O:}{\|}}{S}} - \overset{..}{\underset{..}{O}} - \overset{\displaystyle |}{\underset{\displaystyle |}{C}} - \overset{\displaystyle |}{\underset{\displaystyle |}{C}} - H$$

The reaction is used in the petroleum industry to separate alkenes from alkanes which are unaffected by concentrated sulphuric acid under these conditions. Subsequent dilution of the sulphuric acid solution results in hydrolysis of the esters

$$H - \overset{\displaystyle |}{\underset{\displaystyle |}{C}} - \overset{\displaystyle |}{\underset{\displaystyle |}{C}} - \overset{..}{\underset{..}{O}} - \overset{\displaystyle \overset{:O:}{\|}}{\underset{\displaystyle \underset{:O:}{\|}}{S}} - \overset{..}{\underset{..}{O}}H \;\;\overset{H_2O}{\rightleftharpoons}\;\; H - \overset{\displaystyle |}{\underset{\displaystyle |}{C}} - \overset{\displaystyle |}{\underset{\displaystyle |}{C}} - \overset{..}{\underset{..}{O}}H \;+\; H\overset{..}{\underset{..}{O}} - \overset{\displaystyle \overset{:O:}{\|}}{\underset{\displaystyle \underset{:O:}{\|}}{S}} - \overset{..}{\underset{..}{O}}H$$

Protonation of unsymmetrical alkenes occurs so as to give the more stable of the two possible carbocations. Thus, propene is converted into the 2-hydrogensulphate ester, from which propan-2-ol is obtained

$$CH_3CH = CH_2 \;\overset{H^\oplus}{\longrightarrow}\; CH_3\overset{\oplus}{C}HCH_3 \;\overset{\overset{\ominus}{:}\overset{..}{O}SO_2OH}{\longrightarrow}\; \underset{\underset{:OSO_2OH}{|}}{CH_3CHCH_3} \;\overset{H_2O}{\longrightarrow}\; \underset{\underset{:OH}{|}}{CH_3CHCH_3}$$

An obvious disadvantage from the commercial point of view is the production of large quantities of dilute sulphuric acid, and there are a number of alternative processes involving direct acid-catalysed hydration of alkenes.

Addition of halogen

The rate of reaction, the nature of the products and the mechanism by which they are formed are all very much influenced by the reaction conditions. Very little reaction occurs in the dark between bromine and ethene in anhydrous, non-polar, conditions (for example, in a flask whose walls have been coated with paraffin wax). Conversely, rapid reaction occurs in bright sunlight or on irradiation with ultraviolet light. This involves a free radical mechanism which can also be initiated by the use of peroxides, etc. Most simple alkenes readily decolorise a solution of bromine, and the reaction serves as a useful test for unsaturation. An ionic mechanism is involved, but the actual products depend on the solvent employed. In organic solvents such as tetrachloromethane, the dibromide is formed, for example

$$CH_2 = CH_2 \; + \; :\overset{..}{B}r_2 \quad \longrightarrow \quad CH_2 Br CH_2 Br$$

With bromine in aqueous solution ('bromine water'), decoloration is equally rapid, but the product is a mixture of the dibromide and a bromo-alcohol (known as a 'bromohydrin')

$$CH_2 = CH_2 \; + \; :\overset{..}{B}r_2 \quad \overset{H_2\overset{..}{O}}{\longrightarrow} \quad CH_2 \overset{..}{B}r \; : CH_2 \overset{..}{B}r \; : \; + \; CH_2 \overset{..}{B}r \; :CH_2 \overset{..}{O}H$$

The order of ease of addition of halogens is the reverse of that for hydrogen halides. Fluorine tends to react explosively with alkenes, whereas reaction with iodine is slow and incomplete. Only direct addition of chlorine and bromine is of practical value.

Addition of bromine in organic solvents

Mutual repulsion between the pi electron cloud and sigma electrons in the closely approaching bromine molecule polarises the latter, so that the nearest bromine atom becomes electron deficient

induced polarisation of the bromine molecule

By analogy with the mechanism of addition of hydrogen bromide, it might be supposed that the next stage is addition of $:\overset{..}{B}r^{\oplus}$ to form a bromocarbo-cation

The formation of a 'normal' carbocation is, however, inconsistent with certain observations on the stereochemistry of addition. For example, the cyclic alkene, cyclopentene, has a slightly puckered but essentially planar structure, and would therefore be expected to form *two* addition products with bromine

planar cation,
attacked by : B̤r̤ : ⊖ from
above or below

Bromine is quite a large atom, and the bromide ion might therefore more readily attack the carbocation from the opposite side, giving rather more of the *trans* than the *cis* product. However, when the reaction is carried out, we find that the *trans* isomer is the *only* product.

Similar experiments have been performed with geometrical isomers of alkenes whose structure is such that optical isomers could be formed on addition of bromine. The results again show that only *trans* addition takes place.

To attempt to explain this, it has been suggested that the intermediate in this reaction is one in which the bromine atom is sigma bonded to *both* carbon atoms. It is likely that the two bromine-carbon bonds are formed simultaneously, but on paper we can show it as a stepwise process

The carbon-bromine bonds will be highly polar (why?), and so each carbon atom carries an appreciable positive charge

either carbon atom
can be attacked by : B̤r̤ : ⊖

Exercise 9.3
Write a mechanistic equation for the second step in this reaction —
uptake of the anion, $: \overset{..}{\underset{..}{Br}} :^{\ominus}$.

Formation of a cyclic bromonium ion would certainly account for
exclusive *trans* addition, as the bromide ion could clearly only attack such
an intermediate from the opposite side. However, it does not explain *why*
a bromonium ion should be formed in preference to the normal carbocation. The reason is, of course, that the bromonium ion is *more stable*
and therefore requires less activation energy for its formation. This increased stability results from an additional sigma-bond, and the fact that
all the atoms involved have a complete octet.

Reaction with bromine water

Formation of the bromohydrin product could conceivably be due to
hydrolysis of the first-formed dibromide. However, independent experiments show that under similar conditions, hydrolysis of a dibromoalkane
to a bromoalcohol is extremely slow. So we must look for an alternative
explanation.

An aqueous solution of bromine contains both dissolved bromine
molecules and some bromic(I) acid ($HO\overset{..}{\underset{..}{Br}}$), formed by the reaction

$$: \overset{..}{\underset{..}{Br}}_2 + H_2O \rightleftharpoons H\overset{..}{\underset{..}{Br}} : + HO\overset{..}{\underset{..}{Br}} :$$

Attack by either of these reagents ($: \overset{..}{\underset{..}{Br}}_2$ or $HO\overset{..}{\underset{..}{Br}} :$) gives the intermediate
bromonium ion which can then further react with either a bromide ion,
$: \overset{..}{\underset{..}{Br}} :^{\ominus}$, or a water molecule. The former is the better nucleophile, but
water is present in much greater concentration. (Also, water molecules
solvating the cation will be in a very favourable position to complete the
reaction.)

The formation of two products is, of course, strong support for the proposed mechanism involving a common cationic intermediate. Further evidence is provided by the observation that if sodium chloride or sodium nitrate is added to the bromine water, small amounts of the bromochloroalkane

are produced. Neither sodium chloride nor sodium nitrate react with alkenes, dibromoalkanes or bromoalcohols in cold aqueous solution, so the new products could only be formed by reaction of the bromonium ion with the chloride or nitrate anions. The addition of a competing reagent which may form a new product with a suspected intermediate is a commonly used experimental device known as **trapping**. In the reaction we have been considering, added chloride or nitrate ion 'traps' the bromonium ion intermediate, so preventing its reaction with bromide ion or water molecules. In all such studies it must be demonstrated that the trapping agent will not react directly with the substrate or with the product of the main reaction.

Addition of alkene to alkene: acid-catalysed polymerisation

By varying the reaction conditions, alkenes can be made to polymerise by either an ionic or a free radical mechanism. In acid-catalysed polymerisation of an alkene, the first step, **initiation**, is formation of a carbocation

$$RCH = CH_2 \ \overset{+H^{\oplus}}{\rightleftharpoons} \ R\overset{\oplus}{C}H - CH_3$$

206

This cation is then subjected to nucleophilic attack by another molecule of the alkene

Since the result of this step is the generation of yet another carbocation, the process can be repeated over and over again, leading to the formation of a long chain carbocation

(where n is a large number)

This constitutes the **propagation stage** of the reaction. A sequence whereby an intermediate reacts so as to generate another similar intermediate, which can then repeat the process, is known as a **chain reaction**. Ionic polymerisation of alkenes is therefore said to proceed by a **chain propagation mechanism**. Eventually, the growing carbocation chain will be neutralised in some way, for example by uptake of a nucleophile, or by loss of a proton. This interrupts the propagation sequence and is referred to as **chain termination**.

Using different catalysts, some alkenes may be polymerised by an anionic mechanism, but simple ionic polymerisation is of little commercial importance. Most industrial ionic polymerisations are carried out with the aid of special catalysts developed by Ziegler and Natta, based on complexes of titanium chlorides with aluminium alkyls. The advantage of such catalysts is twofold. They allow polymerisation of alkenes under relatively mild conditions, and they also permit some control over chain length and stereo arrangement — factors which greatly influence the physical properties of the resulting polymer.

Oxidation of alkenes

Alkenes undergo a variety of oxidation reactions, many of which are thought to be initiated by electrophilic attack of the oxidising agent on the alkene.

Reaction with potassium manganate(VII) (permanganate), KMnO₄

Most alkenes rapidly decolorise a dilute aqueous alkaline solution of potassium manganate(VII) at room temperature. Discharge of the characteristic pink colour serves as a useful test for unsaturation. The product is the corresponding diol, known as a *vicinal* (or α) **glycol**.

$$\diagup_{\diagdown}C = C\diagdown_{\diagup} \xrightarrow{\text{KMnO}_4} -\overset{|}{\underset{|}{C}} - \overset{|}{\underset{|}{C}} - \\ \quad\quad\quad\quad\quad :OH\ :OH$$

an α-glycol

Reaction is initiated by attack of the manganate(VII) ion on the alkene double bond. The concept of a negatively charged electrophile must at first seem a little anomalous! However, the manganate(VII) ion can act as an electrophile because the high oxidation state (+7) of the manganese means that electrons in the oxygen-manganese double bonds are attracted towards the manganese atom, leaving the oxygen atoms slightly electron deficient, that is, electrophilic. Such polarisation will increase on close approach of the ion to the high electron density of the pi-bond.

mutual induced polarisation
of the carbon–carbon and
oxygen–manganese double bonds

As pi electrons are withdrawn from the alkene double bond to form a carbon–oxygen bond, so the adjacent carbon atom (which is acquiring positive charge) is able to receive electrons from another oxygen atom of the manganate(VII) ion. No separate carbocation intermediate is involved, but instead, continuation of these electron shifts leads to the formation of a **cyclic transition state**. This then goes on to form the cyclic manganate ester cyclic transition state

cyclic manganate ester

Hydrolysis of the ester, which occurs spontaneously, involves cleavage of the oxygen–manganese bonds, since when ^{18}O-labelled $KMnO_4$ is used, the labelled oxygen atoms are transferred to the glycol

manganate(V) ion

During the course of this reaction, the oxidation state of the manganese atom changes from +7 to +5

$$Mn^{VIII} O_4 \xrightarrow{+2e} H_2 Mn^V O_4^{\ominus} \equiv Mn^V O_3^{\ominus} + H_2O$$

Reaction via a cyclic transition state implies exclusive *cis* addition to the alkene double bond. That this indeed occurs can be demonstrated with a cyclic alkene such as cyclohexene, where only the *cis*-diol is observed

cis-cyclohexane-1,2-diol

Reaction with osmium(VIII) oxide (osmium tetroxide, osmic acid), OsO_4

Osmium(VIII) oxide is a yellow crystalline solid, soluble in water and various organic solvents. Oxidation of alkenes with this reagent gives the

209

same product, a *cis*-1,2-diol, as is obtained with $KMnO_4$. The mechanism, involving the formation and hydrolysis of an intermediate cyclic ester, is also similar. However, osmate esters are somewhat more stable and are usually decomposed by hydrolysis with aqueous sodium sulphate(IV) (sodium sulphite), Na_2SO_3

cyclic
transition state

osmate ester
(insoluble)

a *cis*-1,2-diol

During the reaction, osmium changes its oxidation state from +8 to +6

$$Os^{VIII}O_4 \xrightarrow{-2e} H_2OsO_4 \equiv Os^{VI}O_3 + H_2O$$

Reaction with trioxygen (ozone), O_3

This reaction is usually carried out by bubbling ozone-rich oxygen from an ozoniser into a solution of the alkene in an inert solvent such as tetrachloromethane. A trace of moisture is necessary to bring about polarisation of the ozone. Electrophilic attack on the alkene double bond gives initially a very unstable cyclic ozonide called a **molozonide**

a molozonide

This rapidly and spontaneously rearranges to a less unstable **ozonide** structure

Addition of water results in decomposition of the ozonide so as to give a mixture of carbonyl compounds, the whole process being described as **ozonolysis** of the alkene

Identification of the carbonyl compounds (for example, by conversion into solid derivatives which can be analysed by paper or thin layer chromatography) gives information about the structure of the alkene. For example, the two isomeric butenes are readily distinguished by their ozonolysis products

$$CH_3CH_2CH = CH_2 \longrightarrow CH_3CH_2CHO + HCHO$$

$$CH_3CH = CHCH_3 \longrightarrow 2CH_3CHO$$

Reaction with diborane

Diborane, B_2H_6, is prepared by treating sodium tetrahydridoborate(III) (sodium borohydride), $NaBH_4$, with trifluoroborane, BF_3. In most reactions, diborane behaves as though it had the structure BH_3. Having only six valence electrons, the boron atom is electron deficient, and reaction is initiated by donation of pi electrons to this atom. As in the above oxidation reactions, no ionic intermediate is formed, but instead, reaction proceeds via a cyclic transition state where breaking of the alkene pi-bond and formation of the carbon-boron bond is accompanied by breaking of a boron-hydrogen bond and formation of a new carbon-hydrogen bond

cyclic
transition state

211

Repetition of these steps leads to the formation of a **trialkyl borane**

$$B(CH_2CH_2R)_3$$

The practical importance of this reaction lies in the fact that alkyl boranes are readily oxidised (for example, with hydrogen peroxide) to the corresponding primary alcohols

$$(RCH_2CH_2)_3B \xrightarrow{H_2O_2} 3\ RCH_2CH_2OH\ +\ B(OH)_3$$

Note that the alcohols are the anti-Markovnikov products, and so the process is complimentary to the acid-catalysed hydration of alkenes

$$RCH = CH_2 \begin{array}{c} \xrightarrow{BH_3,\ H_2O_2} RCH_2CH_2OH \quad \text{anti-Markovnikov addition} \\ \xrightarrow{H^{\oplus},\ H_2O} RCH(OH)CH_3 \quad \text{Markovnikov addition} \end{array}$$

Hydrogenation of alkenes

Reaction may be carried out in the vapour phase, or in solution in an inert solvent — usually under pressure. A finely divided metal catalyst is required, commonly platinum, palladium or nickel. Platinum and palladium catalysts on charcoal may often be used at room temperature. Nickel is cheaper, but less reactive and normally requires a high temperature (200-300°C) (473-573K). Addition of hydrogen to an alkene is not an ionic reaction. The exact detail is still a matter for debate, but reaction occurs on the surface of the metal catalyst. Adsorption of hydrogen weakens the sigma-bond between the two hydrogen atoms. The alkene then 'sits' on the metal surface and is attacked by the hydrogen atoms (simultaneously, or step-wise) from within the metal surface

alkene approaching
hydrogen on metal
surface

complex on
surface

alkane product
desorped

Hydrogenation is exothermic, the enthalpy change being between about 110 and 130 kJ mol^{-1}. These values, of course, are unaffected by the use of a catalyst, which simply facilitates reaction by lowering the activation energy requirements: see figure 9.3.

Figure 9.3 *Energy profile for catalysed and uncatalysed hydrogenation of an alkene*

Observation shows that the more alkylated an alkene (that is, the more alkyl groups attached to the doubly bonded carbon atoms) the lower the enthalpy of hydrogenation. For example, the isomeric butenes

3-methylbut-1-ene
a monoalkylated alkene
$\Delta H = -127 \text{ kJ mol}^{-1}$

3-methylbut-2-ene
a trialkylated alkene
$\Delta H = -112 \text{ kJ mol}^{-1}$

If an alkene evolves less energy on hydrogenation, then it must contain less energy. So with catalytic hydrogenation we have a method for estimating the relative thermodynamic stabilities of different alkenes, including *cis* and *trans* isomers. We find that for a series of simple alkenes, the more alkylated the structure, the more stable it is. However, thermodynamic stability must not be equated with reactivity of an alkene towards electrophilic reagents. On the contrary, 3-methylbut-2-ene (enthalpy of hydrogenation -112 kJ mol^{-1}) is more stable than the isomeric 3-methylbut-1-ene (enthalpy of hydrogenation -127 kJ mol^{-1}), but in electrophilic addition reactions, the former compound reacts far more readily than the latter. The difference, as we have seen, is related to the stabilities of the carbocation intermediates involved. 3-Methylbut-2-ene is more reactive because less energy of activation is required for the formation of the tertiary carbocation $(CH_3)_2 \overset{\oplus}{C}CH_2CH_3$, than for the conversion of 3-methylbut-1-ene to the secondary carbocation $(CH_3)_2CH\overset{\oplus}{C}HCH_3$. These points should be made clear by reference to the energy diagram, figure 9.4.

Reactivity of buta-1,3-diene

The structure of this compound was described in chapter 2 (see page 21). Although buta-1,3-diene has two ethene-like double bonds, the compound is more easily hydrogenated, halogenated and polymerised than ethene. Addition of hydrogen bromide is particularly interesting, as two different products are formed, the ratio of which depends on the temperature of reaction

214

Figure 9.4 *Energy relationships for reduction and protonation of two isomeric alkenes*

3-Bromobut-1-ene is the product expected from addition of $H\overset{..}{\underset{..}{Br}}$ across one of the double bonds (1,2-addition), but the other product, 1-bromo-2 -ene (1,4-addition), certainly would not be predicted from the classical structure for buta-1,3-diene. To understand this apparently anomalous behaviour, we have to examine the structure of the carbocation inter-mediate involved.

As in addition of $H\overset{..}{\underset{..}{Br}}$ to propene, initial protonation occurs so as to give the more stable of the two possible carbocations

$$CH_2 = CH - CH = CH_2 \xrightarrow{H^{\oplus}} \begin{array}{l} \overset{\oplus}{C}H_2CH_2CH = CH_2 \qquad (I) \\[2mm] CH_3\overset{\oplus}{C}HCH = CH_2 \qquad (II) \end{array}$$

215

The secondary carbocation (II) is formed in preference to the less stable primary carbocation (I), and uptake of $: \overset{..}{\underset{..}{Br}} :^{\ominus}$ by this cation would give the normal 1,2-addition product. However, the structure shown for carbocation (II) is one in which the positively charged carbon atom is conjugated with the remaining double bond. It is therefore possible to draw an alternative structure showing the terminal carbon atom with the positive charge

$$CH_3\overset{\oplus}{CH} \overset{\frown}{} CH \rightleftharpoons CH_2 \qquad CH_3CH = CH - \overset{\oplus}{CH_2}$$

(II)   (III)

In other words, (II) and (III) are limiting forms, and the actual structure is a mesomer (resonance hybrid), with two electron-deficient carbon atoms available for attack by the bromide ion

$$[CH_3\overset{\delta+}{CH} \mathop{=\!=\!=} CH \mathop{=\!=\!=} \overset{\delta+}{CH_2}]^{\oplus}$$
1   2   3   4

$: \overset{..}{\underset{..}{Br}} :^{\ominus}$ can attack carbon atoms
2 or 4

Keeping in mind that each step in the mechanism is reversible, the following species will exist in equilibrium

$$CH_2 = CH - CH = CH_2 \;+\; H\overset{..}{\underset{..}{Br}} :$$

$\Updownarrow$

$$[CH_3 - \overset{\delta+}{CH} \mathop{=\!=} CH \mathop{=\!=} \overset{\delta+}{CH_2}]^{\oplus} \;+\; : \overset{..}{\underset{..}{Br}} :^{\ominus}$$
1   2   3   4

$$CH_3 - \overset{..}{\underset{..}{C}}HBr : - CH = CH_2 \qquad CH_3 - CH = CH - CH_2\overset{..}{\underset{..}{Br}} :^{*}$$
4   3   2   1   4   3   2   1

At low temperatures, attainment of equilibrium is slow, and the predominant product will be that which is most easily formed (that is, with the lowest activation energy). If we look again at the limiting forms (II) and (III), we can see that although they are both conjugated systems, (II) also has a secondary structure and would therefore be more stable than (III).

*Note that in IUPAC nomenclature the carbon atoms are renumbered in the products so as to give the alkene double bond the smallest number.

In the jargon of resonance theory, we should say that since carbocation (II) is more stable than (III), it will make a greater contribution to the resonance hybrid. The hybrid is nearer to (II) than (III) in structure, and so carbon 2 has more of the positive charge than carbon 4. It follows that activation energy for attack of $: \overset{..}{Br} :^{\ominus}$ on carbon 2 will be less than that for attack on carbon 4. From this we conclude that the product 3-bromo-but-1-ene predominates at low temperatures because it is formed at a faster rate than 1-bromobut-2-ene. This is called **kinetic control** of reaction. At higher temperatures, more energy is available, and equilibrium is attained quickly. Under equilibrium conditions, the major product is 1-bromobut-2-ene, so this must be the more stable product. Its formation is said to be the result of **thermodynamic control** of reaction.

Another interesting observation is that if the 1,2-addition product is heated to about 40°C, it undergoes rearrangement to the 1,4-product. Loss of $: \overset{..}{\underset{..}{Br}} :^{\ominus}$ from 3-bromobut-1-ene is not difficult because the result-ing carbocation is resonance stabilised. Furthermore, at higher temperatures the additional activation energy required for attack on carbon 4 is less of a problem.

One final point concerns the relative stabilities of the two products. Can we explain why 1-bromobut-2-ene is more stable than 3-bromo-but-1-ene? We saw earlier that the more alkylated an alkene, the more stable it is. Looking at the two structures involved

$$CH_3 \overset{\displaystyle |}{\underset{\displaystyle : \overset{}{\underset{..}{Br}} :}{-CH}} - CH = CH_2 \quad \text{and} \quad CH_3 - CH = CH - CH_2 \overset{..}{\underset{..}{Br}} :$$

3-bromobut-1-ene (IV)   1-bromobut-2-ene (V)

it can be seen that whatever the effect of the bromine atom on the alkene, it will be the same for both products, as it occupies the same position rela-tive to the double bond in each case. The difference, then, lies in the fact that the 1,4-addition product (V) is a dialkylated alkene, whereas 3-bromobut-1-ene (IV) is only monoalkylated.

ELECTROPHILIC ADDITION TO ALKYNES

The 'triple' bond in alkynes consists of a sigma-bond plus two pi-bonds, and alkynes undergo many of the electrophilic addition reactions characteristic of alkenes. A comparison of bond strengths reveals that the second pi-bond in alkynes is slightly less stable than an alkene double bond, but despite this, alkynes are frequently less reactive than alkenes towards electrophilic reagents. For example, alkynes do not react with cold concentrated sulphuric acid, and chlorine can be added to the double bond in hex-4-en-1-yne while leaving the triple bond intact

$$CH_3CH = CH - CH_2 - C \equiv CH \xrightarrow{\; : \overset{..}{C}l_2 \;} CH_3CH\overset{..}{C}l : CH\overset{..}{C}l : - CH_2 - C \equiv CH$$

Reagents such as $H\overset{..}{C}l :$, which readily add to an alkene double bond, only slowly react with alkynes unless an electrophilic catalyst (for example $Hg^{2\oplus}$) is present.

The reason for this resistance to electrophilic attack is not all that clear. Of significance is the fact that the triply bonded carbon atoms are sp-hybridised, resulting in a shorter more compact pi molecular orbital than that in an alkene, where the carbon atoms are sp^2-hybridised (see page 36). Another factor may be the relative instability of the 'vinylic' type of carbocation intermediate, $CH_2 = \overset{\oplus}{C}H$. However, the same general mechanistic principles apply to alkynes, and the direction of addition in unsymmetrical compounds is dictated by the difference in stabilities of the possible carbocation intermediates. For example, propyne reacts with hydrogen bromide to give 2-bromopropene rather than 1-bromopropene as the main product

$$CH_3C \equiv CH \xrightarrow{\; H^\oplus \;} CH_3\overset{\oplus}{C} = CH_2 \xrightarrow{\; : \overset{..}{B}r : ^\ominus \;} CH_3C\overset{..}{B}r : = CH_2$$

218

Further addition gives mainly 2,2-dibromopropane, and again this is due to preferential formation of the more stable of the two possible carbocations

$$CH_3C\overset{..}{\underset{..}{Br}} = CH_2 \quad \xrightarrow{\quad H^\oplus \quad} \quad CH_3\overset{\oplus \,..}{\underset{..}{C}Br} - CH_3, \text{ rather than } CH_3CH\overset{..}{\underset{..}{Br}} - \overset{\oplus}{C}H_2$$

Exercise 9.5

The secondary carbocation $CH_3\overset{\oplus \,..}{C}Br - CH_3$ is additionally stabilised by resonance. Draw another limiting form to illustrate this.

---

10 Aromatic Electrophilic Substitution

INTRODUCTION

The resonance structure of benzene was described in chapter 2, and you might find it helpful to re-read that chapter before going on to study aromatic electrophilic substitution. With six pi electrons in a circular molecular orbital above and below the plane of the nucleus, benzene is a molecule with a high pi electron density and is therefore nucleophilic.

The parallel with alkenes is obvious. With both types of compound, reaction is initiated by donation of an electron pair from a pi-bond to an attacking electrophile, $E^{\oplus}$, leading to the formation of an intermediate carbocation

The Kekulé formula is the most convenient to use in writing mechanistic equations, and it is conventional to omit all those ring hydrogen atoms not involved in the reaction.

In the case of an alkene, reaction is completed by addition of a nucleophile, $\overset{\cdot\cdot}{Y}{}^{\ominus}$, to the carbocation

But in reactions of benzene, the role of the anion is to function as a base and remove a proton from the carbocation

You will notice that this is mechanistically similar to the second step in unimolecular β-elimination (page 125)

and the electron pair required to neutralise the positive charge actually comes from the carbon–hydrogen bond.

The reason for this divergence in behaviour is simple enough. Addition of an anion to the alkene carbocation gives a product which is more stable than the original alkene, one pi-bond having been replaced by two new sigma-bonds. Similar addition to the benzene carbocation would give a cyclohexadiene product considerably less stable than the original benzene, because of loss of most of the resonance energy associated with that compound. By expelling a proton, the carbocation is able to get rid of the positive charge while simultaneously restoring the aromaticity of the ring. See figure 10.1.

Figure 10.1 *Energy profile for possible reactions of the carbocation intermediate formed from benzene*

221

Loss of resonance energy also acts as a barrier to the uptake of the electrophile, so another point of difference with alkenes is that benzene is generally much less reactive towards electrophilic reagents. For example, whereas most alkenes rapidly decolorise a solution of bromine in tetrachloromethane, ionic bromination of benzene only occurs with the aid of a Lewis acid catalyst. However, the necessary activation energy is not as high as it might otherwise be, because the intermediate carbocation is itself resonance stabilised. The positive charge introduced by the electrophile is not localised, but is shared by three ring carbon atoms

A reasonable 'one formula' representation would be

resonance structure of the carbocation formed from benzene

Notice that delocalisation is restricted to five ring carbon atoms, as the carbon atom carrying the electrophile has a complete octet (that is, there is no available $2p$ orbital to participate in the molecular orbital). In the carbocation, the electrophile is fully sigma-bonded with the ring carbon atom, and it is commonly referred to as a **sigma complex intermediate**.

This will be formed, of course, via a transition state in which pi electron density is being withdrawn from the ring and used to make the sigma-bond with the electrophile. Bond-making and bond-breaking are represented in the usual way

developing positive charge

bond forming with the electrophile which is losing its positive charge

bond breaking (withdrawal of pi electron density)

For simplicity, the other pi electrons are shown in two 'double bonds', but the transition state, like the intermediate it gives rise to, has a resonance structure and the developing positive charge is likewise delocalised (Hammond Postulate, see page 105).

Expulsion of the proton in the second step also involves a transition state, represented as

It follows, then, that the energy profile for aromatic electrophilic substitution is of the form where an intermediate carbocation lies in an energy trough between two transition states, figure 10.2.

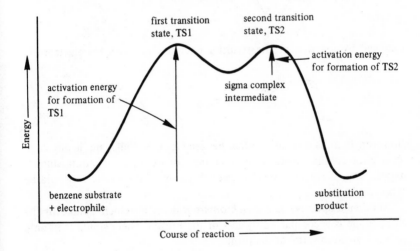

Figure 10.2 *Energy profile for aromatic electrophilic substitution*

223

Activation energy for formation of the intermediate is much greater than for the expulsion of the proton. The first step, uptake of the electrophile, is therefore the slow rate-determining step. When considering the mechanisms of specific reactions, there is no need to draw the structures of the transition states each time, and the intermediate is adequately represented by the classical Lewis formula. Keep in mind, however, that this is only one limiting form for a resonance-stabilised structure.

EVIDENCE FOR THE TWO-STEP MECHANISM

Before discussing evidence for the accepted mechanism, let us briefly consider why the possible alternative mechanisms have been discarded. We could formulate a scheme in which benzene underwent a preliminary ionisation

followed by reaction of the resulting phenyl anion with the electrophile

However, there is no evidence that benzene is at all acidic, and in any case, most electrophilic substitution reactions (for example, nitration, sulphonation, etc.) occur at low pH where ionisation of the substrate would be suppressed.

Another alternative is a *synchronous* process in which uptake of the electrophile is accompanied by loss of the proton. There would then only be one transition state, of the form

with a simple energy profile, figure 10.3.

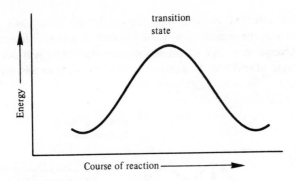

Figure 10.3 *Energy profile for a hypothetical one-step substitution reaction*

That this is *not* the case has been demonstrated by studies with hexa-deuterated benzene. It can be shown experimentally that breaking a carbon–deuterium bond requires more energy (about 5 kJ mol^{-1}) than breaking a carbon–hydrogen bond (see figure 10.4). So that if cleavage of the carbon–hydrogen bond was involved in the transition state, then replacing hydrogen by deuterium should increase the energy of the transition state and so decrease the rate of reaction.

Figure 10.4 *Energy profiles for hypothetical one-step substitution reaction of benzene and hexadeuterobenzene*

You will recall that this is called a **kinetic isotope effect** (see page 134), and the fact that no such effect is observed in most aromatic electrophilic substitution reactions both rules out the synchronous mechanism and supports the accepted two-step mechanism. In the latter, loss of the proton occurs as the second step. Since the first step is rate-determining, any small change in energy of the second transition state will not affect the overall rate of reaction. This should be clear from the energy profile in figure 10.5.

Figure 10.5 *Energy profile for electrophilic substitution of benzene and hexa-deuterobenzene*

In the majority of aromatic electrophilic substitution reactions, the intermediate is far too unstable (that is, short lived) to be detected, yet alone separated and characterised. But in a few special cases, a sigma complex is involved which can be isolated and its structure confirmed. For example, if the symmetrical 1,3,5-trimethylbenzene (mesitylene) is treated with fluoroethane at $-80°C$ (193K) in the presence of boron trifluoride catalyst, the following complex is obtained as a yellow solid

Notice that the three methyl groups are placed on the ring carbon atoms which receive the delocalised positive charge. Additional stabilisation then results from the +I effect of these groups

Another factor is the high stability of the counterbalancing anion, $B\ddot{F}:_4{}^{\ominus}$. If the complex is allowed to warm up to $-15°C$ (258K), reaction continues by expulsion of a proton and formation of the ethyl substituted product

The fact that in a few favourable cases the sigma complex can be isolated, and its structure determined, is good inferential support for participation of similar complexes in reactions where the intermediate is too unstable to be detected.

In the following discussions we shall revert to the normal practice of omitting lone pairs from in-text formulae, and in general equations. But we shall continue to show all the electron pairs in mechanistic equations, and you are urged to do the same.

AROMATIC NITRATION

Nitration of benzene is normally carried out with a mixture of concentrated nitric and sulphuric acids

227

There is much evidence that the effective nitrating agent in this reaction is the **nitryl cation**, $NO_2^{\oplus}$ (also known as the **nitronium ion**). The stronger acid, sulphuric, is able to protonate the ——OH group of a nitric acid molecule

$$H_2SO_4 + HO\!-\!NO_2 \rightleftharpoons H_2\overset{\oplus}{O}\!-\!NO_2 + HSO_4^{\ominus}$$

Uptake of $H^{\oplus}$ converts the hydroxyl group into a good leaving group, the water molecule, and the resulting positive charge weakens the oxygen-nitrogen bond. Consequently, dissociation can occur with the formation of the nitryl cation

$$NO_2\!\overset{\frown}{-}\!\overset{\oplus}{O}H_2 \rightleftharpoons NO_2^{\oplus} + OH_2$$

Water formed in this dissociation is protonated by another molecule of sulphuric acid, thus driving equilibrium to the right

$$H_2SO_4 + H_2O \rightleftharpoons H_3O^{\oplus} + HSO_4^{\ominus}$$

Overall, two molecules of sulphuric acid react with one molecule of nitric acid to produce $NO_2^{\oplus}$, $H_3O^{\oplus}$ and two $HSO_4^{\ominus}$ ions

$$\boxed{2\,H_2SO_4 + HNO_3 \rightleftharpoons NO_2^{\oplus} + H_3O^{\oplus} + 2\,HSO_4^{\ominus}}$$

Much evidence has accrued in support of this scheme, in particular, observations on the depression of freezing point of sulphuric acid by the addition of concentrated nitric acid. You will remember that this phenomenon is what is known as a **colligative property**, depending only on the *number* of particles present, and not on their nature. Experiments with mixtures of concentrated nitric and sulphuric acids show that depression is about 4 (actually 3.8) times that which would be expected from the calculated number of molecules of nitric acid present. This is consistent with the formation of four particles (ions) in the overall equation

$$2\,H_2SO_4 + HNO_3 \rightleftharpoons NO_2^{\oplus} + H_3O^{\oplus} + 2\,HSO_4^{\ominus}$$

A precisely fourfold depression would only be observed if equilibrium was completely over to the right, so the value of 3.8 is not unreasonable.

Confirmation of the existence of the nitryl cation has been obtained by the preparation and characterisation of various salts such as nitryl chlorate(VII), $NO_2^{\oplus}2ClO_4^{\ominus}$. The vibrational (infrared) spectrum of this compound is of particular interest. In aqueous solution, two absorption peaks are observed, at ~ 940 cm^{-1} and ~ 1400 cm^{-1}. The former peak is also present in the spectrum of chloric(VII) acid, and this is attributed to the $ClO_4^{\ominus}$ ion. The peak at ~ 1400 cm^{-1} must therefore be due to the nitryl cation. Since a similar absorption peak is also observed in the vibrational spectrum of mixed concentrated nitric and sulphuric acids, there is little doubt of the presence of the nitryl cation in the nitrating mixture. We should take note of the fact that establishing the *presence* of the cation does not of itself prove that it actually is the attacking species — as likely as this may seem. Confirmation comes from kinetic studies, when it is found that rates of nitration predicted from the calculated concentration of nitryl cation are in good agreement with observed rates. Furthermore, it has been shown that nitryl salts such as the fluoroborate, $NO_2^{\oplus}BF_4^{\ominus}$ can themselves be used to nitrate benzene under quite mild conditions.

MECHANISM OF NITRATION

Since no kinetic isotope effect is observed in the nitration of hexadeuterobenzene, it is concluded that the slow rate-determining step is uptake of the nitryl cation. In support of this, reaction is found to be first order with respect to both benzene and nitric acid

$$\text{Rate} = k \text{ [benzene] [nitric acid]}$$

and since the nitric acid is largely converted into the nitryl cation, the rate equation may be rewritten as

$$\text{Rate} = k \text{ [benzene] } [NO_2^{\oplus}]$$

Spectral evidence indicates that the nitryl cation has a *linear* structure

$$\overset{..}{\underset{..}{O}} = \overset{\oplus}{N} = \overset{..}{\underset{..}{O}}$$

229

and it is the positively charged nitrogen atom which receives electrons from the ring. The two step mechanism may be summarised as follows

The nitryl cation is a poor leaving group, and activation energy for its expulsion is much higher than for loss of the proton. Once formed, the sigma complex can only further react in a forward direction. In other words, nitration is *non-reversible*. Note that the foregoing discussion applies only to nitration of benzene or other aromatic substrates with mixed concentrated nitric and sulphuric acids. With other nitrating media, a different electrophile may be involved.

AROMATIC HALOGENATION

Benzene will react additively with both chlorine and bromine, but only under conditions which favour a radical mechanism. Radical reactions are the subject of another text in this series. Ionic substitution requires the assistance of a Lewis acid catalyst, known as a 'halogen carrier'. This is usually a metallic halide or a metal which gets converted into the halide. For example, iron(III) bromide is used in bromination of benzene

Alkene addition, you will remember, occurs without the necessity for a catalyst. Polarisation induced on close approach of a (correctly oriented) bromine molecule to the alkene double is sufficient to initiate the addition process

230

$$\begin{array}{c} \diagdown \diagup \\ C \\ \| \overset{\delta+}{:\text{Br}} \longrightarrow \overset{\delta-}{\text{Br}} : \\ C \\ \diagup \diagdown \end{array} \qquad \text{induced polarisation}$$

For successful attack on the benzene ring, the halogen molecule must be more strongly polarised, and this is achieved by the Lewis acid catalyst

$$: \overset{..}{\underset{..}{\text{Br}}} \overset{\frown}{\longrightarrow} \overset{..}{\underset{..}{\text{Br}}} : \overset{\frown}{} \text{FeBr}_3 \rightleftharpoons [\overset{\delta+}{:\overset{..}{\underset{..}{\text{Br}}}} - - - \overset{..}{\underset{..}{\text{Br}}} - - - \overset{\delta-}{\text{FeBr}_3} :]$$

It is possible that this brominating complex has an ion pair structure

$$[: \overset{..}{\underset{..}{\text{Br}}}^{\oplus} \quad \text{FeBr} \overset{..}{\underset{..}{:}}_{4}^{\ominus}]$$

The anion $\text{Fe}\overset{..}{\underset{..}{\text{Br}}}:_4^{\ominus}$ would be particularly stable as the iron atom is sur-rounded by a complete octet of electrons, and furthermore, much of the negative charge would be shared by the four electronegative bromine atoms.

However, there is no evidence for the formation of a 'free' $: \overset{..}{\text{Br}}^{\oplus}$ ion. On the contrary, from recent investigations it appears likely that the first step in the reaction is the formation of a so called 'pi complex' between the bromine molecule and the aromatic nucleus

This involves donation of pi electron density to the nearest bromine atom, following which the Lewis acid catalyst 'pulls off' the outer atom as a bromide ion. It may well be that *all* aromatic electrophilic substitution reactions involve the preliminary formation of some sort of pi complex between the nucleus and the attacking electrophile. Nevertheless, bromina-tion of benzene is adequately summarised by the basic two-step mechanism

Bromination, like nitration, is non-reversible, and the absence of a kinetic isotope effect in the bromination of hexadeuterobenzene indicates that uptake of $Br^{\oplus}$ is the slow rate-determining step.

Reaction with other halogens

Direct fluorination of benzene is extremely rapid and difficult to control. Iodination, on the other hand, is slow and incomplete, and usually shows a kinetic isotope effect. Unlike other halogenation reactions, uptake of $I^{\oplus}$ is *reversible*, and in the sigma complex intermediate, loss of $I^{\oplus}$ can compete with expulsion of $H^{\oplus}$

sigma complex
intermediate

Replacement of H by D tilts the balance, and it becomes easier for the sigma complex to expel $I^{\oplus}$ than $D^{\oplus}$, and so the overall rate of production of iodobenzene is decreased. See figure 10.6.

The by-product of iodination, hydrogen iodide, is a powerful reducing agent, and so the addition of a strong oxidising agent such as nitric acid increases the yield of iodobenzene.

AROMATIC SULPHONATION

There is still some doubt as to whether the attacking electrophile in sulphonation is the sulphur trioxide molecule, SO_3, or its conjugate acid,

232

Figure 10.6 *Energy profile for decomposition of the iodobenzene sigma complex intermediate*

$\overset{\oplus}{H}OSO_2$. Reaction of benzene with concentrated sulphuric acid is slow; heating under reflux for several hours is necessary for good yields of the sulphonic acid.

$$\text{benzene} + H_2SO_4 \;\underset{\Delta}{\rightleftharpoons}\; \text{C}_6\text{H}_5\text{SO}_2\text{OH} + H_2O$$

Sulphur trioxide is present in strong sulphuric acid

$$2\,H_2SO_4 \;\rightleftharpoons\; SO_3 + H_3O^{\oplus} + HSO_4^{\ominus}$$

but the concentration in oleum is much greater, and it is significant that the latter reagent sulphonates benzene at a considerably higher rate. Sulphur trioxide is assumed to be the most likely attacking species in most aromatic sulphonation reactions.

The molecule has a polar resonance structure in which the sulphur atom is electron deficient and therefore electrophilic

233

resonance
structure

The two steps in sulphonation of benzene can be shown as

In contrast with bromination and nitration, sulphonation is a reversible process. Sulphur trioxide is a good leaving group and in the sigma complex intermediate, loss of SO_3 can compete with expulsion of the proton

Consequently, sulphonation of deuterobenzene exhibits a small kinetic isotope effect.

Exercise 10.1
Draw a labelled energy profile to illustrate the kinetic isotope effect in sulphonation of benzene and hexadeuterobenzene. *Hint*: re-read the section on iodination of benzene.

234

Good yields of product are possible because the final stage of the reaction is protonation of the sulphonate anion. This has the effect of changing the structure from one with a good leaving group (SO_3) to one with a much poorer leaving group ($H\overset{\oplus}{O}SO_2$)

good leaving group
(displaced as SO_3)

poor leaving group
(displaced as $H\overset{\oplus}{O}SO_2$)

On the other hand, if we wish to desulphonate benzene sulphonic acid, the latter compound is heated under reflux with dilute sulphuric acid. This ensures that most of the sulphonic acid molecules are ionised, again favouring the structure with the better leaving group

poor leaving   large   good leaving
group   excess   group

The mechanistic steps are then exactly the reverse of those for sulphonation, namely, uptake of a proton followed by expulsion of the sulphur trioxide molecule

$$(\overset{..}{S}O_3 + H_2\overset{..}{O} \rightleftharpoons H_2\overset{..}{S}O_4)$$

The idea that in a reversible process the forward and reverse reactions involve the same steps but in the opposite order is known as the **principle of microscopic reversibility**. This is logical in that the shape of an energy profile for a reversible reaction remains the same, whichever way the reacting species are travelling.

AROMATIC ALKYLATION AND ACYLATION – THE FRIEDEL-CRAFTS REACTION

Alkylation

No reaction is observed when a chloroalkane is dissolved in benzene, but on adding a small amount of anhydrous aluminium(III) chloride, the mixture gets quite hot, hydrogen chloride is evolved, and the corresponding alkylbenzene is formed

The overall effect is as though benzene had displaced the halide ion from the haloalkane, but benzene is too weak a nucleophile to do this without the aid of a catalyst.

As in the bromination of benzene, the role of the catalyst is to convert the attacking reagent into a stronger electrophile. It can be shown, for example, that when anhydrous $AlCl_3$ is added to a chloroalkane, a $1:1$ complex is formed. The aluminium atom is able to receive electrons from the halogen atom

$$R - \overset{..}{\underset{..}{Cl}} : \curvearrowright AlCl \overset{..}{:}_3$$

The result may be to simply polarise the carbon–chlorine bond

$$[\overset{\delta+}{R} - - - \overset{..}{Cl} - - - \overset{\delta-}{AlCl} \overset{..}{:}_3] \quad \text{(polar complex)}$$

or to actually bring about ionisation

$$[\overset{\oplus}{R} : \overset{..}{\underset{..}{Cl}} \overset{\ominus}{AlCl} \overset{..}{:}_3] \quad \text{(ion pair complex)}$$

236

Complete ionisation is obviously more likely with tertiary or secondary chloroalkanes than with primary chloroalkanes where the resulting carbocation would be much less stable.

Some insight into the structure of these haloalkane–Lewis acid complexes is given by the following observation. A small amount of anhydrous aluminium(III) bromide containing radioactive bromine was added to a solution of 2-bromopropane in a hydrocarbon solvent, and the mixture allowed to stand at room temperature for some time. Subsequent recovery and analysis of the bromoalkane showed that it had been enriched in the radioactive isotope. So it would appear that the carbocation must have enough mobility to dissociate from the original bromine atom and pair off with a radioactive atom

$$R - \overset{..}{\underset{..}{Br}} : \; + \; Al\overset{*}{\underset{..}{Br}} :_3 \;\; \rightleftharpoons \;\; [R^{\oplus} : \overset{..}{\underset{..}{Br}}Al\overset{\ominus..}{\underset{..}{Br}} :_3] \;\; \longrightarrow \;\; R - \overset{*}{\underset{..}{Br}} : \; + \; : \overset{..}{\underset{..}{Br}} - Al\overset{*}{\underset{..}{Br}} :_2$$

(Br* represents radioactive bromine)

As further evidence, it is found that solutions of certain haloalkane-$AlCl_3$ complexes are electrically conducting, implying that in those cases the ions have even greater mobility. For simplicity, we will regard the attacking electrophile as the carbocation, $R^{\oplus}$. Ethylation of benzene with chloroethane can then be formulated as

$$(CH_3CH_2\overset{..}{\underset{..}{Cl}} : \; + \; Al\overset{..}{\underset{..}{Cl}} :_3 \;\; \rightleftharpoons \;\; [CH_3\overset{\oplus}{CH_2} \quad \overset{\ominus..}{Al}\overset{..}{\underset{..}{Cl}} :_4])$$

Both steps are reversible, and Lewis acids such as $AlCl_3$ are also found to catalyse dealkylation of alkylbenzenes.

Direct alkylation of benzene is of limited practical value because it is difficult to stop at monosubstitution, and with primary and secondary haloalkanes, rearrangement of the alkyl group may occur.

Alkylation with other reagents

Since the electrophile is essentially a carbocation, other compounds capable of generating such species can be used in Friedel–Crafts alkylations. With the aid of suitable Lewis acid catalysts, benzene can be alkylated by alcohols and by alkenes. Manufacture of (1-methylethyl)benzene ('cumene') by reaction of benzene with propene in the presence of phosphoric(V) acid is an example of this.

Acylation

Chloroalkanes used in the Friedel–Crafts alkylation reaction may be replaced by acid chlorides, in which case the product is the corresponding ketone

Introduction of the **acyl** group, RCO —, is known as **acylation**. When ethanoyl chloride (acetyl chloride) is used, the process is called **ethanoylation** (or more commonly, 'acetylation').

The aluminium chloride may complex with the acid chloride

or bring about its complete ionisation

Ionisation seems quite likely, because the **acylinium ion**, $\overset{\oplus}{R}CO$ has a resonance-stabilised structure and is much more stable than a carbocation

$$R \overset{\oplus}{-} C \overset{\frown}{=} \overset{..}{\underset{..}{O}} \quad \longleftrightarrow \quad R - C \equiv \overset{\oplus}{\underset{..}{O}}$$

(I)   (II)

Limiting form (II) will make a significant contribution as the positively charged oxygen atom (unlike positive carbon) has a complete octet.

Assuming that the attacking electrophile is the acylinium ion, the two-step mechanism can be summarised as

It is found that more than a catalytic amount of anhydrous aluminium (III) chloride is needed because of complexing between the catalyst and the carbonyl group in the product

This complex is decomposed by water during 'workup' of the reaction mixture.

Acylation overcomes the two principal disadvantages of the alkylation process in that it stops at monosubstitution and rearrangement of the acyl group does not occur. Furthermore, the acyl group is readily reduced to alkyl, so the method provides an alternative route to straight-chain alkyl benzenes, which are difficult to prepare by direct alkylation.

SUBSTITUENT EFFECTS IN AROMATIC ELECTROPHILIC SUBSTITUTION

Experimental observation shows that when a substituted benzene under-goes electrophilic attack, the atom or group already present affects both the *rate* and *position* of further substitution. In other words, a substituent can influence the **reactivity** of the substrate, and **orientation** of the product.

REACTIVITY OF SUBSTITUTED BENZENES

Methylbenzene (toluene) is more easily attacked by electrophilic reagents than is benzene, so the methyl group is an **activating substituent**. When we speak of increased reactivity, we mean either that methylbenzene reacts under milder conditions (such as lower temperature, reduced concentration of reagents, etc.) than benzene, or reacts faster than benzene under the same conditions.

In practice, it is seldom possible to ensure exactly the same conditions for reaction of two different substrates. Instead, relative rates of reaction are determined by a technique called the **competitive method**. For example, equimolecular amounts of benzene and methylbenzene are placed in the same reaction vessel where they compete for a limited amount of an electrophilic reagent such as a nitrating mixture of concentrated nitric and sulphuric acids, insufficient to completely react with either substrate. At the end of the reaction, the amounts of nitrated products from each substrate are compared. In this way it can be demonstrated that methylbenzene is about 25 times more reactive than benzene towards nitration (under the given conditions).

Although the methyl group is activating in all electrophilic substitution reactions of methylbenzene, the *degree* of activation varies with the particular electrophile. For instance, methylbenzene reacts some 350 times faster than benzene in chlorination.

We have seen that for most aromatic electrophilic substitution reactions the rate-determining step is formation of a sigma complex intermediate. Since this intermediate has an electron-deficient nucleus, we should expect an electron-releasing substituent on the nucleus to have a stabilising effect. Likewise, an electron-withdrawing substituent should destabilise the intermediate, stabilisation and destabilisation, of course, being relative to a similar intermediate formed from unsubstituted benzene. See figure 10.7.

Figure 10.7 *Order of stability of sigma complex intermediates. Note the convention for showing the presence of a substituent without specifying the position of attachment*

We know that both the intermediate and the transition state from which it is formed are high-energy species, comparable in energy, and therefore in structure. We may think of the transition state as a sigma complex 'in the making', and as such it is reasonable to suppose that substituents will have a similar stabilising or destabilising effect on the transition state as on the intermediate. (This is a consequence of the Hammond Postulate which we first discussed in chapter 5, page 105.)

By this reasoning, then, we conclude that electron-releasing substituents are activating because they are able to *lower the activation energy for the rate-determining step*, and electron-withdrawing substituents are deactivating because they *raise the activation energy for that step*.

The magnitude of these effects will vary with the position of the substituent, but for the moment we can summarise the general case in the form of an energy profile. See figure 10.8.

ORIENTATING EFFECT OF SUBSTITUENTS

Analysis of the products of a wide variety of substitution reactions of methylbenzene shows that in each case the predominant products are the *ortho* and *para* isomers. Quite often, as little as 4 per cent or less of the *meta* isomer is obtained. For example, sulphonation of methylbenzene with concentrated sulphuric acid at room temperature gives the following results

Figure 10.8 *Energy profiles for the formation of the sigma complex intermediates in aromatic electrophilic substitution. For simplicity, benzene and the two G-substituted benzenes are shown with similar groundstate energies*

The methyl group is said to be *ortho* and *para* directing. Similar observations are made with other electron-releasing substituents, and we can therefore make the general statement that in aromatic electrophilic substitution, all electron-releasing substituents are activating and *ortho* and *para* directing.

Conversely, it is found that in substitution reactions of nitrobenzene it is always the *meta* product which predominates. Nitration, for example, gives the following proportions of products

From a study of numerous other compounds, it becomes apparent that almost all electron-withdrawing substituents are deactivating and *meta* directing. The only common exception is halogen, which is electron-withdrawing and weakly deactivating, but *ortho* and *para* directing. The effects of some common substituents on aromatic electrophilic substitution are summarised in table 10.1.

Table 10.1 Orienting effects of some common substituents in aromatic electrophilic substitution

Groups which are ortho–para *directing*	*Groups which are* meta *directing*
STRONGLY ACTIVATING	*STRONGLY DEACTIVATING*
— ÖH, — Ö:$^{\ominus}$	— N̈O$_2$, — $\overset{\oplus}{N}$(CH$_3$)$_3$
— N̈H$_2$, — N̈HCH$_3$, — N̈(CH$_3$)$_2$	— C̈Cl:$_3$, — C̈F:$_3$
MODERATELY ACTIVATING	*MODERATELY DEACTIVATING*
— ÖCH$_3$, — N̈HCOCH$_3$	— C̈HO, — C̈OCH$_3$
	— C̈OÖH, — S̈O$_2$ÖH
	— CN
WEAKLY ACTIVATING	
— CH$_3$, etc.	
WEAKLY DEACTIVATING	
— F̈:, — C̈l:, — B̈r:, — Ï:	

243

In attempting to explain the orienting effect of a substituent, we should begin by reminding ourselves of the distribution of positive charge in the sigma complex intermediate. The limiting forms which we can draw indicate that the charge is shared mainly by ring carbon atoms in the 2,4 and 6 positions

limiting forms   resonance structure

This being so, a substituent would be expected to have its greatest effect, whether stabilising or destabilising, when it is on a ring carbon atom bearing positive charge.

Let us look first at the effect of electron-releasing substituents.

ELECTRON-RELEASING SUBSTITUENTS

The two mechanisms whereby an atom or group can release electrons are the inductive effect (inductive stabilisation) and the mesomeric or resonance effect (resonance stabilisation).

INDUCTIVE STABILISATION

Increase in stability of carbocations in the series

(methyl) $(1°)$ $(2°)$ $(3°)$

is most simply attributed to inductive stabilisation by the methyl groups which are able to take a small share of the positive charge. In discussing the mechanism of addition of HBr to propene, we linked the preferential formation of 2-bromopropene with the difference in stabilities of the two possible intermediate carbocations

$$CH_3CH = CH_2 \longrightarrow CH_3\overset{\oplus}{C}HCH_3 \text{ (2°) rather than } CH_3CH_2\overset{\oplus}{C}H_2 \text{ (1°)}$$

244

Furthermore, less activation energy is required for the formation of a secondary carbocation from propene than for a primary carbocation from ethene. Consequently, propene also reacts at a faster rate than ethene. See figure 10.9.

Figure 10.9 *Energy profiles for the formation of primary and secondary carbocations. For simplicity, propene and ethene are shown with the same groundstate energies*

Both the rate of reaction and orientation in electrophilic addition are determined by the relative stabilities of the intermediate carbocations, and this is directly related to inductive stabilisation by the methyl group.

Now let us turn to the structure of the intermediate sigma complex for nitration of methylbenzene. Whether attack occurs *ortho*, *meta* or *para* to the methyl group, the sigma complex in each case can be represented by three limiting forms, figure 10.10.

For both *ortho* and *para* substitution, one of the limiting forms (marked with an asterisk) has the methyl group bonded to a ring carbon atom bearing the positive charge, and for these structures inductive stabilisation is particularly effective. This does not occur with the limiting forms for *meta* substitution, and the *meta* sigma complex is consequently rather less stable. The significance of this is more apparent when we look at the energy profiles for mononitration of benzene and methylbenzene, figure 10.11.

Figure 10.10 *Limiting forms for sigma complexes involved in nitration of methylbenzene. Structures marked with an asterisk (*) are particularly stable*

RESONANCE STABILISATION

The methoxy group, like the methyl group, is an activating and *ortho/para* directing group, but in most reactions methoxybenzene is rather more reactive than methylbenzene. Before attempting to account for this difference between the two substituents, let us again look first at an analogous alkene addition reaction. Methoxyethene, $CH_3 \overset{..}{O} CH = CH_2$, undergoes electrophilic addition of hydrogen bromide at a faster rate than propene, and the increased reactivity is attributed to resonance stabilisation of the intermediate carbocation, not possible in the cation formed from propene

$$CH_3 - CH = CH_2 + H\overset{..}{\underset{..}{Br}}: \longrightarrow CH_3 \rightarrow \overset{\oplus}{CH} \leftarrow CH_3 + :\overset{..}{\underset{..}{Br}}:\overset{\ominus}{}$$
inductively
stabilised

$$CH_3\overset{..}{O} - CH = CH_2 + H\overset{..}{\underset{..}{Br}}: \longrightarrow CH_3\overset{..}{O} - \overset{\oplus}{CH} - CH_3 + :\overset{..}{\underset{..}{Br}}:\overset{\ominus}{}$$
mesomerically
stabilised

246

Figure 10.11 *Energy profiles for mononitration of benzene and methylbenzene. Activation energy is lower for meta nitration of methylbenzene than for nitration of benzene. However, even less activation energy is required for ortho and para attack, and nitration occurs preferentially in these positions. For simplicity, the two substrates are shown with similar groundstate energies*

247

Two limiting forms can be written for the methoxy cation

$$CH_3\overset{..}{\underset{..}{O}} \curvearrowright \overset{\oplus}{CH} - CH_3 \quad \leftrightarrow \quad CH_3\overset{\oplus}{\underset{..}{O}} = CH - CH_3$$

$$(I) \qquad\qquad\qquad\qquad (II)$$

Resonance stabilisation by the methoxy group is particularly effective, because in the right-hand limiting form (II), all the atoms have a complete octet. This means that the oxygen atom is able to take an appreciable share of the positive charge, which in the propyl carbocation is largely localised on one carbon atom — and that atom only has a sextet of valence electrons.

It is the ability of the methoxy group to resonance-stabilise the intermediate carbocations which accounts for the difference in reactivity of methylbenzene and methoxybenzene in aromatic electrophilic substitution.

Whenever we can write a limiting form showing the methoxy group bonded to a positively charged ring carbon atom, an additional, more stable, form can be written, in which the oxygen atom has the positive charge. For example

particularly stable form, as all atoms have a complete octet

In nitration of methoxybenzene, the sigma complex intermediate for *ortho* substitution is represented by the following limiting forms

particularly stable

Analogous forms can be written for *para* substitution, but similar stabilisation of the sigma complex for *meta* substitution is not possible (verify this by drawing the limiting forms). Consequently, in nitration of methoxybenzene, very little of the *meta* isomer is produced.

248

OTHER STRONGLY ACTIVATING SUBSTITUENTS

Amino and hydroxy groups are very powerfully activating substituents. Phenylamine and phenol are both readily brominated in aqueous solution, and phenol can be nitrated with dilute nitric acid. Benzene will not react under these conditions, and the activating effect of the substituents is again related to their ability to utilise the non-bonded electrons on the nitrogen or oxygen atoms to stabilise the carbocation intermediate.

Nitration of phenylamine is difficult because the molecule is easily oxidised, but also because under strongly acid conditions phenylamine is largely converted into the phenylammonium cation, $PhNH_3^{\oplus}$. Positively charged nitrogen is powerfully electron attracting, and so protonation of the amino group strongly deactivates the molecule towards electrophilic attack. To overcome this difficulty, the amino group is 'protected' by ethanoylation (acetylation)

The nitrogen atom is now much less basic, and N-phenylethanamide (acetanilide) can be nitrated and sulphonated, etc., under quite mild conditions. Subsequently, the 'free' amino group is readily regenerated by hydrolysis in either acidic or alkaline solution.

Exercise 10.2

The amido group, CH_3CONH —, has a resonance structure. Draw limiting forms which indicate why the substituted amino group is less basic than the amino group in phenylamine. Take into account the structure of the conjugate acid formed on protonation of the nitrogen atom (chapter 4), and destabilisation resulting from the proximity of positive charges on the nitrogen and carbonyl carbon atoms.

In alkaline solution, the hydroxyl group of phenols is ionised to $— \overset{..}{\underset{..}{O}} :^{\ominus}$, and this is the most powerfully activating of all the common substituents. The reason is that in the additional limiting forms we can write for the *ortho* and *para* sigma complexes, electron donation by the oxygen atom leads to a relatively stable enone structure

As a result, phenols are able to react (in alkaline conditions) with electrophiles too weak to attack benzene. An important example of this is the so called **coupling reaction** of phenols with diazonium salts. On adding an acidic solution of benzene diazonium chloride to a weakly alkaline solution of phenol, a bright red precipitate of 4-(phenylazo)phenol separates instantaneously

If the *para* position is already occupied ('blocked') in the phenol, coupling will occur in the *ortho* position, but *meta* coupling is not observed.

Exercise 10.3
Write mechanistic equations for the above coupling reaction.

ELECTRON-WITHDRAWING SUBSTITUENTS

We can use arguments similar to those developed above to explain the orienting effect of electron-withdrawing substituents. The fact that nitrobenzene nitrates at a slower rate than benzene can be linked to destabilisation of the sigma complex intermediates by the nitro substituent. The predominance of the *meta* isomer implies that sigma complexs for *ortho* and *para* substitution are destabilised to a greater extent that that for *meta* substitution.

The nitro group has a polar resonance structure

which for convenience we may abbreviate to $\overset{\oplus\ominus}{-NO_2}$. The limiting forms for the *ortho, meta* and *para* sigma complexes are shown in figure 10.12.

250

We can see that for both *ortho* and *para* substitution, one of the limiting forms (marked with an asterisk) has the nitro group bonded to a ring carbon atom carrying the positive charge. Strong electrostatic repulsion between adjacent positive charges would make these particular limiting forms extremely unstable, and it is unlikely that they will make much contribution to the resonance structure. In effect, delocalisation is restricted to spreading the charge over only two of the ring carbon atoms.

The electron-withdrawing nitro group will also destabilise the sigma complex for *meta* substitution, but not to the same extent as in the other cases, because the positive charge can still be shared by three ring carbon atoms. The corresponding energy profiles are shown in figure 10.13.

Other dipolar electron-withdrawing substituents such as carbonyl $\overset{\delta+}{-}C\overset{\delta-}{=}O$, and cyano, $\overset{\delta+}{-}C\overset{\delta-}{\equiv}N$, will have similar but slightly weaker effects.

Figure 10.12 *Limiting forms for sigma complexes involved in ortho, meta and para nitration of nitrobenzene. Those forms marked with an asterisk are particularly unstable. The newly introduced* — NO_2 *group will also be polar, but for clarity, charges are not shown*

251

HALOGEN SUBSTITUENTS

Nitrogen, oxygen and chlorine atoms are all more electronegative than carbon, and therefore exert a negative inductive effect when bonded to carbon. On that basis, we should expect substituents like $\overset{\cdot\cdot}{—OH}$ and $—NH_2$ to be weakly deactivating. But as we have seen, these groups are actually very strongly activating, and the reason is that the mesomeric release of non-bonding electrons completely outweighs any destabilisation from the negative inductive effect.

When chlorine is the substituent, the situation is reversed: the negative inductive effect is stronger than the positive mesomeric effect. All three sigma complex intermediates are destabilised, but those for *ortho* and *para* substitution are less unstable because the chlorine atom is able to share the positive charge to a limited extent by a positive mesomeric effect. Thus, in the case of halogen substituents, reactivity is controlled by the inductive effect, but orientation is determined by the mesomeric effect.

Exercise 10.4
Illustrate the above point by drawing limiting forms for nitration of chlorobenzene in the *ortho, meta* and *para* positions.

SUMMARY OF SUBSTITUENT EFFECTS

(1) *Alkyl groups (— CH₃, etc.)*
Weak activation by a positive inductive effect. Preferential stabilisation of the *ortho*, and *para* sigma complexes.

(2) *Amino (— NH₂), substituted amino (— NHCH₃, — NHCOCH₃, etc.), hydroxyl (— OH) and substituted hydroxyl (— OCH₃, etc.)*
Much stronger activation by a positive mesomeric effect, which outweighs a weak negative inductive effect. Preferential stabilisation of *ortho* and *para* sigma complexes.

(3) *Ionised hydroxyl (— O :⁻)*
Very powerful activation by a combination of a positive inductive effect and a positive mesomeric effect. Preferential stabilisation of *ortho* and *para* sigma complexes.

Figure 10.13 *Energy profiles for the formation of sigma complex intermediates in nitration of benzene and nitrobenzene. For simplicity, the two substrates are shown with the same groundstate energies. Note that although substitution occurs preferentially in the meta position, this still requires higher activation energy than attack on unsubstituted benzene.*

(4) *Polar groups such as nitro (*$\overset{\oplus\ominus}{-NO_2}$*), carbonyl (*$-\overset{\delta+}{C}=\overset{\delta-}{\underset{..}{O}}$ *and*

$$\underset{H}{|}$$

$-\overset{\delta+}{\underset{\underset{CH_3}{|}}{C}}=\overset{\delta-}{\underset{..}{O}},$ *etc.), carboxyl (*$-\overset{\delta+}{\underset{\underset{:OH}{|}}{C}}=\overset{\delta-}{\underset{..}{O}})$ *and cyano (*$-\overset{\delta+}{C}\equiv\overset{\delta-}{\underset{..}{N}})$

Strong deactivation because of electrostatic repulsion between positive atom of polar group and positively charged ring carbon atom. Greater destabilisation of *ortho* and *para* sigma complexes favours *meta* substitution.

(5) *Halogen (*$-\underset{..}{\overset{..}{Cl}}:$*,* $-\underset{..}{\overset{..}{Br}}:$*)*

Weak deactivation resulting from strong negative inductive effect, only partly offset by a moderate positive mesomeric effect operating in the *ortho* and *para* sigma complexes.

STERIC EFFECTS IN AROMATIC ELECTROPHILIC SUBSTITUTION

In the above discussion, we were concerned only with the ability of substituents to attract or release electrons, and we ignored any effects arising from the *size* of the substituent. There are two *ortho* to one *para* position in a monosubstituted benzene, and we might reasonably expect *ortho* and *para* products to be formed in the ratio of 2:1. In practice, this ratio is frequently found to be much less than 2:1. For example, nitration of alkylbenzenes gives an *ortho:para* ratio which steadily decreases from right to left in the series

Methylbenzene yields about 60 per cent *ortho*-methylnitrobenzene, but less than 10 per cent of the *ortho* isomer is obtained with dimethylethyl (*tert*-butyl) benzene. The small proportion of *ortho* product from dimethylethylbenzene is thought to be due to destabilisation of the *ortho* sigma complex intermediate as the result of steric compression between the attacking electrophile and the bulky alkyl group

254

Similar compression in the transition state will increase the activation energy for formation of the intermediate, and the phenomenon is described as **steric hindrance** to *ortho* attack. For a given substituent, steric hindrance will be greater, the larger the size of the attacking electrophile. Nitration of chlorobenzene gives about 30 per cent *ortho*-chloronitrobenzene, whereas sulphonation of the same substrate gives less than 1 per cent *ortho*-chlorobenzene sulphonic acid. The sulphonate group is somewhat larger than the nitro group, and so steric compression destabilises the transition state for *ortho*-sulphonation to a greater extent than for *ortho*-nitration. It quite often is not possible to completely disentangle steric and electronic effects. The 'size' of the electrophile may be in doubt, particularly if it is complexed with a catalyst, and the situation may be complicated by some favourable or unfavourable electrostatic interaction between an *ortho* substituent and the electrophile which does not occur in attack on the *para* position.

STERIC EFFECTS AND RESONANCE

Another rather more subtle steric effect is apparent when bulky substituents are present either side of a substituent which activates the nucleus by a positive mesomeric effect. For example, the methoxy group is strongly activating towards electrophilic attack, and methoxybenzene undergoes nitration and halogenation in the *para* position faster than mononitration or monohalogenation of benzene in similar conditions. Introduction of an *ortho* methyl group makes the molecule still more reactive, but a combination of two *ortho* methyl groups has the reverse effect, and 2,6-dimethylmethoxybenzene is less reactive than methoxybenzene

decrease in reactivity (*para* position)

255

The valence bond notation which we use to show activation by the methoxy group

is a shorthand way of saying that the oxygen atom is conjugated with the aromatic nucleus, and is able to take a share of the positive charge. This implies interaction of an oxygen $2p$ atomic orbital, containing an electron pair, with the delocalised molecular orbital of the sigma complex intermediate. Effective orbital overlap requires that the methoxy group is *coplanar* with the ring. With one methyl group present, this still occurs, and activation is increased by the positive inductive effect of the methyl group. But with a methyl group either side of the methoxy group, coplanarity is no longer possible and orbital overlap is reduced or even prevented altogether. Limitation or prevention of resonance in this way is called **steric inhibition of resonance.**

Exercise 10.5
Give an explanation for the observation that although N,N-dimethyl-phenylamine and 2-methyl-N,N-dimethylphenylamine readily couple with benzene diazonium cation, 2,6-dimethyl-N,N-dimethylphenyl-amine does not.

Outline Solutions to Exercises

EXERCISE 1.1

(a) $CH_3 - \underset{\underset{\displaystyle :\overset{..}{O}:}{\|}}{C} - \overset{..}{\underset{..}{O}} - CH_3$, (b) $CH_3 - \overset{..}{N} = \overset{..}{N} - CH_3$,

(c) $CH_3 - \overset{\oplus}{\overset{..}{O}H_2}$, (d) $CH_3 - \overset{\ominus}{CH_2}$, (e) $\overset{..}{C} \equiv \overset{\ominus}{N}$, (f) $CH_2 = \overset{\oplus}{N} = \overset{\ominus}{N}$

EXERCISE 1.2

(a) $CH_3 - \overset{\oplus}{N} \equiv \overset{..}{N}$, (b) $CH_3 - \overset{\oplus}{N} \overset{\displaystyle \overset{..}{O}\,.}{\underset{\displaystyle \overset{..}{\underset{..}{O}}.\,\ominus}{}}$, (c) $\begin{array}{c} CH_2 - C \overset{\displaystyle \overset{..}{O}:}{} \\ | \qquad \qquad \overset{..}{\underset{..}{N}}\!\ominus \\ CH_2 - C \underset{\displaystyle \overset{..}{\underset{..}{O}}:}{} \end{array}$

EXERCISE 1.3

Boron trifluoride has a planar structure with a F — B — F bond angle of 120°.

EXERCISE 1.4

Hydrogen bonding between the nitro and hydroxyl groups is *intra*molecular in 2-nitrophenol, but *inter*molecular in the isomeric 3- and 4-nitrophenols.

EXERCISE 1.5

Both compounds are partially miscible with water because of their ability to hydrogen-bond with water molecules. Butan-1-ol is less volatile because of *intra*molecular hydrogen bonding, which is not possible with ethoxyethane.

EXERCISE 2.1

(a) $\overset{H}{\underset{H}{>}}\overset{\oplus}{N}=C=\overset{\ominus}{\ddot{N}}:$, (b) $CH_2 - CH = \overset{\ominus}{\underset{\cdot\cdot}{Cl}}:$, (c) $CH_3 - \overset{\ominus}{\underset{\cdot\cdot}{N}} - \overset{\oplus}{N} \equiv \overset{\cdot\cdot}{N}$,

(d) $CH_3 - \overset{\oplus}{O} = \overset{\cdot\cdot}{N} - \overset{\ominus}{\underset{\cdot\cdot}{O}}:$

EXERCISE 2.2

(a) $\overset{H}{\underset{H}{>}}C = \overset{\oplus}{\underset{\cdot\cdot}{O}} - H$ Oxygen has a complete octet, and there is one additional electron pair bond.

(b) $\overset{H}{\underset{H}{>}}\overset{\oplus}{N} = C\overset{H}{\underset{H}{<}}$ Nitrogen has a complete octet and there is one additional electron pair bond.

(c) $H - \overset{\cdot\cdot}{N} = \underset{\underset{H}{|}}{C} - \overset{\cdot\cdot}{\underset{\cdot\cdot}{O}}:^{\ominus}$ Charge on more electronegative oxygen.

(d) $\overset{H}{\underset{H}{>}}C = \overset{\oplus}{N} = \overset{\ominus}{\underset{\cdot\cdot}{N}}$ Negative charge on more electronegative nitrogen.

EXERCISE 2.3

$$CH_3 - \overset{\oplus}{C} \overset{\overset{\ominus}{\cdot\cdot}}{\underset{\underset{\cdot\cdot}{NH_2}}{\diagdown}} O \cdot$$

Carbon has only six valence electrons: the other two limiting forms have complete octets.

EXERCISE 2.4

Urea has a mesomeric structure in which the carbon–nitrogen bond has some 'double bond character'. One limiting form is

$$\overset{\cdot\cdot}{NH_2} - \underset{\underset{\cdot\cdot}{:O:_\ominus}}{\overset{|}{C}} = \overset{\oplus}{NH_2}.$$

EXERCISE 3.1

	Attacking reagent	*Substrate*	*Classification*
(a)	$CH_3\overset{\cdot\cdot}{\underset{\cdot\cdot}{O}}:^{\ominus}$	$CH_3CH_2\overset{\cdot\cdot}{\underset{\cdot\cdot}{Br}}:$	Substitution
(b)	$CH_3CH_2\overset{\cdot\cdot}{\underset{\cdot\cdot}{O}}:^{\ominus}$	$CH_3CH_2\overset{\cdot\cdot}{\underset{\cdot\cdot}{I}}:$	Elimination
(c)	$CH_3\overset{\cdot\cdot}{\underset{\cdot\cdot}{O}}H$	$CH_3C\overset{\cdot\cdot}{O}CH_3$	Addition
(d)	$(CH_3)_3C\overset{\cdot\cdot}{\underset{\cdot\cdot}{O}}:^{\ominus}$	$CH_3C\overset{\cdot\cdot}{\underset{\cdot\cdot}{O}}OCH_3$	Substitution

EXERCISE 3.2

(a) nucleophile, (b) neither, (c) electrophile, (d) nucleophile, (e) both, (f) electrophile, (g) electrophile, (h) both.

EXERCISE 3.3

$$-\underset{\underset{\cdot\cdot}{:O:}}{\overset{\|}{C}} - CH_2 - \underset{\underset{\cdot\cdot}{:O:}}{\overset{\|}{C}} - \quad \underset{+H^{\oplus}, -H^{\oplus}}{\rightleftharpoons} \quad -\underset{\underset{}{:OH}}{\overset{|}{C}} = CH - \underset{\underset{\cdot\cdot}{:O:}}{\overset{\|}{C}} -$$

259

EXERCISE 4.1

Energy profile of similar shape to that for ethanoic acid, figure 4.1. Resonance-stabilised structures summarised as

and

EXERCISE 4.2

In none of the limiting forms does the positive charge appear on the ring carbon atom to which the $-\ddot{\text{O}}:^{\ominus}$ group is attached.

EXERCISE 4.3

See text for structures. In the conjugate cation, no limiting form has positive charges on adjacent atoms. Contrast

with

260

EXERCISE 5.1

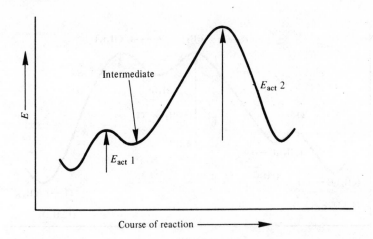

Course of reaction ⟶

EXERCISE 5.2

(a) No change in optical activity, (b) loss of optical activity.

EXERCISE 5.3

EXERCISE 5.4

Course of reaction ⟶

EXERCISE 5.5

$$\overset{\delta-}{:\overset{..}{\underset{..}{I}}} - - - - \overset{\displaystyle CH_3}{\underset{\displaystyle H \quad H}{\overset{|}{\underset{|}{C}}}} - - - - \overset{\delta+}{\overset{..}{\underset{..}{O}H_2}}$$

EXERCISE 5.6

$HOSO_3^{\ominus}$ and $Cl^{\ominus}$ are weaker nucleophiles than $I^{\ominus}$.

EXERCISE 6.1

$$CH_3 - \overset{\displaystyle CH_3}{\underset{\displaystyle CH_3}{\overset{|}{\underset{|}{C}}}} - CH - CH_3 \longrightarrow CH_3 - \overset{\displaystyle CH_3}{\underset{\displaystyle CH_3}{\overset{|}{\underset{|}{C}}}} - \overset{\oplus}{CH} - CH_3 \xrightarrow{rearr.} |CH_3 - \overset{\displaystyle CH_3}{\underset{\displaystyle CH_3}{\overset{\oplus}{\underset{|}{C}}}} - CH - CH_3$$

262

EXERCISE 6.2

Increased elimination, since E_{act} for formation of the bimolecular transition state is higher for elimination than for substitution.

EXERCISE 6.3

The energy profile is of the form

Structures are given on page 132.

EXERCISE 6.4

$$
\begin{array}{c}
\overset{\delta -}{\underset{\cdot\cdot}{\overset{\cdot\cdot}{HO}}} \text{----} H \\
|\\
CH_2 === CH_2 \\
|\\
\underset{\delta +}{N(CH_2CH_3)_3}
\end{array}
$$

EXERCISE 6.5

Attack on the methyl group (β') is less hindered than attack on the ethyl group (β''), hence the main product is but-1-ene. The TS for the formation of but-2-ene is

263

$$\overset{\delta-}{HO} - - - H \quad \begin{array}{c} CH_3 \\ | \\ C \end{array} \overset{H}{\underset{\underset{CH_3 \quad H}{\overset{|}{C}}}{\overset{\overset{|}{\big\|}}{C}}} \begin{array}{c} H \\ \diagup \\ \diagdown \\ N(CH_3)_3 \quad \delta+ \end{array}$$

EXERCISE 7.1

EXERCISE 7.2

Addition of HBr to propene, page 198. Propanone is readily protonated at the oxygen atom, and the resulting cation is resonance stabilised. Propene is more resistant as protonation involves breaking a pi-bond.

EXERCISE 7.3

$$\begin{array}{c} \overset{\delta+}{H_2 \overset{..}{O}} - - - - H \\ | \\ H\overset{..}{O} - \overset{..}{N} ==== C - \\ \quad\quad\quad | \\ \quad\quad\quad : OH \\ \quad\quad\quad \delta- \end{array}$$

EXERCISE 7.4

(a) $(CH_3CH_2CH \overset{\overset{\displaystyle CH_3}{|}}{-} CH - \ddot{O}H.$ (b) $CH_3CH_2\overset{\overset{\displaystyle CH_3}{|}}{\underset{\underset{\displaystyle CH_3}{|}}{C}} - \ddot{O}H$

Aldehydes form 2° alcohols, ketones 3° alcohols.

EXERCISE 7.5

EXERCISE 7.6

$CH_3CH = CHCH\ddot{O},$ $\overset{\displaystyle CH_3}{\underset{\displaystyle CH_3}{>}}C = CHC\ddot{O}CH_3,$ $CH_3CH = CHC\ddot{O}CH_3,$ $\overset{\displaystyle CH_3}{\underset{\displaystyle CH_3}{>}}C = CHCH\ddot{O}$

EXERCISE 8.1

EXERCISE 8.2

265

$$\overset{\ominus}{:}\ddot{O}-\underset{|}{\overset{CH_3}{\overset{|}{C}}}-\ddot{\underset{..}{Cl}}: \longrightarrow \ddot{O}=\underset{|}{\overset{CH_3}{\overset{|}{C}}} \quad + \quad :\ddot{\underset{..}{Cl}}:^{\ominus}$$

where the lower substituent is $:\overset{..}{O}-\underset{||}{\overset{}{C}}-CH_3$ with $\overset{..}{\underset{..}{O}}:$

EXERCISE 8.3

$$CH_3-\underset{:\overset{..}{O}:}{\overset{}{C}}-\overset{..}{\underset{..}{O}}H \quad H-\overset{\oplus}{\underset{..}{O}H_2} \;\rightleftharpoons\; CH_3-\underset{:\overset{..}{O}:}{\overset{}{C}}-\overset{\oplus}{O}H_2 + \overset{..}{\underset{..}{O}}H_2$$

$$CH_3-\underset{H}{\overset{..}{O}:} \quad \underset{:\overset{\oplus}{O}H_2}{\overset{CH_3}{\overset{|}{C}}}=\ddot{\underset{..}{O}}: \;\rightleftharpoons\; CH_3-\underset{H}{\overset{\oplus}{O}}-\underset{:\overset{\oplus}{O}H_2}{\overset{CH_3}{\overset{|}{C}}}-\overset{..}{\underset{..}{O}}:^{\ominus}$$

$$\overset{\ominus}{:}\overset{..}{\underset{..}{O}}-\underset{\overset{\oplus}{:}O-CH_3 \; (H)}{\overset{CH_3}{\overset{|}{C}}}-\overset{\oplus}{O}H_2 \;\rightleftharpoons\; O=\underset{\overset{\oplus}{:}O-CH_3 \; (H)}{\overset{CH_3}{\overset{|}{C}}} \quad + \quad \overset{..}{\underset{..}{O}}H_2$$

$$H_2\overset{..}{\underset{..}{O}}\; H-\underset{\overset{\oplus}{|}}{\overset{CH_3}{\overset{|}{O}}}-\underset{O}{\overset{||}{C}}-CH_3 \;\rightleftharpoons\; H_2\overset{\oplus}{\underset{..}{O}}-H + CH_3-\overset{..}{\underset{..}{O}}-\underset{:\overset{..}{O}:}{\overset{||}{C}}-CH_3$$

EXERCISE 9.1

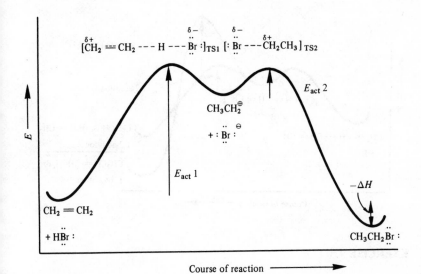

Course of reaction ⟶

EXERCISE 9.2

2-Methylbut-2-ene via the more stable carbocation $CH_3 - \overset{\oplus}{\underset{CH_3}{C}} - CH_2CH_3$.

EXERCISE 9.3

EXERCISE 9.4

EXERCISE 9.5

$$: \overset{..}{\underset{..}{Br}} \overset{\frown}{-} \overset{\oplus}{C} \overset{CH_3}{\underset{CH_3}{\diagdown}} \quad \longleftrightarrow \quad : \overset{\oplus}{\underset{..}{Br}} = C \overset{CH_3}{\underset{CH_3}{\diagdown}}$$

EXERCISE 10.1

EXERCISE 10.2

(a)

(b) Protonation results in an unfavourable repulsion between the positively charge nitrogen and carbon atoms

EXERCISE 10.3

(where $B = H_2O$ or $:\overset{..}{\underset{..}{Cl}}:^{\ominus}$ etc.)

EXERCISE 10.4

EXERCISE 10.5

Steric inhibition of resonance in 2,6-dimethyl-*N*,*N*-dimethylphenylamine.

Brief Bibliography:
Some More-advanced Textbooks

GENERAL

Morrison, R. T. and Boyd, R. N., *Organic Chemistry*, 4th edition, Allyn and Bacon, 1983

Streitwieser, A. and Heathcock, C. H., *Introduction to Organic Chemistry*, 2nd edition, Macmillan, 1981

PHYSICAL AND MECHANISTIC CHEMISTRY

Alder, R. A., Baker, R. and Brown, J. M., *Mechanism in Organic Chemistry*, 2nd edition, John Wiley, 1984

Harris, J. M. and Warmser, C. C., *Fundamentals of Organic Reaction Mechanisms*, John Wiley, 1976

Jones, R. A. Y., *Physical and Mechanistic Organic Chemistry*, Cambridge University Press, 1979

Lowry, T. H. and Richardson, K. S., *Mechanism and Theory in Organic Chemistry*, Harper and Row, 1975

Sykes, P., *Guidebook to Mechanism in Organic Chemistry*, 5th edition, Longman, 1984

Index

α, β nomenclature 3

acetals 154
acidity
  effect of substituents on 68–73
  measurement of 61
  of activated hydrogen 123, 161
  of alcohols 63–4
  of carboxylic acids 64–6, 68–72
  of phenols 66–8, 72–3
acidity constant, pK_a 61
  relationship with pK_b 63
activated complex 84
activated hydrogen atoms 123, 161
activation energy 84–5
alcohols
  acidity of 63–4
  basicity of 111
  elimination in 138–40
  esterification of 189
  nucleophilic substitution in
    111–15
  reaction with hydrogen halides
    112–15
  reaction with sulphuric(VI) acid
    116–17
aldehydes *see* carbonyl compounds
aldol reaction 169
alkenes
  addition of diborane 211–12
  addition of hydrogen halide
    195–201
  addition of halogen 202–6
  addition of hydrogen 212–14
  addition of sulphuric(VI) acid
    201–2
  oxidation of 207–11
  polymerisation of 206–7
  reactivity of 193–4, 214
  stability of 214

alkoxide ion
  as a base 63–4, 136
  as a nucleophile 81, 111
alkynes
  reactivity of 218–19
allylic compounds
  nomenclature of 4
  reactivity of 110
  structure of 25
amines
  as nucleophiles 121
  basicity of 74–8
  classification of 120
  Hofmann elimination in 140
  nucleophilic substitution in 122
annotated equations 41
aromatic electrophilic substitution
  see benzene
association of molecules
  by dipole–dipole interaction 11
  by hydrogen bonding 12

bases, organic
  strength of 73–4
  substituent effects on 74–5, 78
basicity, measurement of 61–2
basicity constant, pK_b 62
  relationship with pK_a 63
benzaldehyde
  reactions of 145
  structure of 22–3, 145
benzene
  acylation of 238–9
  alkylation of 236–8
  bond lengths in 36–7
  electrophilic substitution in
    220–7
  halogenation of 230–2
  nitration of 227–30

resonance energy of 33–4
structure of 22
substituent effects, summary of 252, 254
sulphonation of 232–6
benzylic compounds
nomenclature of 4
reactivity of 110
structure of 110
bimolecular reactions
comparison with unimolecular 104–9, 135–6, 137
conditions favouring 106–7
definition of 98
evidence for, in elimination 134
evidence for, in nucleophilic substitution 108
stereochemistry of 102–3
bonds
length and resonance 34–6
order of 35
partial, representation of 18–19
bromonium ion intermediate 204–5
Brönsted acids and bases 58
buta-1,3-diene
reactivity of 214–17
structure of 21–2

Cannizzaro reaction 171
canonical forms 22 (*see also* limiting forms)
carbanions
as intermediates 143, 163
structure of 25
carbocations
as intermediates 84
nomenclature 49
rearrangement of 93–5
solvation of 90
stability of 25, 50, 51, 104, 105, 226–7
structure of 49, 85–6
carbonium ions *see* carbocations
carbonyl compounds
acidity of 161
formation of acetals 154
formation of bisulphite compounds 149–50
formation of condensation products 170–1

formation of cyanohydrins 146–8
formation of haloforms 173–5
formation of hemiacetals and hemiketals 153
formation of ketals 154
hydration of 151–3
reaction with alcohols 153–4
reaction with ammonia 155, 157
reaction with Grignard reagents 160–1
reaction with hydroxylamine 156–7
reaction with LiAlH$_4$ 158–9
reaction with NaBH$_4$ 159
reactivity of 142–3
resonance in 16–18
tautomerism in 164–8
carboxylic acids
acidity 64–6, 68–72
amides 183–6
anhydrides 183
chlorides 181–3
esters 186–92
reactivity of 176–80
catalyst, role of 213, 230–1, 236–7, 238–9
chain reaction 207
chlorobenzene
structure and reactivity 109
chloroethene (vinyl chloride)
structure and reactivity 109
chloromethyl benzene (benzyl chloride)
structure and reactivity 110
3-chloropropene (allyl chloride)
structure and reactivity 110
competitive method for comparison of reactivity 240
condensation reactions 155, 170–1
crossed condensation 171
configuration
inversion of 102–3, 108
retention of 86
conjugate acids and bases 62–3
conjugated enone 165
conjugated molecules 18–22
contributing forms in resonance 22, 27–31 (*see also* limiting forms)

coordination complexes 59, 115
coupling reaction 250
curved (curly) arrows
   use in mechanistic equations 45
   use in writing limiting forms 16,
     23

Debye unit 10
delocalisation energy 26
delocalisation of electrons 21
dipole–dipole interaction 11
dipole moment, electric 10, 11, 38
displaced group 42
double-headed arrow 17

E1 and E2 reactions *see* β-elimi-
     nation
electromeric effect 33
electronegativity 5
electrophilic reagents
   definition 45
   examples 47
β-elimination
   bimolecular, E2 131–3
   competition with nucleophilic
     substitution 135–7
   control over 136
   evidence for 133–4
   formation of *cis* and *trans* isomers
     131
   formation of mixed products
     127–30
   unimolecular, E1 124–31,
     133–4
energy profiles 86–7
enolate anion 163
enthalpy of combustion 33–4
enthalpy of hydrogenation 34–5
equations, annotated 41
   mechanistic 51–7
ester hydrolysis 188–91
ethanamide
   basicity of 185
   bond lengths in 37
   reactivity of 185–6
   resonance structure 28, 30, 185
ethers (alkoxyalkanes)
   nucleophilic displacement in
     119–20
   structure and reactivity 118

field effects 9, 69

haloalkanes
   classification 79
   elimination in 123–4
     bimolecular, E2 131–3
     competition with substitution
      135–7
     evidence for E1 133–4
     evidence for E2 134–5
     unimolecular, E1 124–31
   nucleophilic substitution
     bimolecular, S_N2 95–103
     comparison of mechanisms
      104–7, 108–9
     evidence for S_N1 107–8
     evidence for S_N2 108
     role of solvent in 87–90
     unimolecular, S_N1 82–95
   structure and reactivity 79–82,
     123–4
haloform reaction 173–5
Hammond postulate 105, 110, 199
hemiacetals and hemiketals 153
heterolysis 44
Hofmann elimination 140
homolysis 44
hydride ion 158–60, 172
hydrogen bonding 12, 13, 153, 165
   with the solvent 88
hyperconjugation 104

inductive effect
   consequences of 10–13
   relay of 8
   summary of 9
   terminology of 6
inductive stabilisation of inter-
     mediates 50–51, 199–200,
     216, 244
inductomeric effect 32
infrared spectra
   as evidence for resonance 40
   in monitoring reactions 191, 229
intermediates
   definition of 84
   distinction from transition state
     99–100
   stability of 50–1, 199–200,
     216, 244

structure of   48–50, 85–6
trapping of   206
inversion of configuration   102–4
ion pair   109
ionisation   84–5
isotopic labels, use of   96, 103,
    152, 188, 190–2, 209, 237

ketals   154
keto–enol tautomerism   164–8
ketones *see* carbonyl compounds
kinetic isotope effect   134, 225,
    232, 234

leaving groups   80, 100, 179
Lewis acids
    as catalysts   59, 112, 115, 218,
        230–1, 236–9
    complexes with   59, 118
    definition of   58
Lewis bases, definition   59
limiting forms
    contribution of   27
    definition of   17
    guidelines for writing   30
    number of   28

Markovnikov's rule   129, 198
mechanistic equations   51–5
mesomer   17, 19
mesomeric effect (*see also* resonance)
    comparison with inductive effect
        20
    definition of   16
    manifestation of   33–40
    relay of   18
microscopic reversibility, principle
    of   236
migratory aptitude of groups   95
molecular orbital approach to
        structure   20–1
molecularity of reaction   83
    distinction from kinetic order   83

nitro group
    effect on acidity of carboxylic
        acids and phenols   71–3
    effect on aromatic electrophilic
        substitution   250–3
    structure   24–5, 250

nitryl cation (nitronium ion)   228
nucleophilic addition with elimination
    aldehydes and ketones   170
    carboxylic acids   178
    esters   190
nucleophilic push   95, 132, 173, 177
nucleophilic reagents
    definition of   45
    examples of   47, 81
    strength of   107
nucleophilic substitution
    reversibility of   100–1 (*see also*
        under haloalkanes, etc.)

orientation of reactants   96, 196

partial structures, use of   55–7
pH, influence on reaction rates   147
phenols
    acidity of   66–8, 72–3
    nucleophilic substitution in   118
phenoxide ion
    as a nucleophile   117
    resonance structure   67
pi complex   231
pK_a, pK_b 61–3
polar bonds   5
polar molecules
    association of   11–13
    physical properties of   10–14
    solubility of   13
polarisation
    induced   32, 46, 96, 193, 196,
        203, 230–1
    permanent   5, 32
polarity   5
propenyl (allyl) structure
    carbanion   25
    carbocation   25
    terminology   4
prototropy   164
pseudo-first-order reaction   99

rate-determining step in a reaction
    83
reaction mechanisms
    approach to formulating   200
    classification as nucleophile–
        electrophile interactions
        53–5

275

reactions, classification of 42–3
reagents, classification of 44–7
rear side attack in bimolecular
    substitution 96
relative permittivities of common
    solvents 90
resonance (*see also* mesomeric effect)
    carbonate ion 28–30
    carbonyl group 16–18
    definition of 22
    effect on physical properties
        33–40
    ethanamide 28, 37
    evidence for 33–40
    manifestation of 33–40
    nitro group 24–5, 250
    propenal 26–7
    propenyl ions 25
    stabilisation of enols 163
    stabilisation of molecules and
        ions 22–6, 65–6, 109,
        110, 163, 179
    stabilisation of reaction inter-
        mediates 222, 246–8
resonance energy
    definition of 26, 29
    determination of 33–4
resonance hybrid 22 (*see also*
    mesomer)
reversibility of nucleophilic substi-
    tution reactions 100–1

saponification of esters 186–8
Saytzeff rule 129
Schiff bases 155
shielding distance 86
sigma complex intermediate 222,
    246–8
solvation energy 90
solvation of ions 75, 88–9
solvent, role in nucleophilic substi-
    tution 87–90, 92
spectator ions 41
stabilisation energy 26 (*see also*
    resonance energy)

steric crowding in a transition state
    in Hofmann elimination 140
    reactions of ethers 120
    reactions of haloalkanes 106–7
    reactions of ketones 144
steric hindrance to reaction 75,
    140, 255
steric inhibition of resonance 255
substituent effects, table of 252, 254
substitution *versus* elimination
    135–7
substrate molecule 41

tautomerism, keto–enol 164–8
transition state (*see also* steric
    crowding)
    cyclic 208
    definition of 84
    distinction from an intermediate
        99–100
trapping of intermediates 206

ultraviolet spectra
    and equilibria 152
    and resonance 39–40
    in monitoring reaction 156, 191
unimolecular reactions
    comparison with bimolecular
        104–9
    conditions favouring 135, 137
    definition of 83
    evidence for, in elimination
        133–4
    evidence for, in nucleophilic
        substitution 107–8
    stereochemistry of 85–6

valence bond approach to structure
    20
vinylic (propenyl) compounds
    nomenclature of 4
    structure and reactivity of 109